ELEMENTS OF FIELD GEOLOGY

by

G. W. Himus, Ph.D., F.G.S.

and

G. S. Sweeting, D.I.C., F.G.S.

Third Edition, revised by

G. S. Sweeting and M. M. Sweeting, M.A., Ph.D.

UNIVERSITY TUTORIAL PRESS LTD

9-10 GREAT SUTTON STREET, LONDON, E.C.1

Published 1951
Second Edition 1955
Reprinted 1957, 1959, 1962, 1965, 1968
Third Edition 1972

ISBN: 0 7231 0577 4

PRINTED IN GREAT BRITAIN BY UNIVERSITY TUTORIAL PRESS LTD
FOXTON, NEAR CAMBRIDGE

FOREWORD TO THE THIRD EDITION

It is a pleasure to be asked to write a brief Foreword to the Third Edition of so successful and valuable a work as Himus and Sweeting's "Elements of Field Geology", a book which must have done more than most others of its kind to help the beginner in our science to set his steps in the right direction. In the twenty years that have elapsed since the appearance of the First Edition, "Himus and Sweeting" has firmly established itself as an essential manual for every serious student of geology, amateur or professional.

Since the Second Edition was published in 1955, the death of Dr Himus has occurred and the major part of the work of revision has fallen upon Mr Sweeting, who has been able to call upon the willing assistance of his daughter, Dr Marjorie M. Sweeting, of the Oxford School of Geography, who has been responsible, in particular, for enlarging and rewriting the section on physical features in connection with geological mapping. The general style and layout of the work has been little changed; an entirely new chapter on the Geology of Water Supply has been added, while the chapter dealing with the field identification of fossils has been checked and brought up-to-date by my colleague, Dr W. S. McKerrow, of the Oxford Department of Geology and Mineralogy.

As well as the useful and often original keys to the field identification of minerals, rocks, and fossils which comprise about half the work, "Himus and Sweeting" is well-known for its detailed and straightforward account of how to set about preparing a geological map of a piece of ground, the excellent example chosen being the Ashover area in Derbyshire. In the new edition, the opportunity has been taken to replace the term "Kinderscout Grit" by "Ashover Grit" in conformity with more recent detailed work carried out in the district by the Institute of Geological Sciences.

The need to produce a Third Edition in itself testifies to the value of the book and to its deserved popularity among teachers and students of geology, both at home and overseas. It may with some confidence be prophesied that still further new editions will be called for before the useful life of this unique little book is ended.

Professor E. A. Vincent,
Department of Geology and Mineralogy,
University of Oxford.

PREFACE

THE data on which the science of geology is founded are discovered not, as in the case of, say, physics or chemistry, by experiments in a laboratory, but by observations in the field. Many a student, who, from reading, is familiar with the methods and results of geological reasoning, is at a loss to know how to proceed when he finds himself in the field. This book will help him to make a geological examination of a given area.

When studying a district, the first questions to be answered are, what are the rocks, how are they distributed and arranged, what do they contain, and what are their relative ages? Their distribution and arrangement can be ascertained by examining a geological map of the area; this can be done in the study, without going into the field, but the information so gained, though better than none at all, is second hand and does not constitute the best kind of knowledge. It is far better for the beginner to make his own geological map, and our main object has been to indicate how this is done.

While mapping, it is necessary to identify the various rocks which are found; this presupposes the ability to determine a number of minerals, while to ascertain the relative ages of rocks requires a study of the fossils which are found in them.

The book is therefore divided into two parts. Part I is concerned with the procedure to be followed when examining a district of simple structure, either with the aid of a geological map or, better still, when making a geological map from one's own observations. Part II provides keys for the identification in the field of those minerals, rocks, and fossils, which the geologist is most likely to find in Great Britain. For the serious student of geology, Part II is an essential adjunct to Part I.

There are, however, others whose object is not that of studying an area as a whole, but who are mainly concerned with the amassing of as large a collection as possible of named geological specimens. To these, Part II should appeal, since it will help them in the problem of attaching names to their finds. At the same time, they may be sufficiently interested to read Part I and as a result be persuaded that there is more in geology than the collecting and naming of specimens.

In preparing Part II we have drawn up a number of tables and keys whereby the reader is led to the identification of a specimen from a study of its easily ascertainable characters. We have eschewed the usual method of *definition*, in which the name of a fossil (for example) is given first, and *then* the diagnostic characters. While this may be satisfactory for the advanced student and the

iv

expert, it is of little help to the beginner, and may easily sicken him with the difficulties which he meets. As a result, he may either give up the subject as hopeless, or adopt the superficial method of "identification" by merely glancing through a series of pictures of fossils, or making rough comparisons with named specimens through the glass of a museum case. Our plan has been to divide the limited number of minerals, rocks, and fossils which we have chosen, into groups having recognisable characters in common, and then to subdivide them into smaller and smaller groups until finally the identification is accomplished.

We have not envisaged the use of more elaborate apparatus than may easily be carried and applied either in the open air, or in the geologist's quarters after the day's field-work is done. The equipment assumed to be available includes hammer, pen-knife, pocket-lens, one or two minerals of known hardness, a carborundum slip with coarse and fine faces, and a small box of blowpipe apparatus and reagents.

For the identification of minerals, we have presented the necessary information in the form of tables. The preliminary division is into minerals that are as hard as or harder than quartz, and minerals that are softer than quartz. The larger group of softer minerals is then divided into a number of classes according to the colour of the specimen in mass and in fine powder. The rocks are treated under three headings, sedimentary, igneous, and metamorphic: for each class, a scheme is provided, in which the members are sorted primarily with regard to texture, and then into smaller groups on a basis of composition.

As aids to the identification of fossils, we adopted a method which we believed to be original. This consists in providing an artificial key to the genera on the lines of the *flora* of the botanist. After this section was in proof, we discovered that A. W. Grabau and H. W. Shimer, in their *North American Index Fossils*, published in 1909, had applied the same principle, but on much more comprehensive lines. In fact, keys are given for the identification of nearly 1,300 genera of invertebrates, while the characteristics (with figures) of some thousands of species are set out in the two valuable volumes. It is greatly to be regretted that nothing similar has been attempted by British palaeontologists.

Our keys for the identification of fossils deal with eight important classes of invertebrates, and, in addition, fourteen plants are described and illustrated. With some modifications and additions, our selection is based on the series of fossils used in teaching elementary palaeontology. While our choice may be open to criticism, we have no doubt that no authors or groups of authors would produce identical lists, although there would be a number of forms common to all. We make no excuse for retaining a number of "composite" genera, such as *Productus, Terebratula, Rhynchonella*, and others, for we feel that any attempt to subdivide them in accordance with modern views would be beyond the scope of the elementary student.

We are aware that we may be criticised for the omission of any reference to the *Foraminifera* which are of increasing importance to the oil-geologist in the correlation of strata. With few exceptions, the members of this important group are so small that they require the use of a microscope for their detection and identification. Therefore, we have not dealt with them. Also, we have made no mention of vertebrate fossils, which are represented generally by detached fragments (chiefly vertebrae and teeth), and we have been unable to produce any simple scheme for their identification.

A student who uses the schemes for identifying his fossils may often fail to recognise that a specimen belongs to one of the genera which we have described and illustrated. We do not regard this as a serious blemish; what would be dangerous would be a *wrong* identification, since this might lead to erroneous conclusions as to the age of a deposit. The student should therefore take pains when attempting to identify a genus to ascertain that the specimen in hand possesses all the necessary qualifications. When there is a doubt, he should reserve judgment and, if possible, obtain advice from one more expert than himself.

A number of the illustrations may appear somewhat crude and sometimes semidiagrammatic; these represent the kind of sketches which may be found in any geologist's notebook. They have been reproduced regardless of their artistic merit, without being subjected to any process of "improvement".

Acknowledgments.—For advice, assistance, and criticism in the preparation of the chapter on fossils, we are indebted to Dr H. M. Muir-Wood, Dr H. Dighton Thomas, Dr J. F. Kirkaldy, Dr L. R. Cox, F.R.S., and Mr L. Bairstow. Our proofs have been read, and valuable advice offered, by Dr Francis Jones, Mr Gwyn Thomas, and Mr E. E. S. Brown. For permission to make use of certain figures, we desire to thank Professor A. Morley Davies and his Publishers, Thomas Murby and Co., Professor F. Debenham and his Publishers, Edward Arnold, and Messrs John Murray, for permission to use illustrations from the classic works of Sir Charles Lyell. A former student, Mr P. B. Cornwell, kindly supplied us with the original of the sketch showing the view up the Ashover Valley from near Milltown. The inset maps at the end of the book are based on the Ordnance Survey Maps with the sanction of the Controller of H.M. Stationery Office.

G. W. H.

G. S. S.

NOTE TO THE THIRD EDITION

For this edition the text has been carefully and extensively revised. A new chapter (Chapter X) on Water Supply—a matter of increasing importance—has been added. The sections on the study of maps have been rewritten, and changes have been made to the diagrams of fossils to accord with modern classifications and nomenclature.

The proofs have been read by Dr W. S. McKerrow, of the Oxford Department of Geology and Mineralogy, and Mr Iain Williamson, M.Sc., Mining College, Wigan, Lancs. Their help is much appreciated. My best thanks must also go to my daughter, whose help has been indispensable.

G. S. S.

NOTE

ASHOVER, DERBYSHIRE

The publishers and authors have learnt with regret that the popularity of this book has been the indirect cause of annoyance to the residents of Ashover. Users of the geological maps of Ashover on the ground are urged to respect private property, boundaries and hedges, and to try to ensure that their interest in this subject does not conflict with the rights of residents and the aims of the conservation societies.

CONTENTS

PART I

CHAPTER   PAGE
I. FIELD GEOLOGY. WHAT IT IS 1
II. EQUIPMENT FOR THE FIELD 5
III. ON THINKING IN THREE DIMENSIONS 15
IV. GEOLOGICAL MAPPING (1): INTRODUCTION 26
V. GEOLOGICAL MAPPING (2): SOME GENERAL CONSIDERATIONS 37
VI. GEOLOGICAL MAPPING (3): TRACING BOUNDARY LINES 48
VII. GEOLOGICAL MAPPING (4): APPLICATION OF PRINCIPLES 63
VIII. GEOLOGICAL MAPPING (5): PLOTTING THE BOUNDARIES 78
IX. THE INTERPRETATION OF GEOLOGICAL MAPS 91
X. WATER SUPPLY 103

PART II

XI. COLLECTING 113
XII. IDENTIFICATION OF MINERALS 123
XIII. BLOWPIPE ANALYSIS 152
XIV. THE IDENTIFICATION OF ROCKS 166
XV. FOSSILS 186
APPENDIX I: SAFETY PRECAUTIONS 264
APPENDIX II: THE GEOLOGICAL COLUMN 265
SUGGESTIONS FOR FURTHER READING 271
INDEX 273
INSET MAPS AT END OF BOOK:
    I. BASE-MAP OF ASHOVER (DERBYSHIRE).
    II. GEOLOGICAL MAP OF ASHOVER (DERBYSHIRE).

THE ELEMENTS OF FIELD GEOLOGY

PART I

CHAPTER I

FIELD GEOLOGY. WHAT IT IS

"Geology is a capital science to begin, as it requires nothing but a little reading, thinking and hammering."—CHARLES DARWIN, 1835.

Geology was defined by Sir Charles Lyell, in the opening words of his immortal *Principles of Geology* (1830) as "the science which investigates the successive changes that have taken place in the organic and inorganic kingdoms of nature; it enquires into the causes of these changes, and the influence which they have exerted in modifying the surface and external structure of our planet."

Geology is a science based on observation and experiment; it brings the student into direct contact with nature, for geology must be studied in the open air. Reading books and examining specimens in the laboratory or museum will never make a geologist; geologists are made in the field, not in the study or laboratory. It is by no means part of our purpose to decry the value of indoor work, including reading and examining specimens; both are aids to, but no substitute for, field-work, and as such they should be regarded.

Many a beginner has his first introduction to geology in the class-room, museum, or laboratory, where he sees and probably handles selected specimens of minerals, rocks, and fossils. He may also be drilled in identifying them, and he may prove an apt pupil. But, however varied and numerous those specimens may be, their true significance, mode of occurrence, and environment are completely lost on the beginner; they are truly "dead bones." It is only when he goes into the field and sees how things occur in nature that the embryo geologist begins to realise what "geology" really means.

The false perspective which is the consequence of lack of field-work was brought home to one of us by a student, who, after handling a number of specimens in the laboratory, remarked on being taken into a large limestone quarry, "I never thought so much rock of one kind occurred in one place." It is remarkable how many students taking geology as part of a university course have never previously been into a quarry of any sort.

Our object is to try to help the beginner in his first essays in field-work, and to give him some idea of how he should proceed in making a study of an area whose structure is simple; how to work in "difficult" country is only learned by experience. The study of even a simple area demands not only a close examination of the ground, but the identification of the minerals, rocks, and fossils which are found there. We have therefore made a feature of synoptical tables and schemes as an aid to the determination in the field (that is, without the aid of elaborate apparatus) of the commoner types.

The beginner's introduction as an observer in the field will depend to a large extent on the district in which he lives or to which he has easy access. He who can get easily to the country or to the sea coast will find a wealth of geological features available for study and, probably, also opportunities for collecting. But even the dweller in a town or built-up area may have opportunities which are by no means contemptible. Parks, recreation grounds, gravel- and sand-pits, temporary excavations for drainage and foundations are all worth examination, and provide information about what lies below the surface.

Even in the heart of large cities, something may be done, and the observer might do worse than make a census of the types of building stones which are displayed; their variety is apt to come as a surprise. A churchyard will often show a fine selection of rocks which have been used as tombstones, and useful information may be obtained by noticing the extent to which stones of various ages and materials have suffered from the effects of weather.

Londoners have conveniently situated pits, commons, and heaths (Hampstead, Wimbledon, Plumstead, etc.) where they can examine and study at leisure practically the whole of the Lower London Tertiaries, and also the Thames gravels. Likewise, in and around other large towns, similar facilities for study are available. Even where the hand of industry has fallen most heavily on the land- scape, there is often a conveniently situated tip-heap from a coal-mine from which plant remains of Coal Measure age may be obtained.

In fact, there are few areas in Great Britain where, given enthusiasm and the will to take a little trouble, it is not possible to study field geology. There is probably no area in the world which affords better opportunities for the study than the British Isles. With but one exception (the Miocene), every system in the Geological Column is represented, while the rocks themselves show well-marked lithological differences and are arranged in an almost unbroken sequence. For example, in proceeding from London to Holyhead, we find an orderly succession of clays, sands, chalk, and limestones, followed by igneous and metamorphic rocks.   The strata are of varying thickness, and have a general regional dip towards the south-east; thus they present their upturned edges towards the north-west, and the farther we proceed in that direction, the older the rocks become.

The surface appearance or "topographical expression" of such a varied suite of deposits depends on the materials of which they are composed and their state of aggregation.   Hard, resistant rocks such as limestones, grits, and slates, show bold and abrupt edges. The less compact and less consolidated rocks, such as sandstones and chalk, have softer and more rounded outlines, while the soft and loosely-cemented sands, clays, and shales form more or less low-lying areas.   The consequence is that in a traverse from London to Holyhead we pass across a series of roughly parallel alternating hills and valleys, whose general trend is from north-east to south-west.

Again, the rocks have their own distinctive characters, including mineral composition and, which is important from the point of view of mapping them, their fossil or organic contents.

Field-work (or what sometimes passes for such) may be carried out in a number of different ways; the observer may visit all the quarries and sections which are within reach with the object of amassing a collection of minerals, rocks, and fossils, and this may be accomplished without his gaining anything more than the vaguest notion of the relations of the various rocks to one another, or of the structure of the area.   He may combine collecting with genuine observation of the stratigraphical succession and the structure of the area.   Or, he may set out with the avowed intention of making a detailed study of a piece of country, either by using information which has already been published as maps and memoirs, or (best of all) by setting out to construct his *own* geological map.

It is not for us to criticise any of these modes of procedure. The first appeals pre-eminently to those who are possessed by the magpie instinct, and who are content to amass a large collection of interesting objects without any desire to know anything more about them than, perhaps, their systematic names.   At least, the magpie has an excuse for getting healthful exercise in the open air, and, mayhap, will be led by some chance observation to go further into the subject and to acquire a better appreciation of the area to which he has access.   The true student, however, who has the makings of a geologist will be less easily satisfied, and as a beginning he can gain much by acquiring the relevant maps and memoirs of his area and setting out to verify what he finds therein.   It is a good exercise in the early stages to take one of the admirable maps issued by the Geological Survey, preferably a 6 in. to the mile sheet of a hilly area, and to try and discover the evidence on which the mapping is based. Why is the boundary line between two formations drawn in the particular position in which it is shown on the map? Having done this, it is but a small step to the more ambitious plan of setting out to make one's own geological map of an area.

To do this, great patience is required; it is necessary to traverse the district on foot, to observe in detail every exposure, however small, and to plot as accurately as possible the observations on a large-scale map. In the initial stages the difficulties may seem almost insuperable, but, with practice, the power of noting apparently trifling bits of evidence and of reading their meaning increases; the habit of observation and accurate recording becomes second nature, and as the map grows there is the pride of achievement and the consciousness of a job well done.

The object of the present book is to introduce the student to the subject of geological mapping; to provide him with hints on how to go about it; and to give him, in a handy form, tables for the field identification of the commoner minerals, rocks, and fossils which he may meet in the carrying out of this pursuit.

But first he will require a certain amount of equipment, and some notes on this subject are given in the next chapter. Here, however, we would like to emphasise that the possession of good tools will not necessarily make a good field geologist. While it is desirable to acquire a good outfit in which one can take pride, a practised observer acquires the invaluable faculty of an *eye for a country* and the *power of thinking in three dimensions*, and so becomes more or less independent of apparatus.

CHAPTER II

EQUIPMENT FOR THE FIELD

The equipment required by the field geologist is fortunately neither costly, bulky, nor heavy. The smallness of the bulk and weight can be judged by the fact that everything required in the mapping of an ordinary area can be stowed away in the pockets without there being any outward or visible sign to show what the bearer is engaged in.

The apparatus required will depend on the object of the field-work and on the rocks in the area to be examined. The particular items which it is necessary to carry on the person will vary somewhat from day to day, according to the nature of the day's work. When making a detailed study of the area it is necessary to cover the ground on foot, walking many miles, often over rough and rugged country. The geologist, therefore, soon realises the desirability of reducing his impedimenta to the smallest possible weight and bulk which are consistent with their being adequate for the purpose which he has in view.

As a guide to the selection of equipment the following suggestions are put forward:—

MAPS.—The systematic study of the geology of any district involves the construction of a geological map, or of examining it in detail with the aid of an existing map. Although a great deal may be learned by going over the ground with one of the one-inch maps issued by the Geological Survey, the best training in field geology can only be acquired by setting out to do the mapping oneself. In any case, observations (particularly of temporary sections) should be plotted on a six-inch map. Sooner or later the urge to go further and complete the map will probably come, and the beginner's true initiation as a field geologist will have commenced.

A geological map demands that all the outcrops of the various rocks which appear at the surface should, as far as possible, be delineated accurately on a good topographical map, together with all available information as to dips, strikes, faults, etc. This renders necessary a thorough examination of the ground; every exposure, however small and insignificant, must be examined and plotted. The necessity for careful observation and accurate delineation on a map, irksome though it may seem at times, develops those habits of meticulous attention to detail, accuracy, and neatness, which are the essential qualities of the field geologist.

With practice he develops a kind of extra sense which enables him to ferret out trifling items of evidence of the nature of the rocks and their structure which would have escaped him in his earlier days in the field. Moreover, with experience he acquires an eye for country and the faculty of "reading" and appreciating its geological structure from inspection of the ground itself or of a good topographical map. This faculty is valuable when mapping, for it not only saves time and labour by suggesting the most likely places at which to seek for evidence, but it enables the geologist to visualise the beds in three dimensions so that he can grasp the structure of the area as a whole. To begin with, the geologist will find that the mass of detail is liable to overshadow the broad outline of the geology, and it is some time before he can perceive the meaning of his observations and build up a comprehensive idea of the structure they disclose.

For use in conjunction with a gridded map, a *Romer* should be provided. A suitable pattern is the "Militia Romer, Mk. III," which is graduated in metres and yards on scales of 6 in. to the mile, 1/25,000 (approximately $2\frac{1}{2}$ in. to the mile), and 1 in. to the mile. This piece of equipment may be purchased cheaply from the agents for Ordnance maps.

THE MAP-CASE.—The functions of the map-case are: (i) to provide a firm and stiff support to the field-map when plotting observations, and (ii) to protect it from dirt and wet.

The map-case consists of two plates of stiff cardboard or other suitable material, covered with leather, and provided with means for holding the sections of the map in position. Either sewn-on "corners" can be fixed to the case or else elastic (white, and $\frac{1}{2}$ in. wide) can be used. It is a good plan to provide two sheets of celluloid, which can be used to cover the sections of the map when they are not required to be exposed for working.

THE HAMMER.—This is the characteristic tool of the geologist, and the manner in which he wields it is an infallible indication of his technique. The tyro loads himself with a large and heavy implement and with it attacks an exposure of rock with a view to securing a specimen. After the expenditure of much toil and sweat, he is at

last rewarded with a pile of powder and a badly bruised and shape-
less lump of rock which is almost useless as a sample.   In the same
time, with a lighter hammer and with far less expenditure of energy,

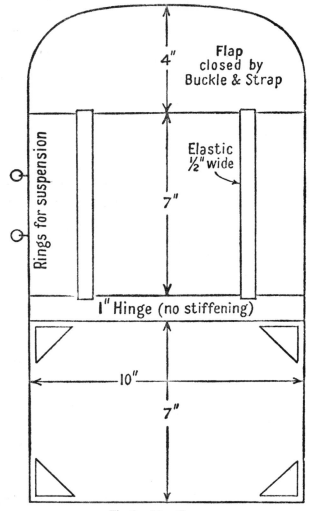

4"   **Flap
closed by
Buckle & Strap**

**Elastic
½" wide**

7"

Rings for suspension

1" Hinge (no stiffening)

10"

7"

Fig. 1.   MAP-CASE.

the experienced executant would have procured a shapely fragment
of reasonable dimensions, free from bruising, and with a minimum
of fuss and flurry.   The secret of using this indispensable tool lies

in the correct selection of the point of attack (a projecting edge or corner) and in the manner of delivering the blow; this is a matter of practice, and although much can be learned by watching an expert, the beginner must nevertheless work out his own salvation in the field.

There are numerous types of geological hammers available, and all are obtainable in a number of different weights. The hammer is used to strike off specimens, to trim them, for splitting fissile rocks, and often to clear overburden or talus which may obscure a critical section. For these purposes the head should be of good steel, tempered so that it will not chip or burr at the edges when in use; it should be firmly attached to a shaft of straight-grained hickory or ash wood. It is desirable that the shaft should be thicker at the grip and taper towards the head, otherwise the hand is liable to become cramped after long hammering.

The shape and weight of the head depends to some extent on personal idiosyncrasy; unnecessary weight should be avoided, for it will become apparent at the end of a long day in the field. A head weighing a pound is ample for nearly all purposes, except where it is necessary to obtain large specimens of very hard and tough rocks. The most satisfactory head is square at the striking end and drawn out at the other into a wedge- or chisel-shape which is at right angles to the line of the shaft. A hammer weighing a pound has a head about 6 in. long and 1 in. square at the rear; the shaft should be about 15 in. long over all. The head of the 12-oz. hammer, which is adequate for most purposes, is 4 in. long and $\frac{3}{4}$ in. square at the striking end; the shaft is 12 in. long. It is a good plan to graduate the shaft (by branding with a hot iron) with a scale of inches; this is useful for measuring sections.

For trimming specimens, a smaller hammer weighing 4 oz. is a useful tool.

When choosing a hammer, select that which has the largest possible "eye" consistent with the size of the head; the larger the eye, the less the end of the shaft need be trimmed when re-shafting. The head should be set "square" when viewed from the side and the rear. It is useful in the field to carry one or two wedges of suitable size so that if a new shaft must be fitted, a good wedge is available. Good ribbed and toothed iron wedges can be purchased cheaply from the ironmonger. The wedge shown in Fig. 2 is the No. 4 size, which is suitable for a 16-oz. hammer.

A hammer of the type described will deliver a hefty blow if well handled, while the chisel end serves to split fissile rocks and can be used as a pick when it is necessary to clear the face of an exposure. On steep, grassy slopes, which are frequently slippery, the chisel end can be dug into the ground and thus assists in climbing. A "straight-peen" hammer (*i.e.* one in which the chisel edge is parallel with the shaft) does not fulfil these functions so well.

COLD CHISELS.—When collecting fossils it is useful to carry a couple of cold chisels, each about 6 in. long and ⅜ to ½ in. wide. Two chisels are recommended, since it sometimes happens that the first becomes wedged firmly and may be irrecoverable unless cut out by means of the other. Moreover, it is very easy to lose a chisel by leaving it behind in a quarry.

THE LENS.—Very few observers are so keen sighted that they do not feel the need of a good lens. The most useful is one having two or three powers with a maximum magnification of 10 to 12 diameters. The low power should have a large field for examining the general texture of a rock, the component grains, and their arrangement. The higher powers permit the examination of fine detail such as the striae or cleavage on the surface of a crystal or the minor detail of the ornament on a fossil. A little experience will show that a single high-power lens (× 12) which, incidentally, is more costly, is less useful than one with two or three powers. Examination of a specimen should always begin with the low power, and not until the information derived from its use is exhausted should the higher powers be brought into play.

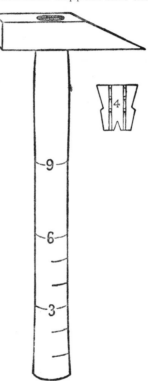

Fig. 2. GEOLOGICAL HAMMER AND WEDGE.

THE COMPASS.—Apart from its normal use as an aid in finding one's position, a compass is required to determine accurately the direction of dip or strike of the rocks, of joints, and of the strike of cleavage; it is also necessary to ascertain the directions of the faces of sections where inclinations oblique to the true direction of dip are measured. Any compass which will enable bearings to be taken to within one or two degrees will suffice.

All bearings plotted on the map and entered in the notebook should be "true" and corrected for the deviation of the compass. To ascertain the correction which must be applied, sights should be taken between prominent objects marked on the map or along straight stretches of road. Several observations should be made in a number of different directions and the bearings determined by the compass compared with the true bearings measured on the map by means of a protractor.

THE CLINOMETER.—This instrument is used to measure dips, i.e. the inclination of rocks from a horizontal plane. In its simplest form a clinometer consists of a pendulum which swings freely in front of a graduated arc. The straight edge of the arc is held against or parallel with the edge of the plane whose dip is to be measured, and the reading shown by the pendulum is noted.

A clinometer can be improvised from an ordinary protractor and a thread of wire carrying a weight. The thread is attached accurately at the central mark of the protractor, the edge of which is held against the rock whose dip is to be measured. The reading where the wire or thread cuts the edge of the protractor is the complement of the angle of dip, since the long edge of practically all protractors is the datum. The dip is therefore 90° *minus* the angle read off.

A combined rule and clinometer can be made from two thin leaves of wood, each about 6 in. long and 2 or 2½ in. wide, hinged together at one end so as to form a foot-rule when opened out. A semicircle, graduated to 90° on each side of the verticle, is attached to one of the leaves, and a pendulum (conveniently made from a clock hand of suitable size) is suspended from the centre of the semi-circle. The edge of the rule may be bevelled off and graduated, on one side in inches and fractions, the other in divisions of 100 yd. (0·342 in.) on a scale of 6 in. to the mile.

Combined forms of compass and clinometer are obtainable. The case of a compass is provided with a "foot" which is attached parallel to the E.-W. line, and a pendulum is suspended from the pivot of the compass needle. When the case of the compass is held upright the pendulum swings before a scale of degrees graduated from 0° to 90° on either side of the N.-S. diameter of the compass to 90° at the E. and W. points.

The determination of dip is dealt with further in Chapter III.

NOTEBOOK AND PENCILS.—The notebook is destined not only to receive manuscript notes, but also sketches and rough plans; it should therefore not be too small. A convenient size of page is

5 in. by 7 or 8 in. or thereabouts, bound along the short edge of the leaves. The paper should be of good quality, capable of taking ink or pencil; it is useful if the pages are ruled feint in squares of $\frac{1}{8}$ or $\frac{1}{10}$ in. Loose-leaf notebooks are convenient, since the pages can be grouped together according to the subject-matter of the notes.

When mapping, it is necessary to write finely and neatly, since even on a six-inch map there is not overmuch space for notes. It must be remembered that a line $\frac{1}{100}$ in. thick represents a width of 8·8 ft. on a scale of 6 in. to the mile. Hard pencils which will take and keep a sharp point are therefore required, preferably 2H or even harder. For use in the notebook, softer pencils (say, HB) are satisfactory; it is better, however, to write in ink in the notebook, for which purpose a good fountain pen or stylo (filled with an ink which will not run if wetted) should be carried.

A great deal of labour and unnecessary writing can be avoided if a number of coloured pencils are carried; exposures may be indicated by dots or short lines of a colour which is chosen to fit in with the colour-scheme of the finished map. The disadvantage of coloured pencils is that they are too soft to take a sharp point, and it is therefore possible only to make a rather large mark with them.

A *sharp* knife will be required to keep the pencils in good condition. It is useful to carry a small "slip" of carborundum (preferably with two faces of different degrees of fineness) to keep the knife in order. The carborundum slip fulfils another useful function, for it can be used to smooth down surfaces of such fossils as corals which may be difficult to identify in the field in their pristine rough condition.

A TROWEL OR PUTTY KNIFE.—This is useful when collecting from unconsolidated deposits, such as clays. A builder's pointing trowel is convenient; some prefer a long-bladed fern-trowel.

COLLECTING BAG.—To carry the equipment and also specimens gathered during the day, some sort of bag is necessary. Where a good deal of collecting is to be done, and particularly if rough and hilly ground must be traversed, a ruck-sack has obvious advantages. It is roomy and has great capacity, and, since it hangs from the shoulders, is not likely to get in the way or to cause the bearer to overbalance. The disadvantages are that (i) because of the great capacity there is a tendency to overload oneself with apparatus and specimens, and (ii) to get at the contents of the bag it is necessary to unship the whole thing from the shoulders. While a large ruck-sack is useful as a means of carrying spare clothing and other gear to the district where it is proposed to work, *in the field* a haversack slung over the shoulder will generally prove adequate.

The bag should be made of strong canvas; brown post canvas or green rot-proof ("deck-chair") canvas are satisfactory. A convenient size is 12 in. × 9 in. × 4 in. at the bottom and 12 in. × 3 in. at the top. The flap should come well down over the front and be provided with suitable means of fastening. A home-made bag is, in many ways, preferable to the stock pattern; most workers have their own fads and fancies about the number and arrangement of the pockets, and these can only be satisfied in a bag of one's own design and construction.

BLOWPIPE APPARATUS.—In areas where minerals of economic importance are likely to be found it is often useful to have a box of blowpipe apparatus, so that confirmatory tests may be carried out in the evening. This will be dealt with at greater length in Chapter XIII. It is not suggested that the blowpipe box should be carried on the person in the field, but a few carefully selected pieces of apparatus and reagents can be packed in a small box which will go comfortably into a corner of a suitcase and will often prove serviceable in the evening or on a wet day when it is out of the question to go mapping.

AUGER.—Where exposures are few and where the mantle of soil is thick, some means of obtaining samples of soft rocks* from a depth of several feet is often needed. For this purpose an auger is useful. An overall length of three feet will often suffice, and a carpenter's auger, suitably modified, $\frac{5}{8}$ or $\frac{3}{4}$ in. diameter, may be used. Since these augers are usually only about 18 in. long, the stem should be cut in the middle and a piece of mild steel of the same diameter should be "shut in" by a blacksmith, to give an overall length of 3 ft. For convenience of carriage, a bamboo sheath is easily made. A piece of bamboo curtain-rod of the required diameter and length is cut; one end is plugged by a piece of wood, and the septa between the joints of the bamboo are cleared by means of the auger. To obviate any tendency of the bamboo to split, it is useful to shrink on a short collar of brass tube at each end.

The auger is screwed into the ground, using a tommy bar made of a piece of dowelling about 18 in. long, and of the required diameter to pass through the eye on the auger-stem. When screwed down to the required depth the auger is withdrawn by a *straight pull*, the surface of the sample is carefully inspected, and any

* Such as clays, shales, sands, etc.

contamination material which may have been picked up during withdrawal from the ground is scraped off. The auger must never be "unscrewed" or the sample from the bottom of the hole will be, at any rate, partially detached, and what is brought up will certainly be contaminated with the upper layers through which it is drawn. The material adhering to the thread is detached and either examined on the spot or transferred to a clean, labelled container for more detailed examination later.

Where it is desired to work at greater depths, the business end of the auger can be welded or brazed into a length of gas-pipe of appropriate diameter, and the eye end into a separate section. The two can be joined by ordinary screwed unions, and additional lengths of piping may be introduced, so that lengths of 10 ft. or more can be built up. The disadvantage of the telescopic auger, of course, is the weight; it is awkward to carry, and much more difficult to withdraw from the ground than a shorter tool. It is necessary to carry at least one pipe-wrench for use when taking a telescopic auger down, for when screwed into the ground the joints are tightened; furthermore, a certain amount of fine grit will get into the screw-threads and cause binding.

When a depth of 5 or 6 ft. from the surface has been reached it is advisable to withdraw the auger at intervals of 6 in. This makes for easier work and tends to prevent wedging and binding.

CLOTHING.—While we do not suggest that there is any special form of geological clothing, we have observed that beginners frequently are unsuitably clad, and therefore we feel that a few notes on the subject may not be out of place. The essential is that clothing (and particularly footwear) should be adequate and fitted for the functions it has to perform.

Footwear. Since a good deal of scrambling over rough country is involved, we recommend boots rather than shoes, since they give protection to the ankle. Boots should be comfortable, strong, waterproof, and provided with vibram type soles. It is advantageous to buy field-boots a size larger than one is accustomed to wear, sufficiently large to allow of wearing an extra pair of heavy woollen socks. The outer socks can be turned down over the top of the boot, when they prevent the entry of small pieces of stone, sand, etc. Moreover, the double layer of wool provides extra spring in walking, and reduces the wear and tear on the feet which is otherwise experienced at the end of a long day's work in heavy boots.

The *outer clothing* should be strong, warm, and capable of standing up to rough usage. An important consideration is that clothing should be free and should not hamper one's movements.

We stress the importance of *warm* clothing, for it often happens that after a rough and hot scramble to a point of vantage, some considerable time may be spent in an exposed position, perhaps in a cutting wind.

Protection from the rain.   There is a difference of opinion between those who prefer a raincoat and those who favour a cape.   Whichever is chosen, the prime requirement is that it really be waterproof. A cape allows freer play to the arms, and it can be used more easily than a coat as a shield when it is necessary to refer to the map. Whichever form of waterproof is chosen, the map-case should always be slung *underneath* it.

A certain amount of mapping can be carried out in the rain if a large plastic bag is used to cover the map-case and so enabling the observer to write with his hand inside the bag.

CHAPTER III

ON THINKING IN THREE DIMENSIONS

A map is a two-dimensional diagram of part of the surface of the earth; it is, in fact, a representation on a plane of something which is irregular and possesses "relief," or a third dimension at right angles to the plane of the map. Everyone who is accustomed to handling maps is able to visualise from the contours the shape of the country. The geologist is concerned, however, not only with the shape of the surface, but also with what is happening below the surface; how the beds "run," where they are likely to intersect the surface of the ground (or crop out), and at what depth they may be expected at any given point. He is concerned, in fact, with three dimensions, and the sooner he can accustom himself to think in these terms, the better. There is a definite relation between the relief of the ground and the trend of the boundary lines between beds, and it is the purpose of this chapter to point out what this relation is, and also to show how underground trends may be forecast from a knowledge of dips, etc.

The data which are required in solving the various problems propounded are the shape of the ground as deduced from the contour lines on the map, the dip, and strike of the rocks. It is therefore reasonable first to consider the determination of the dip and strike.

DETERMINATION OF DIP AND STRIKE

The *dip* of a plane is its maximum angle of inclination to the horizontal, expressed in degrees, and the compass bearing of the dip is its *direction*. The *strike* of a plane is a horizontal line along the "run" of the bed at right angles to the direction of the dip (Fig. 3). When the dip and strike of a bed are known, the "attitude" of the bed is defined, and it is important when mapping to take every opportunity of determining the inclination and strike of the rocks.

To measure the dip, a flat surface is chosen, the clinometer is placed thereon and turned until the maximum reading is obtained. This is immediately recorded in the notebook, and the true bearing of the dip is then determined and recorded. Using a protractor, the direction of the dip is marked on the map by means of a neat, small arrow whose point is at the exact spot where the observation was made; the number of degrees of dip is then neatly written against the shaft of the arrow, thus: $\nearrow_5$. The arrow should not exceed a quarter of an inch in length and should be marked with a hard, sharp pencil. In the evening the direction of the arrow should be carefully checked, and both arrow and figure should then be inked in with indian ink and all traces of the pencil mark erased.

If, as often happens, the surface of the bed is irregular, the effect of minor inequalities can be overcome by laying the closed notebook over them and setting the clinometer on it. To determine the dip correctly it is necessary to see that the clinometer stands on a bedding surface. Rocks such as sandstones and grits often exhibit current- or false-bedding which gives "apparent dips" which differ both in amount and direction from the true inclination of the strata.

Fig. 3. DIP AND STRIKE.

If the dip of the current-bedding is determined by mistake, entirely false ideas of the structure of the country will probably result. *It is always dangerous to place great reliance on dips which are measured on small exposures of sandstones or grits*, they may only represent current-bedding. As a guide to minimise the chance of errors, the following points should be remembered:—

Ripple-marked surfaces, sun-cracks, and fossils mark surfaces of true bedding. Also, if the rock is jointed, the joints are approximately perpendicular to the bedding planes.

"Soil-creep" down a hillside sometimes bends the edges of fissile strata so that the dip of the uppermost edges is in the opposite direction to that of the real dip (Fig. 4). A common indication of hill-creep is the presence of miniature terraces ("terracettes") more or less parallel with the contours. The terracettes may be from a few inches to a couple of feet high.

Similar inversion of the dip, and even contortion of the rock near the surface of the ground may be observed where the rocks have been bent and crushed by the passage of a mass of ice.

Although it is customary to determine the dip and its direction and to deduce the direction of the strike, it is sometimes convenient to determine the strike first. To do this, the clino-

meter is placed on the surface of the bed and turned so that the reading is zero; the position of the instrument is then marked with a pencil or by scratching the rock with a chisel. The clinometer is then turned at right angles to the mark, the dip is read, and *its* direction is marked on the map.

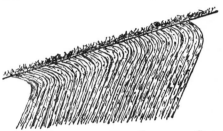

Fig. 4.   ANOMALOUS DIP, CAUSED BY SOIL-CREEP.

Often only the edges of the strata are visible, and it is then necessary to proceed with caution, since a strike section of dipping strata will show apparently horizontal beds, while any section at an angle oblique to the direction of dip will show an apparent dip which is less than the true dip (Fig. 5).

[*After Lyell.*

Fig. 5.   APPARENT HORIZONTALITY OF INCLINED BEDS.

Sometimes, in a quarry or on a sea cliff, two sections are visible and on neither of them are the beds horizontal, but on both dips are seen. It is then necessary to measure the dips on both faces and to determine the true value by construction as follows:—

Supposing, as in Fig. 6, that the dips are 10° in the direction *AB* and 5° along *AC*. To find the true dip and its direction.

On *AB*, in any convenient units, set off the number of degrees of dip on the other face (i.e. *AC*); in this case the distance *AD* is 5 units. On *AC*, in the same units, set off the length *AE* (10 units) which represents the dip on *AB*. Join the points *D* and *E* by a straight line. *DE* gives the direction of the strike. From *A* draw *AF* perpendicular to *DE*; this is the direction of the true dip.

To find the *amount* of the dip, measure *AF*, which is 4·7 units. Now, since 5 units represent a dip of 10° and 10 units a dip of 5°, 4·7 units will represent a dip of $\dfrac{10 \times 5}{4\cdot7}$ or 10·6°.

This method of construction is only reasonably correct where the dips are low. The more mathematically-minded reader will perceive that the lengths *AD* and *AE* should really be proportional

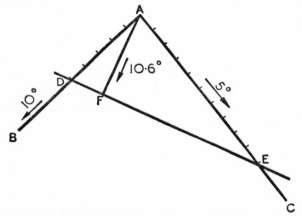

Fig. 6. DETERMINATION OF TRUE DIP FROM TWO OBSERVATIONS.

to the cotangents of the dips along *AB* and *AC* respectively. If *AD* and *AE* are set off in this way, then the direction and magnitude of the true dip will be correct, however high the observed dips may be.

If one of the dips is towards *A* and the other away from *A*, the construction is slightly different and may be carried out as in Fig. 7, in which the 10° dip is from *B* to *A*.

In this case it is necessary to prolong *BA* by 5 units to *D*; the distance *AE* is 10 units as before, and *DE* is the direction of the strike. The length of *AF* is 4·35 units, when the true dip is $\dfrac{5 \times 10}{4\cdot35}$ or 11·5°.

VERY LOW DIPS: THE THREE-POINT PROBLEM

If the dip is very low (say, only two or three degrees), accurate measurement by means of a clinometer is out of the question.

Moreover, the less the angle of dip, the greater are the effects of errors in its measurement, and this may have serious consequences for economic purposes where it is necessary to calculate the distance that a particular bed is below the surface.

Provided that the height of a fixed horizon in the bed above some fixed level (usually Ordnance datum) can be determined at three points which are not in a straight line, the strike and dip can be found by construction.

Thus, supposing the top of a bed has been identified at three points on the map A, B, and C (Fig. 8), the respective heights being 800, 650, and 700 ft. O.D., and the distances between the points as

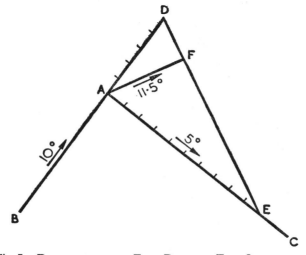

Fig. 7. DETERMINATION OF TRUE DIP FROM TWO OBSERVATIONS.

follows: AB 10,000, AC 8,000, and BC 12,000 ft. To find the dip and strike of the plane in which A, B, and C lie.

The points are set out on paper in their correct relative positions on a convenient scale. Since the fall from A to C is 100 ft., and C is at 700 ft. O.D., there will be a further fall of 50 ft. in a distance of $\frac{50 \times 8000}{100}$, or 4,000 ft. Therefore, if AC is produced 4,000 ft. to E, this point will be at 650 ft. O.D., and BE will be the line of strike.

Now drop a perpendicular AD from A on BE, this will give the direction of the dip. AD is 8,100 ft. in length, thus the tangent of the angle of dip is $\frac{150}{8100}$, or 0·0185, and the dip is very slightly over 1°.

Provided that the surface of the bed is a plane, that is, that it is devoid of minor undulations, it would be possible to predict its level with reference to Ordnance datum within the triangle and for some distance outside it.

THE RELATION BETWEEN WIDTH OF OUTCROP, DIP, AND SLOPE OF THE SURFACE OF THE GROUND

The question has to be studied from two distinct standpoints: (*a*) how the width of outcrop *on the ground* is related to the dip and the slope of the surface of the country, and (*b*) how the width of the outcrop *on the map* is similarly related. Fig. 9 shows some of the answers. In every diagram the thickness of the deposit is the same.

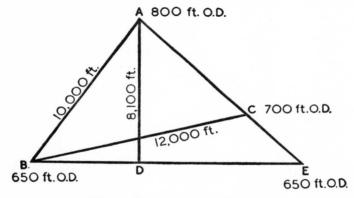

Fig. 8. THE THREE-POINT PROBLEM.

(i) Slope of ground and dip of bed coincide. As long as these conditions are fulfilled, only one bed can appear at the surface.

(ii) Dip at right angles to slope of ground. The width of the outcrop *on the ground* equals the thickness of the bed. *On the map*, the width of the outcrop is less than that of the bed.

(iii) Beds dipping obliquely to the slope of the ground. The width of the outcrop on the ground is always greater than the thickness of the beds. The width of the outcrop on the map, however, may be equal to, or greater or less than, the thickness of the bed.

(iv) Bed horizontal and ground vertical, that is, a cliff section. Width of outcrop equals thickness of the bed. *On the map*, the outcrop will be reduced to a line, which has length but no breadth. In nature a truly vertical cliff is a rarity, but when the slope is very steep the width of an outcrop in plan will be much less than the thickness of the bed.

From the diagrams it can be seen that the true thickness of a bed can be determined either by construction or calculation if the width of its outcrop and its dip are known.

By Construction.   Draw a straight line to represent the surface

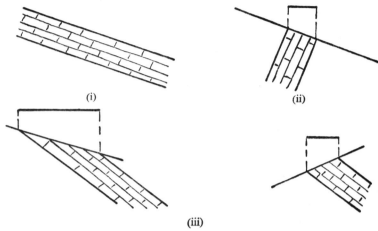

(i)

(ii)

(iii)

Fig. 9.   Relation between Width of Outcrop, Dip, and Slope of Ground.

of the ground, giving it the correct slope.   On any convenient scale set off the measured width of the outcrop, and draw in the upper and lower surfaces of the bed at the correct dip (Fig. 10).   Drop a perpendicular between the two lines, and on the same scale measure the length of the per-pendicular; this gives the thickness of the bed.

By   Calculation. Thickness of the bed equals width (w) of outcrop in feet × sin of the acute angle (a) between   surface   of ground and surface of bed.

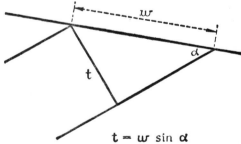

$$t = w \sin a$$

Fig. 10.   Determination of the True Thickness of a Bed.

THE RELATION BETWEEN THE RUN OF A BOUNDARY LINE AND THE SHAPE OF THE GROUND

It is evident that the line of junction between two horizontal beds must follow a contour line, and a little reflection will show that the junction between two vertical beds will run straight across country without deviating, no matter what the shape of the country may be.   In nature, contacts are seldom either strictly horizontal or absolutely vertical over any appreciable area; they are generally inclined to the horizon, often at low angles.   Furthermore, the dip is liable to vary from point to point, and the surface of a bed is often not plane.   Therefore, so far as mapping is concerned, what follows can only be applied over very restricted areas.   Nevertheless, it is useful practice to investigate geometrically how the outcrop of a bed of constant dip will vary with the shape of the ground, for such a study brings out clearly how boundary lines may be expected to behave in the field.   Also, it provides a check which will enable the geologist to judge whether a line he proposes to draw is likely to occur in nature.

As a simple exercise, on a contoured map, plot the outcrop of a bed of uniform thickness and constant dip.   The position of the exposure at which the dip was measured is clearly indicated.

Fig. 11 shows a contoured plan of a small island, and at the point A, on the contour marked 2, a bed having a dip of 10° due west is seen.   The point A is on the upper boundary line of the bed, which is assumed to be 150 ft. thick, of uniform thickness and dip over the area of the plan.

Beneath the plan draw a straight line parallel to the direction of dip, and above it draw parallel straight lines, each distant from the line immediately below it by an amount equal to the contour interval on the plan.   These are numbered from 0 to 5 to correspond with the contours on the map.

From A drop a perpendicular on to line 2, or in more general terms, the straight line which represents the height of A above datum level.   Call this point A'.   Through A' draw a straight line $A'T$, dipping at an angle of 10° from left to right—equal to the angle of dip of the bed.   All straight lines at right angles to the dip are strike-lines, therefore, every point on each of them is at the same level.   Where TA' cuts each of the straight lines from 1 to 5 at $1T$, $2T$, $3T$, and $4T$, draw perpendiculars so as to cut the corresponding contours on the plan.

The points of intersection between the contours and the vertical lines are points at which the surface of the bed coincides with that of the ground.   Therefore, by joining the points with a smooth curve, the trace of the upper limit of the bed can be drawn.

The lower plane of the bed is then drawn in on the profile at the bottom of the diagram, and the same procedure is followed to plot in the lower contact.

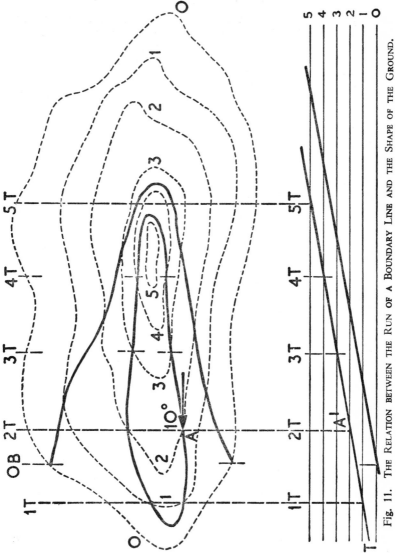

Fig. 11. The Relation between the Run of a Boundary Line and the Shape of the Ground.

A certain amount of judgment must be used in places. For example, consider the upper contact of the bed. At the eastern end of the summit of the island the perpendicular $5T$ passes across country well to the east of the contour line marked 5 over distinctly lower ground. The junction must therefore wrap round the No. 5 line between the perpendicular $5T$ and the eastern end of the contour line, somewhat as is shown in the figure. In a similar way the closure of the western end of the boundary line is arrived at by considering the balance of probabilities, having regard to the way the surface is likely to slope between the mapped contours.

The student should construct a number of similar diagrams for himself, plotting the outcrops of beds of constant dip on small plans showing various types of topography. He should then verify the following statements :—

(i) The junction line between beds which dip *up* a valley, **V** *up* the valley; the steeper the dip, the wider and more open the **V**. In the limit, when the beds are vertical, the line of junction will cross the valley as a straight line.

(ii) Where the beds dip *down* the valley, if the dip of the beds is less than the slope of the ground, the line of junction will **V** *up* the valley with a more acute angle than in (i).

(iii) When the dip is *downstream* and when it exceeds the slope of the floor of the valley, the junction will **V** *down* the valley, the acuteness of the angle decreasing as the dip increases.

(iv) Unless a plane of junction is vertical, a boundary line on the map can never cut a contour at right angles. The higher the dip, the greater the possible angle of intersection between a boundary line and a contour.

The rules and examples given in this chapter are not intended to supply the student with an easy road to the construction of his map. No suggestion is made that it is permissible to plot an out-crop on a contoured map from a single observation of dip. Thickness of beds and their dips are far too variable in nature for geometrical methods to give reliable results. A knowledge of the rules and the construction of maps on the lines suggested provide practice in visualising how beds may be expected to behave beneath the surface in ideal conditions. The student will also be protected, to some extent, from gross errors in plotting; the failure to **V** a junction in the correct direction when running it across a valley, and the drawing of a line at right angles to the contours are cases in point.

An appreciation of the rules is also indispensable in *reading* a geological map, for they increase the geologist's ability to appreciate what is happening beneath the surface. The chief value of geometrical methods is, however, negative. They may show that certain things cannot happen—unless—; but we find that these very things appear to have happened, which means that the evidence must be reviewed, and the possibility of unexpected perturbations having taken place must be explored.

CHAPTER IV

GEOLOGICAL MAPPING (1). INTRODUCTION

THE REQUIREMENTS OF A GEOLOGICAL MAP

A geological map should show—

(i) *The topography of the country* as fully and as accurately as is consistent with the scale of the map.   The form of the surface and the heights should be delineated by contour lines and not by hill-shading.   Contours give a quantitative expression of the rise and fall of the surface; hill-shading cannot give more than a general impression.

(ii) *All geological formations,* from the most ancient to the most recent, which appear in the area covered by the map must be shown with their boundary lines accurately traced and their relation to the form of the ground clearly indicated.

(iii) *All igneous rocks,* effusive being clearly distinguished from intrusive.

(iv) *The geological structure or "grain" of the country,* that is, the relation of the rocks to each other, their inclination from the surface, and their curvatures and dislocations must be shown. Dips should be inserted wherever seen, to show exactly the direction and inclination of the strata.

(v) *Economic information,* such as the position of available building materials, the direction and extent of ores, coal-seams, and other useful minerals, the best sources of water-supply, mine-shafts, etc., should also be indicated on the ideal geological map.

THE BASE-MAP

The base-map must be accurate; much use will be made of such features as the junctions of streams, walls and hedges, bends in roads and footpaths when locating positions in drawing boundary lines. Hence, unless these features are correctly portrayed, the positions and directions of boundaries will be falsely shown and a wrong picture will be given of the geology.

The scale of the map must be suited to the purpose in view. The smaller the scale, the less the detail and the more difficult it will be to fix positions accurately. Also, the smaller the scale, the more necessary it is to generalise, and the more important it is to make a correct selection of what is to be shown.

A line $\frac{1}{100}$ in. thick will cover a band 52·8 ft. wide on a one-inch map, and a dot $\frac{1}{100}$ in. diameter on the same scale would cover an area of 2,790 sq. ft. Since $\frac{1}{100}$ in. is the minimum practicable thickness of a line or diameter of a dot, it is not possible, without gross exaggeration, to show anything on a one-inch map whose lineal dimensions are less than 53 ft. The corresponding figure on a scale of six inches to the mile would be 8·8 ft.

The most suitable scale for field-maps in the British Isles is the 6 in. to a mile. For comparatively small areas, where the detail is fine and the structure complicated, it may be necessary to use a 25-in. plan, but for most purposes, the 6-in. map will suffice. This is the scale employed by the Geological Survey, and is the basis of the one-inch geological maps which are published.

Signs and Symbols Used on Geological Maps

The function of the field-map is for the plotting of *observations of facts* such as types of rock, dips, and the like. All information marked on the map should be plotted *in the field* at the time and place where the observations were made. Any alterations which may be required should be made *in the field*. If an entry on the map seems doubtful, the fact should be recorded in the notebook, and the earliest possible opportunity taken of verifying the doubtful entry on the spot where the original note was made. It is often very tempting to move the position of a boundary line somewhat after returning from the day's work, but if a line has been plotted carefully with the evidence at hand, it is scarcely likely that any real amendment can be made when the necessary data are not available. The ideal to be aimed at in mapping is that what is once put down on the map shall stand; in other words, nothing should be marked on the field-map without very good reason. To have to erase from the map is an indication of shoddy work.

Even on a 6-in. map there is not a great deal of room for writing information; therefore, it is necessary to use signs and symbols, which should be drawn or written in a small, neat hand, and it is worth while taking great pains (especially in the early stages) to acquire the habit of writing clearly and neatly.

In the field we map rock types, and, in its early stages at any rate, a geological map is a *lithological map*. Shorthand symbols for different types of rock are therefore required, such as *ss* for sandstone, *lst* for limestone. If two separate bands of sandstone must be shown on the same map, it is quite easy to use *ss* for one and *SS* for the other, and similar devices may easily be adopted for other types of rock. As an alternative, coloured pencils may be used, and small dots of blue, for example, can be used to indicate limestones, greens for sandstones and grit, various reds for igneous rocks, while greys are suitable colours for clays, shales, and slates.

In addition, there are certain conventional signs in common use, some of which are shown in Fig. 12. In the field the various signs are drawn in pencil (H or 2H is generally recommended); for this purpose the point should be kept really sharp, and a penknife, supplemented by a small block of fine glass-paper, should be carried. In the evening all necessary entries which are to remain on the map should be carefully inked in with waterproof ink and the pencil marks should be carefully erased. Anything which is doubtful may remain in pencil until the doubt has been cleared up, but pencilled notes should not remain longer than necessary because in time they become more or less fixed and difficult to remove; they are also liable to become blurred and illegible.

Preparing the Base-Map

Six-inch Ordnance maps are at present supplied as the old quarter-sheets, each 18 × 12 in., covering an area of 6 square miles, or as the new edition of sheets 5 kilometres square, which are 18·65 × 18·65 in. The most convenient unit for use in the field is a quarter of a quarter-sheet (or, in the new edition, a quarter of a sheet), which is often known as a "field-slip".

If the map is engraved with the National Grid, the numbers of grid lines should be carefully written alongside the lines in waterproof ink and within the *frame*, since they will be required when making reference to positions on the map. It is useful, also, to ink in carefully *one* true N.-S. line on each slip to use as a reference when it is necessary to set off bearings on the map. If the map is not gridded it may be possible to extend the grid from an adjacent sheet.

The border of the map is then cut off with a *sharp knife*. It is useful to preserve that portion of the bottom margin which bears the scale; this can be carried in the map-case and used when measurements of distance must be made. After being trimmed, the map is cut into four quarters, again using a sharp knife for

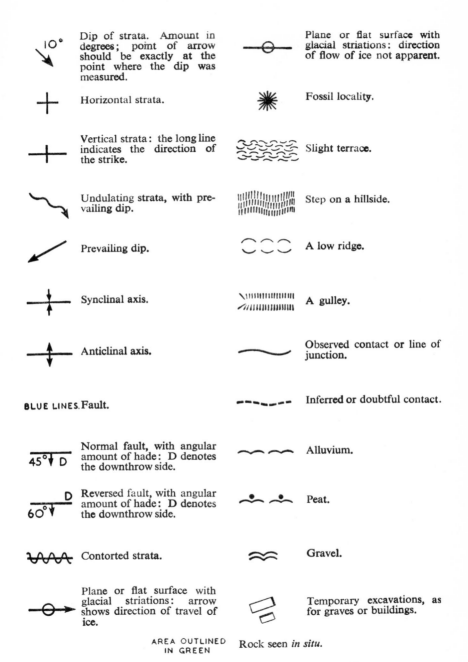

10°	Dip of strata. Amount in degrees; point of arrow should be exactly at the point where the dip was measured.		Plane or flat surface with glacial striations: direction of flow of ice not apparent.
	Horizontal strata.		Fossil locality.
	Vertical strata: the long line indicates the direction of the strike.		Slight terrace.
	Undulating strata, with prevailing dip.		Step on a hillside.
	Prevailing dip.		A low ridge.
	Synclinal axis.		A gulley.
	Anticlinal axis.		Observed contact or line of junction.
BLUE LINES.	Fault.		Inferred or doubtful contact.
45° D	Normal fault, with angular amount of hade: D denotes the downthrow side.		Alluvium.
60° D	Reversed fault, with angular amount of hade: D denotes the downthrow side.		Peat.
	Contorted strata.		Gravel.
	Plane or flat surface with glacial striations: arrow shows direction of travel of ice.		Temporary excavations, as for graves or buildings.
	AREA OUTLINED IN GREEN	Rock seen *in situ*.	

Fig. 12. Signs and Symbols Used on Geological Maps.

29

the purpose; scissors are not satisfactory since it is practically impossible to cut sufficiently straight with them.

On the back of each slip particulars which will enable it to be identified should be written, including the name of the county, the number of the sheet, the letters giving the designation of the quarter-sheet, and the section thereof; for example, DERBYSHIRE, 29, SE./SW. This enables the slip to be identified with certainty.

CARE OF THE FIELD-MAP

Although the initial cost of a 6-in. map is comparatively small, the value of the map to the geologist increases with the extent to which it has been used. The older the map, the greater the store of information which it comes to bear. Some of the observations recorded will almost certainly be derived from temporary sections and are therefore irrecoverable should the original copy be lost or destroyed. Field-maps should therefore always be treated with the greatest respect and stored with the owner's most cherished possessions.

When in use, the field-map must be protected from rain and kept free from dirty finger-marks and the like. We therefore advocate the use of a map-case such as that illustrated in Fig. 1 (p. 7). The case is conveniently slung over the shoulder on an endless strap, to which it is attached by swivels carried on rings which run freely on the strap; the case can then readily be detached when required. We suggest, further, that the sling should be worn *underneath* the jacket; a certain amount of extra protection is thus obtained, and if it is desired to remove the jacket, there is no need to take off the map-case and its sling.

Only those sections of the map which are required for immediate use in the field should be carried in the map-case; the remainder should be kept in a secure place under cover. In high wind there is a risk that the map may be blown out of the case; to guard against this, it is useful to carry four *small* "Bulldog" spring-clips, one of which can be used at each end of the two field-slips to anchor them more securely into position.

It should be a point of honour with the geologist to ensure that in wet weather, whoever and whatever may get wet, his field-map is kept dry. A few drops of water will so soften the surface of the paper that any attempt to write or draw thereon will result in a mess which cannot afterwards be cleaned up.

PRELIMINARY STUDY OF THE MAP; PHYSICAL FEATURES

Before starting the actual mapping of an area it is advisable to make a preliminary study of the relief, both from the map and on the ground. For this purpose the scale of the relief map may well be smaller than that of the field geological map; an inch to a mile, or the 1/25,000 (the two-and-a-half-inch map), are good scales, for they allow the general shape of a reasonably large area to be studied and the trends of various features to be appreciated. A contoured one-inch or two-and-a-half-inch map will generally give a better picture of an area than the corresponding six-inch sheets, because the area which can easily be taken in by the eye at one time is strictly limited.

The relief features of an area result from the action of erosive agents, such as water and ice acting upon the rocks. Thus a study of the map will give an indication of the nature and disposition of the rocks, and also of the type of erosion to which they have been subjected. The following features are among those which might be noted:—

(*a*) *Long ranges of hills* may indicate harder rock and may follow the strike of the rocks; as in the Purbeck Hills. Folded rocks may sometimes give rise to alternating vales and ridges, as in the Cork and Kerry districts of Ireland. The presence of a dome is sometimes indicated by a radial or annular drainage pattern, as in the Woolhope dome in Herefordshire.

Fig. 13. ESCARPMENT AND RIDGE RESULTING FROM HARD BAND WITH LOW OR HIGH DIP.

(*b*) *Steep slopes* backed by long gentle slopes may indicate did and scarp relief. The long gentle slope is called the dip while the steeper is the scarp. Escarpment relief is formed by the prolonged erosion of rocks which consist of alternating hard and soft bands, usually dipping at a relatively low angle. In descending the steep scarp slopes the observer proceeds from newer to older rocks, and vice versa (Fig. 13). The Cotswold Hills and the Chiltern Hills are examples of escarpments in England. Steep slopes, particularly when they are unindented, may also owe their origin to faults (fault-scarps) or to erosion along faults (fault-line scarp). The steep eastern side of the Eden valley in Westmorland, is a fault-line scarp.

(*c*) If there is *little difference in the slopes* over an area, the rocks are probably relatively homogeneous, as in Dartmoor (on granite) or in Exmoor (on sandstones).

(*d*) *Flat-topped hills* which in profile show a series of "steps" are probably carved out of alternating hard and soft rocks which are nearly horizontal or only slightly dipping (Fig. 14). Reference to a geological map will show that the outcrop of horizontal rocks follows the contour lines of an area, in other words they will have the same outlines or shapes as the contours. Examples of such step-like profiles are seen in Robinswood Hill near Gloucester, an outlier of the Cotswold Hills, and in Ingleborough Hill in N.W. Yorkshire.

Fig. 14.   STEP-LIKE PROFILE OF HILL MADE UP OF ALTERNATING HARD AND SOFT BEDS.

(*e*) *A gorge in a river valley* may mean that the river is cutting through hard rocks, often limestone, as in the Avon gorge at Bristol. Within the gorge, the direction of the river is frequently at right angles to the strike or at a marked angle to it.

(*f*) *A sharp break in the profile* of a river's bed may give rise to a waterfall or to rapids. A waterfall may be caused by the outcrop of a hard bed above a soft one, the dip being at a low angle and

Fig. 15.   WATERFALL AND RAPIDS, CAUSED RESPECTIVELY BY HARD ROCKS DIPPING AT LOW AND HIGH ANGLES.

upstream; this accounts for the waterfall of Hardrow Scar in Wensleydale in Yorkshire, where the water falls over limestone lying on top of shales. Rapids are often caused by an outcrop of hard rocks running transverse to the river and dipping at a high angle (Fig. 15). Features of river erosion, such as potholes and swirlholes, are usually associated with both waterfalls and rapids. A sharp break in the profile of a river may also be brought about by a change in the base-level (often sea-level) of the river, when it constitutes a *nick point*.   The falls of the Ystwyth river at Rheidol in Central **Wales** are probably situated at a nick point.

(*g*) *Straight stretches without any indentation* along a river may indicate a fault line.   Narrow belts of marshy ground, again if they are fairly straight, often occur along the shatter-zones of faults.

(*h*) *Right-angled bends* in streams or valleys may follow joints or faults.   This may be seen in valleys in the chalk in the Berkshire Downs, in streams, on the granites of Dartmoor, or in the River Swere near Banbury.

(*i*) *A river which disappears underground* into a swallow hole or cave (or "pot hole") does so when it passes from an area of impervious and insoluble rocks to a pervious and soluble rock, usually a limestone.   Fell Beck on the slopes of Ingleborough rises on impervious shales and sinks into the Carboniferous Limestones at Gaping Gill Hole.   If massively-bedded limestone is present in an area, then the map may indicate this by the general lack of surface drainage and its diversion into caves;   by the presence of bare rock surfaces and cliffs as on Ingleborough;   by the occurrence of enclosed hollows (often circular);   and by the development of dry valleys, *i.e.* water-formed valleys which do not now contain a stream. Several of these features are seen in the Malham district of Yorkshire or in the Mendips.   Dry valleys are also particularly well developed in the softer limestone area of the Cotswolds and the chalk of Southern England.

(*j*) *Large springs* usually occur where the basal beds of a limestone sequence overlie an insoluble bed as at Austwick Beck Head in Yorkshire where the Carboniferous Limestone overlies slates. The junction of pervious rocks such as sandstones with impervious beds (*e.g.* clays), also gives rise to springs but these are usually not nearly so large as in limestone country.   Lines of springs therefore indicate a junction or fault in the vicinity.   However, one or two isolated springs may have no geological significance.

(*k*) *Valleys whose cross-section is an open* **V**-*shape* and in which the view is obstructed by interlocking spurs projecting from alternate sides are evidence that they have been formed by the action of rivers (Fig. 16).   Bed rock outcrops frequently occur along the valley sides and also in areas of waterfalls and rapids.   Rivers which meander over a wide flat plain are likely to be flowing on alluvium and their floors and banks are unlikely places for bed rock to be found. Oxbow lakes may occur and these indicate the sites of former river meanders.   A river may terminate in a lake or in the sea by a *delta*, where the suspended load of the river has been dropped suddenly; an example occurs in the River Dee as it enters Lake Bala in North Wales.

(*l*) *Old river deposits* or erosion flats may form *terraces* running along the sides of valleys and can be seen along the River Thames. River valleys which are deeply incised (with *incised meanders*) may indicate relatively recent uplift of the land.

Fig. 16.   RIVER VALLEY SHOWING OVERLAPPING SPURS.

(*m*) *Valleys of* U-*shaped cross-section*, the view along which is unobstructed by interlocking spurs, may have been modified by glaciers (Fig. 17).   Armchair-shaped hollows (*cirques*) which occur in highland areas are also evidence of glacial erosion.   Both U-valleys and cirques are found in the Nant Ffrancon area of North Wales.   On a two-and-a-half-inch map further evidence of glacial erosion may be seen, as on the two-and-a-half-inch sheets of Sutherland in Scotland where ice-scoured rock pavements and cliffs are clearly shown.

(*n*) The evidence for the deposition of material by glaciers is diverse.   *A glacial till plain* has usually little relief and may be badly drained.   *Moraines* may be represented by hummocky relief;

terminal moraines are often crescentic, like the York terminal moraine.

Oval or whale-backed hills rising from 50-150 ft. above the surrounding relief and more or less parallel to one another may be *drumlins;* drumlins are made up of ice-moulded glacial till and are aligned in the direction of movement of the last ice sheet, the steeper side usually being on the up side of the ice movement; examples occur in North Ribblesdale, Yorkshire. Long winding ridges in a glaciated area may represent *eskers,* which are formed of fluvio-glacial gravels, and are common in central Ireland. Former *glacial lakes* may leave old beach lines which may appear as flat terraces along the valley sides as in the parallel roads of Glen Roy.

Fig. 17.   GLACIATED VALLEY.

(*o*) Along the sea coast there may be evidence of *raised beaches* or *wave-cut platforms;* on a map these might appear as nearly flat areas above the present sea-level. Such beaches may not be represented on the one-inch map but can often be seen on the two-and-a-half-inch sheet as around the coast of the Isle of Arran, Scotland.

(*p*) *Active coastal erosion* may be suggested by the presence of cliffs as in parts of Devon and Cornwall; *coastal deposition* is indicated by the presence of spits and bars as on the north Norfolk coast. The longshore movement of material can be deduced from the presence of groynes built along the beaches in holiday resort areas, as at Brighton, and from the direction of growth of spits as at Orford Ness.

(q) **Areas** of *coastal sand dunes* and of *marshland* should be noted. The sand dunes may have resulted from the drifting action of wind upon large expanses of coastal sand, as at Perranporth in Cornwall. Salt marshes may form extensive flat areas along the coast where, as in the Dee estuary, they are frequently formed by the combined deposition of rivers and sea.

CHAPTER V

GEOLOGICAL MAPPING (2)

SOME GENERAL CONSIDERATIONS

The construction of a geological map is the result of a process of induction; data are first collected, and, as the result of deduction therefrom, the map is built up, boundary lines are drawn between the various formations, and the necessary symbols are inserted to show the structure of the area.

Data consist of *facts* which may be first-hand or second-hand. First-hand facts are derived by observation (in quarries and other exposures) and experiment (such as augering and the digging of holes or pits) *by the geologist himself.* Second-hand facts include all information gathered from other people; they may be in the form of published or unpublished records of details of sections of wells, borings, cuttings, and the like, or they may consist of verbal information given by people in the locality.

First-hand data as recorded on the map or in the notebook should never be susceptible of doubt; observations must be recorded when and where they are made, a clear distinction being drawn between what is actually seen and what is inferred. If a limestone is encountered in a quarry, that is an observed fact; the dip, its direction, the type of bedding, the presence of fossils, etc., are all *facts.* The geological age of the limestone, however, is arrived at by inference (probably by a study of the fossils); it does not come into the category of first-hand data. Therefore, on the map, a symbol representing limestone is all that should be recorded while data are being collected; the colouring or shading which indicate the age of the limestone should be added later, after the bearing of the observations has been considered.

Second-hand data may or may not be reliable; the source of any information should always be recorded in the notebook. Full references to a published paper should be given, and the reliability of other second-hand data assessed as far as possible and a note thereof should be made. The log of a boring which has been made under the supervision of a trained geologist has obviously a very different degree of credibility from information picked up in conversation with a casual acquaintance in the village inn. It should be remembered that few people are good observers, while still fewer are capable of *reporting accurately what they saw*; the human mind is sadly hampered by an inveterate mythopoeic faculty as a result of which observations and interpretations become inextricably interwoven. The consequences are seen in the perennial reports of the sea-serpent, mermaids, or the Loch Ness monster. Doubtless *something* has been seen, but precisely *what*, is a matter which has never been settled. Every opportunity should be taken of collecting local information, which is often very useful; at the same time, such information should always be checked as far as possible, and a visit should always be paid to the spot referred to in the hope that "information received" may be converted into "information confirmed by observation."

First-hand facts must be obtained and recorded about the rocks in the area, the minerals, the fossils, and details of the country which are not shown on the map.

THE ROCKS

(i) *Their nature*, whether sandstone, limestone, clay, shale, granite, mica-schist, gneiss, etc. It is not always possible to identify a rock by field-tests (although every endeavour should be made to do so), nor is it absolutely necessary. Provided that a rock can be *recognised* in the field, wherever and however it occurs, its outcrop can be mapped. The beginner will often meet, and may have to map a rock (as, for example, the Toadstone in the Ashover district) whose nature he cannot fully determine while in the field, but which he can recognise as a definite contributor to the make-up of the country. When this occurs, specimens of the unidentifiable rock should be collected from several exposures and taken home for further examination.

The *geological age* of a rock and its *mode of formation* are matters of inference; they do not constitute data.

(ii) *Their attitude*. The attitude of a rock is defined by its dip and strike, both of which can be measured. Dip and strike should be determined and recorded wherever possible.

When dealing with foliated and cleaved rocks it is necessary to determine the dip and strike of the foliation or the cleavage; the *dips* of foliation and cleavage are liable to vary very rapidly, but the *strikes* are usually constant over wide areas.

(iii) *The succession*. If long continuous sections, such as in cliffs, rivers, or streams, are available, the succession can often be made out by direct observation. Large quarries and cuttings sometimes pass through one or more junctions which can actually be seen. Usually, however, the succession must be *inferred* from observations of dip and strike, coupled with the position on the map of the exposures at which the measurements were made.

(iv) *Exposures.*   Every exposure of every rock must be accurately located on the map and marked with a symbol or colour indicating the *type* of rock, together with any observations of dip which may have been made there.   Accurate descriptions, illustrated when necessary by sketches, should be made.

(v) *Bedding.*   If the rock is bedded, the type should be recorded. Bedding may be thick or thin, regular or irregular; lamination and current-bedding may be visible.   The bedding planes may show cracks or pits (*inference,* sun-cracking or rain-pitting) or ripple-marking.   If ripple-marks are observed their direction should be recorded and the dimensions of the marks measured and noted.

(vi) *Jointing.*   Whether open or closed, fine or coarse, regular or irregular, direction of the main joints.

(vii) *Signs of disturbance,* such as folding, contortion, slicken-siding, faulting, and thrusting.   Large- or small-scale slipping can be observed at times.

(viii) *The junction between adjacent types of rocks.*   When two different rocks are actually seen in contact with one another, the fact should be marked accurately by a short line on the map, running along the direction followed by the contact.   The greater part of the boundary lines will have to be mapped *by inference,* therefore any short lengths of *observed* junction are of the utmost value; it is only rarely that considerable lengths of boundary line can be plotted by direct observation.   The type of junction should be carefully studied; it may be regular and conformable, for example, where a sedimentary formation overlies another.   It may be irregular, such as a contact between a sedimentary and an igneous rock, or between two igneous rocks.   The junction may show unconformity, the upper formation lying across the upturned edges of the lower.   Often the upper rock may rest on a somewhat hummocky surface of the lower; when this occurs there is often a mass of pebbly material at the junction.

(ix) *Their physiographical expression.*   Hard rocks tend to form "features" which stand out above the lower ground formed by the softer rocks.   Some rocks produce decidedly craggy masses, others give rounded masses when weathered.   These facts are of value when tracing their outcrops, and give rise to what is known as "feature-mapping." (See p. 53.)

(x) *The assemblage of plants on the various types of rock.* Valuable information is often given in the tracing of outcrops by the vegetation. Well-grown oak-trees generally tend to be restricted to shaley and clayey soils; bracken, heath, gorse, birch, and fir-trees are more likely to be associated with less fertile sandy soils.

The Fossils

(i) *Their nature*, so far as this can be determined in the field. See Chapter XV. The fossils from each exposure should be collected and kept together and separate from those from other exposures.

(ii) *Mode of occurrence*, whether in the position of growth or not, complete or fragmentary, rolled or unrolled; the mode of preservation, whether as casts, moulds, or "entires"; whether distorted or not.

(iii) *Whether any species are restricted* to special bands or zones, and the assemblages present therein.

(iv) *The extent to which the fossils* contribute to the make-up of the rock or to any particular layer thereof.

The determination of the *age* of a deposit from fossil evidence is a matter of *inference*; it is not directly *observed*.

The Minerals

The following remarks apply specially to those minerals which are not essential constituents of the rocks. The particulars which should be observed and recorded include—

(i) *Their nature*, so far as this can be determined in the field. See Chapter XII.

(ii) *Mode of occurrence*, including the rocks in which they are found and whether they occur in veins, segregations, or cavities.

(iii) *Their associations.* A knowledge of mineral associations is important, since certain minerals may act as "pointers" to others. Thus, if topaz, tourmaline, and white mica are found together, it is always worth while making an extended search for cassiterite (tinstone).

Particular attention should always be given to old mine-dumps, where good specimens may often be found; moreover, a good idea may be formed of what minerals occur in the district.

If minerals are found in the bed of a stream, the course of the stream should be followed both upwards and downwards with a view to ascertaining the limits within which they occur. The upper limit must mark the point from which the minerals are derived, and a search in the neighbourhood may disclose a vein or lode.

EXAMINING AND RECORDING SECTIONS

Whenever a section (temporary or permanent) is examined, careful and comprehensive notes should be made on the spot; nothing should be left to the memory. The increased use of machinery for quarrying and excavating has led to sections being opened and covered over within a matter of a few weeks, or even, in extreme cases, a few days; unless, therefore, the earliest possible opportunity is taken of recording full details, particulars of importance may be missed and never noted, let alone put on record. In the more leisurely days of thirty or forty years ago, a section might remain open and in use for years, during which time careful study might be made and specimens collected. Work was carried out by hand, and the opportunities of obtaining specimens from workmen were usually good. Now, however, excavation is by mechanical means; sections are rapidly cut back and the sites are abandoned or filled with rubbish as soon as the required material is worked out. Valuable specimens have less chance of being observed and put aside; the chances of breakage are increased, so that although the quantity of material shifted in a given time is much greater, the likelihood that important fossils will be observed and preserved for study is diminished.

Sections in quarries do not usually cross geological junctions; the object of the contractor is to obtain the maximum yield of a commercial material in the shortest possible time, and with the minimum expense. He therefore prefers to work where the rock is thick and not likely to be mixed with that which he does not want. Road-cuttings, on the other hand, frequently cross from one formation to another, and boundary lines can often be accurately located and studied, provided the geologist sees the cutting when it is being made. But the road-maker has an unfortunate habit of sloping back his cutting and rapidly turfing it over, and hiding the desired information. Therefore, unless the geologist is living in the immediate neighbourhood of the ground on which he is working, he will do well to arrange with one of the local inhabitants to let him know when any fresh excavations are in progress or are about to be carried out. It is then often possible to make a special trip to examine what may prove to be a key section.

Here it should be stressed that no section is too small to deserve examination. Trenches for drains, foundations of houses, and the like are all worthy of attention, particularly in towns, where the chance of seeing below the subsoil is generally poor. Foundations for houses are generally mere scrapings on the surface, but occasionally they go deeper, as, for example, where a hotel or public house has new cellars dug. Pylons carrying electric cables are provided with deep foundations, and since the lines go more or less straight across country, the throw-out is always worth examining, for there is less tendency to choose the site with special regard to what is underneath. In fact, a good traverse-section might be constructed if it were possible to examine the material thrown out when a line of pylons was constructed over several miles of country.

The exact position of the section or exposure should be carefully recorded; this may be done in a number of ways. Quarries are often marked on the map; great alterations in shape and size may, however, have taken place since the map was last revised. It may therefore be necessary to correct the map in order to show the quarry correctly, for which purpose aerial photographs are often useful. This may be important, for as a result of recent work, features may be brought to light which require to be accurately located on the map.

Often, exposures are more or less "up in the air," in the sense that they are not actually on a line (such as the border of a road, the banks of a stream, or a hedge-row between fields) which is marked on the map. It then becomes necessary to locate them by some other means. This may be by measurement of distance from one or more recognisable objects or features which can be identified both on the map and on the ground. Alternatively, it is occasionally necessary to fix a position by taking sights with a prismatic or other suitable compass on two, or (preferably) more prominent objects on the map, and plotting the bearings thus obtained. It is not proposed here to go into the details of locating positions; it is assumed that readers are familiar with the methods of using topographical maps, otherwise they would scarcely set out to construct a geological map. Attention should, however, be drawn to two points, both of which ought to be familiar. (*a*) When taking bearings to fix a position on the map, the internal angles between the "rays" should be at least 45°, if possible. (*b*) Sights should be short, half a mile or so, for the longer the sight, the greater is the error resulting from the inevitable imperfections in the apparatus used and in protracting the bearing on paper. (*c*) The point on which the sight is taken must be *accurately* identified; when working on a six-inch map, if the object is a building, the sight should be taken on one corner which can be recognised both on the map and on the ground. (*d*) The compass must be carefully calibrated, and, of course, kept well away from steel objects while sights are being taken. It is not enough to make use of the statement of magnetic variation and rate of change thereof which is marked on the border of the map. Compasses have an individual error; therefore, the best thing is to make a check on the ground by direct observation.

Probably as simple a way as any of calibrating the compass is to take one or more (preferably several) sights along straight runs of road or between easily identifiable objects on the map. From the directions of the straight lines on the map, and the bearings, it will then be possible to draw the line of *compass-north* on the map, from which subsequent observations can be laid off. The advantage of using compass- instead of true-north is that no correction of bearings which are read need be made; furthermore, the side-lines of even a six-inch sheet do not run true north and south, and the farther north we go, the greater is the discrepancy.

Having fixed the position of the exposure on the map and, if necessary, drawn it in as accurately as possible, it is a good plan to surround it by a fine line *in green ink*. The advantage of green-lining exposures is that at any later date, inspection of the map will show clearly where rock was actually seen *in situ*. This may be a matter of great convenience either to the original observer or to some later investigator who uses the original or a copy of the original map.

Even on a six-inch map, there is very little room for making notes, and in any case, it is undesirable to write more than the shortest possible abbreviations or to introduce more than the smallest and neatest symbols to indicate *matters of fact*, such as the nature of the rocks, dips, etc., at exposures. All else, particularly *deductions* from observations and matters of opinion, should be relegated to the notebook, where also descriptions and measurements of sections, together with sketches, should be entered. Means whereby notes may be referred to the appropriate position on the map are suggested below.

(i) *National-grid reference.* This is the best and most convenient method. The co-ordinates of the point are given in terms of the national grid, the easting being given first, then the northing. Unfortunately, not all copies of the six-inch map are yet gridded, although those sheets constituting the "Provisional" and subsequent editions are. It is possible to transfer the grid accurately from the corresponding sheet of the 1/25,000 map if sufficient care is taken.

(ii) *In terms of longitude and latitude.* While this would be "absolute," two scales would be required for each sheet of the map, for while the value of one minute of arc in a north-south direction is always as nearly as possible 1·15 miles, the equivalent distance in an east-west direction diminishes as the latitude increases, so that at a latitude of 53° (Ashover), the value of a minute of arc is only 0·69 mile.

A reference given in terms of either the national grid or of longitude and latitude enables a point to be located accurately whatever the scale of the map.

(iii) *By co-ordinates.* In this method, each slip is divided into a number of squares of convenient size; the east–west co-ordinates are lettered, while the north–south are numbered. A convenient size of square for a six-inch map is $1\frac{1}{2}$ in., or a quarter of a mile. The position of a point would be defined as in (say) square C 2; its exact position would be determined by imagining that each side of the square was divided into ten equal parts, so that the reference might be C 5, 2 3. It would be necessary to define also the particular slip on which the point was located, so that the complete reference might be, "Derbyshire, 30, NW./SE., C 5, 2 3."

The method is simple, and if the system of numbering the squares on each slip is always the same, namely letters from A to F in the west–east sense, and numbers from 1 to 4 in a north–south direction, a point can be located rapidly and with certainty on any copy of the particular quarter-sheet, whether the original or otherwise. If the necessary lines are drawn on tracing-cloth, the cloth can be laid over the map when notes are to be made, and the map need not be ruled.

(iv) *Point system.* Each note is given a serial number, which is neatly written at the appropriate point on the map and enclosed in a small ring. The reference in the notebook might then be, "Derbyshire, 29, NE./NE., 6." The number of the sheet of the map and the particular slip should always be quoted. Although a simple solution, it suffers from the disadvantage that a large number of figures may have to be marked on each slip, and their positions are quite arbitrary. If the original slip is not available, it is wellnigh impossible to relate the notes to the map, unless the method is combined with one of the others described.

(v) *By reference to prominent objects.* The position is defined by giving the distance and/or the bearing from two or more easily identifiable points on the map. When employing this method, care must be taken to select reference-points which are easily identifiable and which are not likely to be altered on subsequent editions of the map. Junctions of hedges, isolated barns, large trees, although convenient as fixed points, are not good to use when fixing positions in the field. They are by no means permanent, and in a matter of a few years may be removed and forgotten. The method is cumbersome and entails more writing than the others; it may, however, sometimes prove useful.

WHAT TO OBSERVE AND RECORD

The next question is, what should be observed and recorded? In broad general terms, the answer is "everything." Every observable fact has some meaning, and it is the duty of the geologist to take note of even trifling pieces of information, for he can never be sure that what appears at first sight to be irrelevant, may not become of great evidential importance, and throw light on some obscure and troublesome problem.

Points which should be recorded include—

The nature of the rock or rocks. Determinations should be made of dip and strike, if observable, directions of joints (if seen), and details of stratification, cleavage, and foliation should be noted. In stratified rocks, every opportunity should be taken of obtaining fossils, including the matrix in which they are enclosed, and it is desirable that specimens should be taken of the various types of rocks exposed, since at a later date it may not be possible to make up for any deficiency in this respect.

The section should be measured, layer by layer, and full notes taken, together with a sketch of the section and a photograph or photographs. Generally, a photograph without a sketch is less useful than a sketch without a photograph, since the camera often fails to bring out just those features which are of most importance. In addition, a diagrammatic sketch is a useful supplement to a photograph, since it serves as a key to the latter, enabling important points to be picked out which may not be very obvious on a print.

If the geologist has any aptitude for rapid and accurate sketching he should cultivate it to the utmost. But let him beware that his artistic propensity does not run riot so that he concentrates more on the pictorial than the geological aspects of his sketch.

Some sections are almost impossible to describe adequately; here a sketch, even if diagrammatic, is essential. Examples of recorded sections are given below; others will be found on pp 67 and 72.

Example of a carefully measured section.   [G. W. Himus and A. Wood, *Proc. Geol. Assoc.*, **55** (1944), p. 21.]   Reference, Kent, 15, SE./NE.

		Ft.	In.
	Soil, very thin .. .. about	3	
	Fine sand with flint pebbles and fragments of Chalk, possibly replacing laterally some of the previous beds..	4	0
	Bed of small flint pebbles, sometimes cutting down into the bed below		1½
	Fine brown sand thickening to north-west 4 ft. to	6	0
	Pebble beds, with rolled flints, some white and weathered right through, others with a black surface. Cutting down sometimes 3 ft. into the beds below .. .. .. 3 ft. to	6	0
Blackheath Beds, say 20 ft.	Clay silt, with eroded top .. .. 1 ft. to	2	0
	Bedded clay silt, passing into sandy silt with patches of rolled clay	1	4
	Brown, fine-grained sand with fragments of *Cyrena* in lower portion	1	6
	"Shell bed," mainly *Ostrea bellovacina* Lam. and *Cyrena* sp. (the latter dominant in the upper layers) converted into a hard stone	3	0
	Brown sand .. .. 1 ft. 6 in. to	2	0
	Comminuted shells in sand		4
	Fine brown sand, passing down into silt	2	0
	Silty clay, passing down into grey and brown clay	1	0
	Grey clay		4
Woolwich and Reading Beds, 15 ft.	Comminuted shells		4
	Brown clay, passing down into grey clay with shells	1	6
	Shell bed; comminuted shells in clay	1	0
	Brown clayey silt, passing down into grey and brown variegated clay; brown, bedded clay at base	3	3
	Comminuted shells in grey clay		9
	Brown and grey clay with tiny fragments of shells	5	0
	Remainder of section obscured by talus.		

The following is an example of a classic section which is both illustrated (Fig. 18) and described.   It is taken from *The Antiquity of Man*, by Sir Charles Lyell, first edition (1863), p. 135.

Section of a Gravel-Pit at St. Acheul, near Amiens.   Observed in July, 1860.

1. Vegetable soil and made ground—two to three feet thick.
2. Brown loam with some angular flints, in parts passing into ochreous gravel, filling up indentations on the surface of No. 3—three feet thick.
3. White siliceous sand with layers of chalky marl, and included fragments of chalk, for the most part unstratified—nine feet.

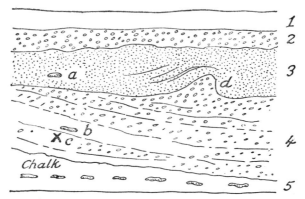

Fig. 18.   SECTION IN A GRAVEL PIT AT ST. ACHEUL.

4. Flint-gravel, and whitish chalky sand, flints sub-angular, average size of fragments three inches diameter, but with some large unbroken chalk flints intermixed, cross stratification in parts.   Bones of mammalia, grinder of elephant at *b*, and flint implement at *c*—ten to fourteen feet.

5. Chalk with flints.

   a, Part of elephant's molar, eleven feet from surface.

   b, Entire molar of *E. primigenius*, seventeen feet from surface.

   d, Projecting ridge of the gravel, No. 4.

Sometimes a section is so complicated that it defies description in words.   The only means of recording its appearance is then by means of a sketch, such as is reproduced in Fig. 19.

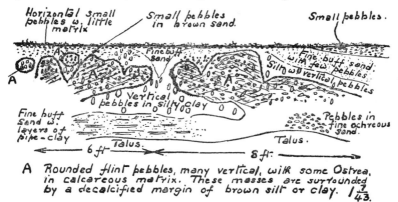

Fig. 19.   SECTION IN BLACKHEATH BEDS, WEST WICKHAM, KENT.

The section sketched was about 14 ft. long, and about 5 ft. vertical was observable; the lower portions were obscured by slip.

CHAPTER VI

GEOLOGICAL MAPPING (3)

TRACING BOUNDARY LINES

The line of junction between two rocks is seldom visible for more than a few feet continuously; it is nearly always covered by a mantle of soil, and not infrequently by superficial deposits such as alluvium, gravel, or glacial drift. The business of the geologist is, therefore, often to map what he *cannot see*, in contrast with the topographer, who maps visible features only.

Sometimes, the observer is fortunate and finds exposures at such frequent intervals that he can locate a junction with certainty within a distance of a few feet. These conditions are exceptional; boundaries must therefore be mapped partly by direct observation and partly by inference, every possible source of information being used to the full. How the necessary data should be collected and used forms the subject of the present chapter.

EXPOSURES

Every exposure has a story to tell; wherever rock is seen, it should be carefully examined and the site marked on the map (green line) with an appropriate symbol to show the nature of the rock. Care must be taken to see that the rock is *in situ*; sometimes, the observer may be led astray by an isolated boulder which has been deposited by glacial action or which has slipped or tumbled downhill in the course of ages. Unreliable evidence of this kind may lead to serious errors in the interpretation of the structure of a region, and every endeavour should be made to obtain more reliable information.

Exposures may be obvious or "not so obvious." The former category includes quarries, cliff, river, and coast sections; road and railway cuttings; and temporary excavations. The less obvious exposures may require more search, and include ditches, the throwout from the installation of telegraph posts, gate posts, electric pylons, rabbit scrapings, mole-hills, and the like.

Quarries have already been dealt with on p. 41.

Cliff sections, if followed for a sufficient distance, are almost certain to intersect boundary lines, while wave-cut platforms often provide valuable information. Beach-reefs sometimes permit observations of dip and strike to be made. Inland cliffs (escarpments), which result from sub-aerial denudation, are generally confined to a single formation.

River and Stream Sections. In hilly and moorland areas, where vegetation is heavy or thick deposits of peat or boulder clay occur, the only exposures may be in stream courses. Even if the banks have been rounded off and slumped so that good exposures are not seen in them, occasional ribs of rock will often be found crossing the bed of the stream, while pebbles and boulders, other than those derived from the boulder clay may provide valuable information.

If there is no boulder clay, the presence of fragments of two rocks, *A* and *B* would indicate that both cropped out in the vicinity. On following up the bed of the stream, the fragments of both rocks would become larger and more angular. At some determinate point, pieces of *A* only would be found; it would therefore be concluded that the outcrop of *B* had been passed, and that the junction between *A* and *B* was in the neighbourhood of the point at which the last fragments of *B* were found.

Cuttings for roads and railways may provide permanent or temporary exposures; they may, however, with advantage be dealt with in the following paragraph.

Temporary excavations. Trenches for drains, sewers, and telephone lines are likely to be particularly informative, because they provide long, continuous sections, often sufficiently deep to cut into bedrock. They run across country in predetermined lines and are not likely to be restricted to a single formation. Where they run at a considerable angle to the strike, they may intersect lines of junction which can then be located accurately.

Road cuttings are available to inspection, more particularly during the period of construction. Railway cuttings, however, are not open for examination by the casual geologist; it is necessary to obtain permission from the superintendent of the section of the line in which they run. It is important that when a railway cutting is to be examined, two persons should always be present, one of whom should keep continuous watch for and give timely warning of the approach of trains. More than one geologist has been killed when examining a railway section for the lack of this precaution.

The material brought up during the excavations for deep air-raid shelters has provided important information, while a deep cellar will often reach ten feet or more beneath the surface. Careful watch should also be kept on burial-grounds, for a hole which is seven or eight feet long and six feet deep may provide information in a critical spot.

Less obvious exposures. By closely scanning the edges of country roads, small exposures may often be seen, particularly when the banks have recently been cleaned to enable water to drain more freely. Ditches in and between fields which have recently been made or cleared are useful sources of information; to examine them requires careful traversing. When it is necessary to cross enclosed country, permission should always be obtained; provided the approach is made tactfully and pleasantly, there is seldom difficulty in obtaining sanction from landowners and farmers. Care should be taken that gates are not left open and that no damage is done to crops.

SOILS AND SUBSOILS

When examining quarries, careful attention should be given to the upper part of the sections with a view to noting how the rocks behave when they disintegrate. Where exposures are few, much reliance must be placed on the nature of the soil and subsoil; for, provided there has not been serious drifting or slipping down hill, the soil is derived from the disintegration of the rock which lies immediately beneath it.

Damp, heavy soils are indicative of clays (including boulder-clay), shales, and mudstones.

Sandy and gritty soils may arise from sandstones or grits.

Calcareous soils, which are generally dry and friable, probably overlie limestone or chalk.

Included fragments and pebbles are of great importance and should always be examined; they are usually best seen when the ground has recently been ploughed.

Angular fragments of sandstone in a sandy matrix would suggest an underlying sandstone, whereas the presence of water-worn pebbles might arise from a superficial layer of gravel or a decomposing conglomerate.

Flints are indicative of post-Cretaceous rocks beneath the soil. Unworn flints may be the residuum from the solution of chalk and indicate that chalk is present directly underneath, while if they are enclosed in a matrix of tenaceous yellow-brown clay, the rock is probably "Clay-with-Flints" and may be mapped as such.

Chert often occurs in the Weald to such an extent that in many orchards practically nothing else is visible at the surface; the indication is that Hythe Beds* lie below.

Well-preserved fossils sometimes abound in the soil or subsoil and are turned up by the plough. If they can be identified, the age of the underlying rock may be determined.

Sub-angular to angular stones, some of which are, perhaps, striated, in a stiff clay, show the presence of till or boulder-clay.

The value of the information to be obtained from an examination of the soil depends, of course, on whether it has been transported from a distance or has been formed directly from the rock beneath. *When mapping* on steep slopes, it is necessary to allow for natural downward trend of the soil or "soil-creep." This is illustrated in Fig. 20, where three rocks, grit, shale, and limestone respectively,

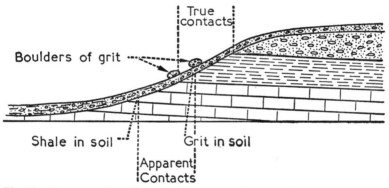

Fig. 20.   EFFECT OF HILL-CREEP IN DISPLACING APPARENT LINE OF CONTACT.

are shown making up the section of a hill, the surface being covered by a thick mantle of soil.

Owing to downward migration, fragments of grit and shale will be found lower down the hillside than the limits of the outcrops of the parent rocks; therefore, the boundary line, as judged by a superficial examination of the soil, would tend to be drawn too low. If, however, on working up the slope of the hill, the grit/shale junction were located by taking note of the point at which the *uppermost* particle of shale was found in the soil (neglecting the probably abundant pieces of grit derived from above), the position of the junction would be closely arrived at. On steeply sloping

* In Kent, the Hythe Beds (Lower Greensand) consist of bands of rather friable sandstone (" hassock ") which alternate with bands of hard, blue-hearted limestone ("Kentish rag"). In the upper portion of the sequence there is much chert.

ground, the golden rule is *map well up*. If the contact runs directly up the slope of the hill, there is little tendency for particles of either rock to migrate laterally; therefore, the problem is simpler.

Soil-creep often affords sufficient sandy or clayey soil—as the case may be—to allow the growth of bracken or gorse, sedge or marsh grass; it may thus lead to the incorrect mapping of geological boundary lines where reliance is being placed on the observation of plant communities or *ecology*.

Irregularities and features are generally most easily visible, both on the ground and on aerial photographs, (*a*) when the ground is lightly covered by snow, (*b*) when the lighting is oblique (early morning and late evening), and (*c*) after prolonged drought.

PLANT AND ANIMAL LIFE

Closely connected with the soils are the plants and animals which live on and in them, and the correlation should be established in each area and used as an aid to mapping. It is common knowledge that certain plants prefer some soils to others; thus, oak-trees flourish and grow to perfection on clay, and are stunted and decay prematurely on light soil. The well-known beechwoods of the Chiltern Hills, although they are sometimes said to grow on Chalk, do so only indirectly, for here, beechwoods are indicators of the overlying Clay-with-Flints. Bracken, gorse, rhododendrons, and Scots firs grow profusely on the Millstone Grit in the Ashover area of Derbyshire, while heath and heather flourish on moorlands where there is little or no lime in the soil. In Kent, the orchards of Kentish cobs are generally situated on Hythe Beds.

Animals also are helpful; moles and rabbits burrow into light soils and eschew clay. In grassland, where other exposures are seldom found, it may be possible to draw the boundary between (say) sandstone and clay by reference to the position of molehills on the one and their absence on the other. In addition, both rabbits and moles throw up fragments of what is below the surface, and these may provide useful clues.

Snails abound on limestones but are rare elsewhere; partridges generally prefer light and sandy soils, where they most easily find food. Adders prefer sandy soils and are rare on clays.

THE SHAPE OF THE GROUND: FEATURE-MAPPING

Every piece of country exhibits minor irregularities and features which are not shown on the map, because the contour-interval is too great. All these irregularities and features are the expression of geological facts, and it is the business of the geologist to riddle out their meaning and to make use of them in his work.

The shape of the surface of the ground is the product of a number of factors, including the types of rock which crop out, their disposition, and the extent and form of denudation to which they have been subjected. In general terms, rocks which are relatively resistant to denudation, or whose structure confers the power of resistance, tend to form higher ground than those which are more easily denuded. It is sometimes stated that each type of rock has its own way of weathering and so gives rise to a particular type of landscape. This, while broadly true, must be accepted with some reserve, for a great deal depends on the denuding influences which have been brought to bear, how the rock is disposed, and how far denudation has proceeded. Thus, granite in relatively sheltered positions weathers to more or less rounded outlines, whereas it may also weather into rough crags. Clays, too, while they generally form low-lying and rather damp areas, may, on occasion, form comparatively high ground, and may even stand up as steep slopes where they are protected by a capping of more resistant rocks. Chalk and limestone generally form high land, for although neither is very resistant to abrasion, and both are sensitive to chemical attack by water containing carbon dioxide, they are pervious to water, which cannot remain on the surface to give rise to streams.

Features, or *form lines*, are often well seen under the following conditions: (*a*) after a light covering of snow; (*b*) in oblique lighting, *i.e.* early in the morning or late in the evening, and (*c*) after a prolonged drought. These conditions also apply in connection with the study of aerial photographs.

It is necessary, therefore, for the field geologist to see how the rocks express themselves in the landscape in his special area and to make use of the information to the fullest extent.

Whether or not a particular rock will form an upstanding feature in the landscape depends very largely on the associated rocks. Dykes of basalt, for example, when injected into sediments, by their superior resistance, tend to weather out into wall-like masses, as may be seen on the coast of Ayrshire. On the other hand, only a few miles away, on Ailsa Craig, the basalt dykes, which have been injected into granite, weather into deep hollows. Sometimes, a dyke is less resistant than the altered sediments on either side of it, and as the result of weathering, the baked sediments stand up like walls above the surrounding unaltered sediments with a slit-like hollow between them, where the dyke has been denuded away.

A common example of mapping by feature is drawing the boundary of alluvium. Where a river runs through a valley which is not gorge-like, it is generally situated in a flat area consisting of alluvium, and the flat almost always butts against a change of slope, where the alluvium thins out against the underlying rocks. The river flat is not strictly horizontal when considered in the transverse direction, but slopes *downwards* very gently as one passes away from the river. The alluvium would be mapped by carefully observing the line along which the change of slope took place.

Similar changes of slope, and also "steps," are often observed on hillsides; these probably represent the expression given to the slope by a change of type of rock. By carefully mapping the position of such a change of slope, or the limits of a step on the hillside, *and* by taking every opportunity of ascertaining the nature of the rocks which crop out above and below, the positions of boundary lines may often be accurately plotted.

Fine examples of features made by rocks of different types are to be found in the Yoredale Series of the Yorkshire Dales, where there are alternations of limestones, sandstones, and shales. Here, the hillsides show a series of steps, the "treads" consisting of the shale bands, and the "risers" of the limestones.

THE USE OF THE AUGER

This instrument is particularly useful when dealing with comparatively soft rocks into which the bit of the auger will penetrate, for can thus be obtained samples from several feet below the surface. On one occasion, in the Weald, one of us (G.W.H.) was engaged in mapping the line of junction of the Gault clay with the underlying Folkestone Sands. The day was a hot one during a somewhat protracted dry spell, and a three-foot auger was being used. It was quickly found that the auger failed completely to penetrate into the Gault, which had baked hard, while the Folkestone Sand was so dry that the auger easily went down to the full depth, was easily withdrawn, and brought up very little sample.

KEY HORIZONS

Sometimes, the bed to be mapped obstinately refuses to show itself at the surface. It may be that the particular stratum is of great importance, such as a seam of coal. Now, supposing that there is an easily recognisable band which is persistent over a wide area, 100 feet *above* the seam of coal; then by mapping the band, the position of the coal can be deduced by geometrical methods.

WELLS AND BORINGS

Shallow wells (such as those marked on the six-inch map) are generally situated at the junction of a pervious with an impervious stratum, and consequently near to a junction, and if a line of wells is found, as in the case of springs, it will generally indicate a boundary line, or perhaps a fault. Enquiry will often elicit information about the rocks which were dug out when the well was sunk. When making enquiries, leading questions should not be asked; it is better to ask whether anything is known of the rocks which were turned out when the well was sunk, than to ask if a *particular* rock was met with.

Records of deep wells and borings can be obtained at the library of the Geological Survey in various papers and memoirs dealing with water-supply. In towns and cities, application to the Borough Engineer will often result in useful data being obtained, while water-supply undertakings can often give great help. Commercial undertakings are sometimes willing to assist if tactfully approached, and it is made clear that the geologist has no ulterior motive. See also Chap. X, p. 103.

TIP-HEAPS, MINE-DUMPS, AND THE LIKE

Mine-dumps are always worth examination, for apart from the fact that good specimens of minerals and fossils may often be collected from them, they provide information about the rocks below the surface. In the Ashover area, for example (p. 80), the throwout from two shaft sinkings about 200 feet apart gave much Carboniferous Limestone in both, but black shales *in one only*. It was concluded, therefore, that the boundary between the limestone and the overlying black shale passed between the two sites.

TRACING THE BOUNDARY LINES

The precise procedure to be followed will depend on local circumstances. Sometimes it may be best to make a series of traverses more or less at right angles to the strike, and thus to pick up a number of points on the boundary lines. In this way, the general direction of the line is determined, while the intervening detail is arrived at by following *along* the approximate run of the line between the fixed points. Alternatively, the observer can set out with the object of following along a single contact over the limits of a quarter-sheet or a single slip of the map. By traversing across the strike, it is probable that more than one contact will be crossed, so that the observer meets with a variety of rocks; when "walking" a line, there may be a tendency to sameness and resultant boredom. But whichever method is adopted, attention must be paid to all exposures which can be seen even though they are some distance from the line which is being plotted, for it is the business of the geologist to study the *whole of the ground* and to avoid converting himself into a kind of a "line hound" who keeps his nose down to the ground

and sees a line of junction and nothing more.   Where there are
many rocks cropping out over a relatively narrow belt, it is generally
unwise to make long traverses across the strike; if this is done,
too many outcrops will be crossed and the observer may become
obsessed by the difficulties of the area.   In this, as in all other proceedings, the object should be to attain a happy medium.

INTRUSIVE CONTACTS

The procedure to be followed when mapping sills is that out-
lined above, for an intrusive sill behaves in a similar way to a bed
in a sedimentary series, with the exception that it may cut across
from one horizon to another.   Dykes, which may be vertical, or
nearly so, run in much straighter lines than the outcrops of sediments,
although sometimes they may have been injected in more or less
concentric rings.

Where a dyke is more resistant to atmospheric influences than
the country-rock, it may stand out as a wall-like excrescence.
Sometimes, however, the topographic expression of a dyke may take
the form of a long, narrow trough with a slight rim on either side;
this occurs where the dyke is less resistant to weathering than the
country-rock.   The small rim on each side is caused by the harden-
ing of the surrounding rock by contact with the dyke, thereby
increasing its resistance to weathering.   A third possibility is that the
dyke and country-rock may be equally susceptible to denudation;
there will then be neither hummock nor hollow to indicate the
presence of the intrusion.

Large intrusions of plutonic rocks require that the contacts be
followed in great detail, for they often send out offshoots into the
country-rock, and these must be traced foot by foot.   Even though
the actual contact of a plutonic mass with associated sediments may
not always be visible, a good idea of its position may often be
obtained if the effect of the intrusion on the country-rock can be
established.   It will be found that in the immediate neighbourhood
of the contact, the country-rock is much altered; it is probably
highly indurated and fresh minerals may be developed.   If it can
be established by observation that "spots" are developed in slates
at a distance of (say) half a mile from a granite mass, then wherever
the slate is found to be spotted, it can be concluded that the contact
is in the vicinity, probably within half a mile.

The intrusive rock will probably show a "chilled margin"
which is more finely crystalline than the main body of the intrusion,
or the composition of the rock may be noticeably different near
the contact; it is often necessary to use these indications as pointers
in mapping.

SUPERFICIAL DEPOSITS

The superficial deposits are of Pleistocene and Recent age, and include alluvium, peat, gravels, and boulder-clay, which generally rest unconformably on the underlying rocks; they are usually comparatively thin and irregular in their occurrence.

Alluvium is the fine-grained silty material which is deposited on river flats and where rivers enter lakes.   The surface of an alluvial area is horizontal, so far as the eye can judge, and the junction with the underlying rocks is marked by the line where the level surface of the alluvium gives place to a slope.   The change of slope may be gentle or abrupt, depending on the nature of the rocks on which the alluvium rests.

Peat may occupy high or low ground; on Dartmoor and in the Cheviots, the thickest peat occupies the highest ground; in Somerset and on the banks of the Solway, the peat-bogs are only a few feet above sea-level.   Peat often occurs in shallow basin-like depressions, having been formed by the gradual ingrowth of plants from the banks of lakes and ponds.   Peat may have been formed from lowly plants like mosses, or from highly organised forms such as trees. In mapping an area of peat, it is necessary to follow the boundary carefully and in detail, for its position cannot be predicted on geometrical grounds.

Gravels may or may not be related to the present system of river valleys.   Those which are mapped as river-gravels usually occur as terraces, each of which is often at a constant height above the present river.   The Geological Survey also map *flood-plain gravels* distinct from the alluvium, but level with the existing flood-plain of the river.

Terraces may occur on either or both sides of a river valley; they may occur for only a few yards, or they may be continuous for distances of several miles.   The terraces represent the remains of gravels laid down by rivers when flowing at higher levels than at present; therefore, normally, the greater the elevation above the river, the older the terrace.   On the other hand, *within the terrace itself*, the principle of superposition holds, and the upper layers of gravel are of later date than the lower.

In addition to gravels, which are related to the present river valleys, there are other *high-level* gravels which represent deposits laid down by rivers whose valleys no longer exist.   These can only be mapped by closely following and plotting their boundaries. When doing so, it is important to take careful note of the nature of the included pebbles, since information is thus obtainable of the direction in which the rivers once flowed.

Boulder-clay is highly irregular in its occurrence; it may be present as thick masses in valleys and the surrounding hills clear of the deposit, or, vice versa, the boulder-clay may be found on the hills and not in the valleys. Boulder-clay can only be mapped by careful direct observation; its presence or absence cannot be predicted by geometrical considerations.

In districts where there is much boulder-clay, the *green-line* method of mapping, described by E. Greenly and H. Williams (*Methods in Geological Surveying*), is of great value. Those areas which are free from drift are carefully and accurately marked on the map by a thin black line, surrounded by a grass-green line. Within the black lines, the country-rock is visible and can be mapped accurately, while outside the green lines, the nature of the country-rock can only be inferred. A geologist who is provided with a map on which the drift-covered and drift-free areas are thus distinguished can form an opinion of the validity of the lines drawn thereon, and can save time by being thus directed to those places where evidence is available, without the necessity of seeking over the whole area of the map.

FAULTS, UNCONFORMITIES, AND OVERLAPS

A fault is often rather elusive to trace, for although there may have been a vertical shift of the rocks on either side of the break amounting to several hundred feet, there may be no more than a slight feature at the surface to bear witness to the movement. Where a fault is intersected by a line of natural section, such as a ravine or cliff, the position of the fracture is likely to be concealed under superficial accumulations; in fact, a major fault is not often seen in section, even where conditions would seem to be most favourable. One important reason for this is that a major fault is rarely, if ever, a simple and clean-cut fracture, but involves a belt of shattered and broken rocks, with the result that the course of the fault is sometimes marked by a valley or by a relatively narrow strip of marshy ground.

It is true that where two groups of rocks which differ much in their resistance to denudation are brought into contact by a fault, there is occasionally a cliff or escarpment, the more resistant rock standing up above the more easily denuded. Generally, however, denudation has kept pace with the progress of faulting, and there are few obvious outward and visible signs.

Faults have very great importance in the structure of the land,

and it is essential that the field geologist should be able to recognise and map them when they occur.

EVIDENCES OF FAULTING

At the outset, we would sound a note of warning. A fault should never be invoked simply as a means of getting over a difficulty in mapping; until other explanations have been tried and found wanting, and until positive evidence has been obtained, the geologist should refrain from suggesting the existence of faulting in his area.

The evidence on which faulting would be inferred may be summarised as follows:—

(i) *Visible displacement of strata, veins, and dykes.*

(ii) *Repetition or omission of outcrops* (Fig. 22).

(iii) *Strata striking "at" one another,* without room for the change of strike to take place by curving.

(iv) *Abrupt termination of an outcrop;* this might also be due to the disappearance of a bed beneath an unconformable overlying series, or to unconformable deposition against a steep slope. If, however, the outcrop were found to have been offset to one side or the other, the presence of a fault would be almost certainly proved.

(v) *"Offsetting" and duplicating of features,* such as escarpments, ridges, etc. This is often best seen on a closely-contoured or hill-shaded small-scale map (Fig. 23).

(vi) *Anomalous dips.* Sometimes, considerable distortion of the beds takes place in the neighbourhood of a fault; on the upthrow side the broken ends may be bent downwards towards the line of fracture, while on the downthrow side the ends may be bent upwards, and even inverted. When a line of anomalous dips is found in otherwise gently-dipping strata, a fault may be suspected.

(vii) *Smash-zones.* These are particularly noticeable where dislocations are of large magnitude. The fault, instead of being clear-cut, is marked by a belt of crushed and brecciated rock (fault-breccia) produced by the grinding action of the broken ends against one another. A crush-zone is often expressed by a boggy hollow.

When, in the course of mapping, one or more of the above indications is observed and plotted, *then* is the time to begin to speculate on the existence of a fault. It should be remembered that the evidence is cumulative and that the confidence with which a fault can be introduced into the map increases with the number of criteria from which its presence is inferred.

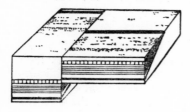 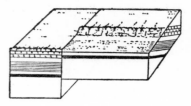

DIP-FAULTS CAUSING TRUNCATION AND SEPARATION OF OUTCROP.

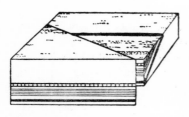 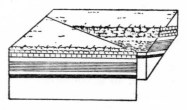

OBLIQUE FAULT, DOWNTHROW WITH DIP, CAUSING SEPARATION OF OUTCROP.

OBLIQUE FAULT, DOWNTHROW AGAINST DIP, CAUSING PARTIAL DUPLICATION OF OUTCROP.

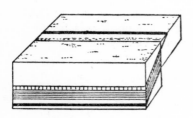 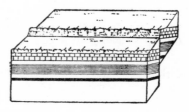

STRIKE-FAULT, DOWNTHROW WITH DIP, CAUSING OMISSION OF OUTCROP.

STRIKE-FAULT, DOWNTHROW AGAINST DIP, CAUSING COMPLETE DUPLICATION OF OUTCROP.

From Barrington Brown and Debenham, Structure and Surface.

Fig. 22.   EFFECT OF FAULTING ON OUTCROP.

An important question to consider when dealing with a fault is, what happens to it at the ends, for no fault can continue for an indefinite distance. It will very likely be found that when the faultline is followed, the throw gradually decreases and finally dies away to zero; frequently, the major fault disappears in a ramifying plexus of minor dislocations, each causing very small displacement of the rocks affected.

OFFSETTING BY DIP-FAULT

UNCONFORMITY AND OVERLAP

The term *unconformity* is used in two senses: (i) to convey the idea of a discontinuity in sedimentation, whereby a younger series of rocks is brought into immediate contact with an underlying older series which do not, in the geological column, *immediately* precede them; this is the broader meaning. (ii) Where a younger series of rocks shows a marked discordance of bedding with an older series; here, the essential point is that the older series must have been disturbed, and have therefore acquired a dip which is manifestly not that of the younger rocks. This is sometimes known as "angular unconformity."

PARTIAL DUPLICATION RESULTING FROM OBLIQUE FAULT

COMPLETE DUPLICATION AS THE RESULT OF STRIKE-FAULT

[*From Barrington Brown and Debenham,*
Structure and Surface.

Fig. 23. OFFSETTING AND DUPLICATION OF ESCARPMENT DUE TO FAULTING.

Angular unconformity, when seen in section, is more easily recognised in the field than a break in the succession, where the bedding-planes of the two series of rocks may be parallel, or completely conformable. A good example is the great unconformity between the almost horizontal Carboniferous Limestone and the steeply-dipping Ingletonian Slates (Fig. 24). *On the map* (Fig. 45) the unconformity is shown by the fact that the overlying series is nearly horizontal, while the underlying beds are highly inclined.

Where there is no marked discordance in bedding, however, there may often occur at the base of one series a conglomerate composed of fragments of the underlying rocks, or even of rocks intermediate in age between the overlying and underlying series. This demonstrates clearly that there must have been a break in the succession.

Fig. 24.   UNCONFORMITY NEAR AUSTWICK, YORKSHIRE.

Frequently, the presence of an unconformity (or non-sequence) only becomes apparent as the result of careful mapping with the correlation of the various beds on palaeontological evidence.

Overlap is the term applied where the upper beds of a continuous series extend beyond the limits of the beds immediately beneath them.   Overlap is detected in the field as the result of careful mapping for it will be found that the outcrop of an inferior bed gradually narrows in a particular direction, without there being any other assignable cause, such as thinning of the lower bed. When overlap is encountered, it may be concluded that deposition was taking place in an area of continuous subsidence, with the result that the area available for sedimentation was progressively increasing.

The existence of overlap is generally suspected only as the result of studying the boundary lines on a complete or partly completed map; readers are therefore referred to Chapter IX.

CHAPTER VII

GEOLOGICAL MAPPING (4)

APPLICATION OF PRINCIPLES

The purpose of this chapter is to show how the methods of geological mapping which have been developed in Chapters IV to VI may be applied to the study of an area of simple structure. To this end, we propose to outline the steps taken in making a geological map of the district round the village of Ashover, Derbyshire, situated about 4½ miles from Matlock and 7 miles from Chesterfield. Over a period of more than twelve years, we have made numerous visits to Ashover, and as a result, one of us (G.S.S.) published "An Outline of the Geology of Ashover, Derbyshire," in the *Proceedings of the Geologists' Association,* in 1946.

The area comprises parts of the following six-inch sheets of the Ordnance Survey: Sheets SK 36 SW and SK 36 SE. The relevant portions have been combined into one map in Plate I. On both sheets the National Grid lines are shown, consequently points at which observations were made are identified on the map by their grid references.

PRELIMINARY RECONNAISSANCES

Before attempting to begin the geological map, a careful study should be made of the topographical map of the area, and this should be reinforced by making traverses over the ground. The geologist thus obtains a good idea of the lie of the land which is of assistance to him in his subsequent proceedings. It is useful, while making the preliminary examination, to make panoramic sketches from one or more vantage points, to bring out the salient features in the relief. Here, the geologist who has artistic ability will find scope for the display of his talents; but let him beware lest he spends too much time in producing artistic effects. Let him rather strive to catch and portray on paper the general relation of hill and valley, of river and cliff, as they impress him when his mind is fresh. At a later stage, he should be able to riddle out the meaning of what he has seen.

Even though he may be devoid of artistic ability, the observer should make sketches, crude though they may be; they may not be intended for publication, but as aids to memory and pegs on which to hang later observations.

The first studies of map and ground around Ashover bring to light the following facts:—

The village is situated on relatively flat ground at about 600 ft. O.D., and rather more than 100 ft. above the River Amber which runs from north-west to south-east. About two-thirds of a mile to the east of the village, there is a steep tree-clad slope, rising to between 700 and 800 ft. O.D., and trending almost south-north. This continues to rise (to above 900 ft. O.D.) and swings round to the north of the village, forming a steep escarpment (off the map reproduced in this book) which trends slightly north of west.

On the opposite (or right) bank of the river, the ground rises to a well-marked hilly ridge which, south-east of the village, shows well-marked cliffs. This ridge runs approximately from north-west to south-east; the southern end is well wooded, but farther to the north, the ridge forms a rather bare hummock which is divided into large meadows by stone walls consisting of vertical slabs. The hill rises to over 600 ft. O.D., with two small areas over 700 ft.

Looking south-westwards from the village, a second ridge, rising to about 1,000 ft. O.D., running nearly parallel with the river, is seen. The southern half is heavily wooded; farther north, the ground carries a heavy growth of bracken, and is covered with short, wiry turf. This outer ridge forms a well-marked escarpment facing the river, *i.e.* about north-east. A conspicuous feature of the landscape towards the south-east corner of the map is Ashover Hay, which stands up as a prominent whale-backed hill orientated nearly due north-south, in rough prolongation of the steep ground which forms the eastern border of the map. Between the Hay and the "outer ridge" which, towards its southern extremity, swings first to south-east and then almost east, there is a considerable area of low-lying ground. A general view from the Hay, looking northwards, is shown in Fig. 25.

In the foreground is the northern slope of Ashover Hay, divided by dry stone walls into numerous small enclosures; in the middle distance, the well-marked hummock, cleft down the middle by the valley of the Amber, can be seen. Separated from the hummock by rather low-lying marshy ground are the two escarpments which form a frame to the central hilly ground.

The map shows a number of quarries and old lead mines, all of which must be visited, since each will provide useful information from which to deduce the geological structure of the district.

COLLECTING THE DATA

Having made a preliminary traverse, the next step is to examine and plot on the map all the available exposures. With such a wealth of quarries, no question of having to seek for exposures arises; visits should be paid to the various workings, and the details noted. Naturally, when proceeding to the quarries, observations will from time to time be made; the places where anything is seen should be carefully identified on the map and notes taken.

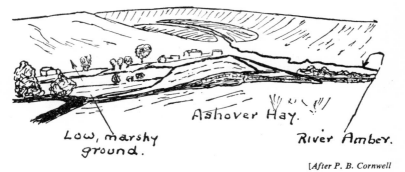

Low, marshy ground.   Ashover Hay.   River Amber.

[*After P. B. Cornwell*

Fig. 25. THE ASHOVER VALLEY FROM THE HAY.

Part of the map, with the various observations marked thereon, is reproduced in Fig. 26, and a number of the accompanying notes are appended. Since the map has been gridded, it was not necessary to refer the notes to the individual slips; where possible, quarries are referred to by the names given on the map, while some points are identified by their grid references.

THE INNER HUMMOCK

The first traverse may be supposed to be along the road which runs south-east from Ashover to Milltown.

Hockley Quarry (Fig. 27). A large, unworked quarry in blue-grey limestone,* showing a long, cliff-like section about 75 ft. high, which follows almost exactly along the strike. Near the top of the quarry, the rock is thinly bedded; the greater part of the section is massively bedded and well jointed. In the upper portion, there are four or five persistent grey-black bands traversing the limestone. A specimen proved harder than steel (in fact, a steely streak was left on the surface after the test), and proved to be of practically the same hardness as quartz (Table A). The mineral much resembled flint, but broke with a flat, instead of a conchoidal

* For identification, see pp. 170 and 172.

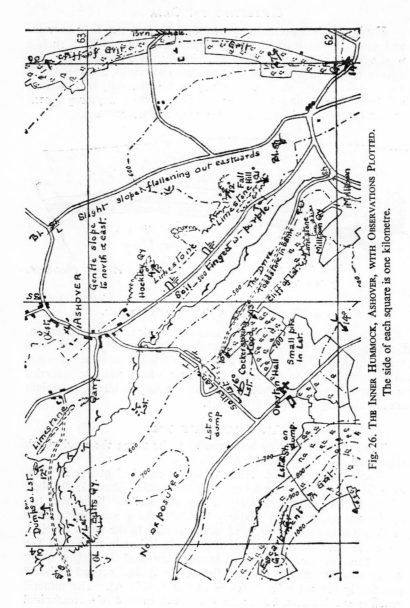

Fig. 26. The Inner Hummock, Ashover, with Observations Plotted.
The side of each square is one kilometre.

fracture, and was brecciated, which flint seldom is. It was therefore concluded that the mineral was CHERT, which is practically restricted to limestones older than the Chalk.

The fossils collected included *Productus** (large and small species), *Spirifer*, *Lithostrotion*, and *Dibunophyllum*. There were also numerous stems of crinoids, sometimes 6 in. long. (These are locally known as "fossil" or "Derbyshire screws".) Sometimes stems of crinoids make up whole beds, giving rise to "crinoidal limestone".

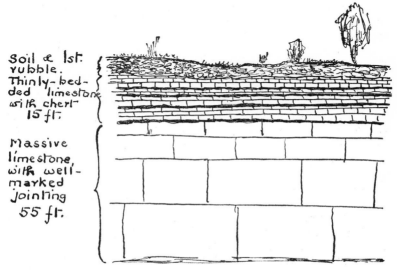

Soil & lst. rubble. Thinly-bedded limestone with chert 15 ft.

Massive limestone, with well-marked jointing 55 ft.

Fig. 27.   SECTION IN HOCKLEY QUARRY, ASHOVER.

Some specimens contained *Spirifer* and stems of crinoids, preserved in *silica*.

At the eastern end of the quarry, near an old lime-kiln, there is a deep trench in which, below the limestone, there is an entirely different rock. About 14 ft. of the rock was seen, conforming completely with the bedding of the limestone. The rock was dark green, sometimes passing into purple, well laminated, and made up largely of rounded particles varying in size from a bean to a walnut. Under the lens, fragments of limestone, chert, and speckled pellets were detected. The rock, from its contact with the limestone, was veined with a white fibrous material which was identified as calcite (easily scratched by knife, perfect cleavage into rhombohedra).

*For identifications, see pp. 191, 192, and 193.

The rock was therefore apparently some sort of shaley *Conglomerate*. It is known locally as *Toadstone*.* The veining of calcite is probably due to solution by percolating waters of calcium carbonate from the limestone and subsequent redeposition in the interstices of the toadstone. Marked *T* on the map. (Specimens taken for examination.)

In a corner of the quarry, and in the trench referred to above, the dip was measured and found to be 3° to 4° on a true bearing of 45°.

Since the actual contact of limestone with toadstone was observed, a suitable symbol, such as *Lst/T* is written on the map at the point where the junction was observed.

In the north-eastern corner of the main quarry, the limestone was observed to be dipping at 4° on a true bearing of 45°. The information is marked on the map by means of an arrow, and the angle of dip is marked alongside it. The precise point at which the dip was measured is recorded in the notebook, together with the dip. Thus: "Limestone at point 3516 6276, dipping at 4° to 45° true." Records of dips should always be made in the notebook, as well as on the map. Furthermore, if the grid reference is given, the position at which the dip was observed can be plotted on any gridded map, whatever the scale.

About 300 yards down the road, in the direction of Milltown, another cutting was observed. In this, a junction of limestone/toadstone was seen. The soil in the upper part of the fields between the road and the river is tinged strongly with purple, probably resulting from the decomposition of toadstone.

Still farther down, on the left of the road, a long, low, cliff-like section in limestone was seen. The western end is very rubbly and shows signs of disturbance. The limestone is very irregularly bedded, widely jointed, and the surfaces of the joints are often polished and scratched ("slickensides"). This suggests that there may be faulting, or, at any rate, differential movement between the faces of the joints. No toadstone was found here.

From the slickensided surfaces and cracks, good specimens of *Calcite*, in rhombohedral crystals and as dog-tooth spar, were collected (Table J, p. 148). Also there was a cubic mineral, coloured white, pale yellow, and various shades of purple. It was slightly harder than calcite, and gave a colourless powder (Table J, p. 150), the mineral showed perfect cleavage; the coigns of the cubes were easily broken off, leaving flat, smooth surfaces, which if developed sufficiently far would evidently leave an octahedral form. The mineral was therefore *Fluorspar*.

* See pp. 89 and 90.

Piles of broken stone, containing lumps of a soft, lustrous, lead-grey mineral which broke easily into cubes, were observed. This was identified as *Galena*, p. 163. Associated with the fluorspar and galena, was a small quantity of a dark-brown, resin-like mineral. This was identified (p. 164) as *Zinc Blende*, or *Sphalerite*.

In abandoned workings in the northern part of the quarry, at point 3548 6245, a dip of 12° to a true bearing of 51° was observed; here also, there was a good deal of an ochre-yellow, powdery mineral in wide cracks. Numerous specimens of a large *Productus* were also found. At point 3552 6228, a dip of 21° to 159° (true) was recorded.

The change in direction of the dip, and the increase in its amount, indicate that the limestone is plunging below the rather featureless area to the east. The inference is that the toadstone has been carried far below the surface.

At 3567 6222, signs of excavation were observed, and it was found that a large tank had recently been constructed. When digging for the foundations, many pieces of a soft, black, and very compact fissile rock had been thrown out. The rock had a characteristic "earthy" smell when breathed on and split easily into thin laminae; it was therefore identified (Scheme on p. 171) as *Shale*. The site on the map was carefully marked and the symbol *Sh* written against the position. The shale evidently overlies the limestone, so we therefore conclude that the succession, as far as it has been ascertained, is—

Black Shale,   Limestone,   Toadstone.

The traverse might well be completed by following up the right bank of the river and returning to Ashover by Salter Lane.

At the bridge over the river, black shales are observed low down in the banks. By the side of the Drive, which leads towards the north-west, there are numerous small exposures in limestone, which should be marked on the map. Hereabouts, there are large dumps of broken limestone and also a screening and washing plant at which fluorspar is being recovered and dressed before despatch to Sheffield and Glasgow.

About 220 yards above the bridge, there is a small digging on the left of the track, and in this, unmistakable toadstone is observed; here, the rock closely approximates to the more compact and less shaley variety which was obtained at the Hockley Quarry. This point is quite close to the entrance to a large quarry in limestone, Milltown Quarry. Here, the limestone is more rubbly and less regularly bedded than that at Hockley; in places, the joints are enlarged to wide cavities, the walls of which are sometimes lined with fluorspar, fine masses of cubic crystals, an inch or more in size, being obtainable. Good specimens of *Productus* and *Syringopora* are to be found.

Although the actual contact of the limestone with the toadstone is not observable, exposures in the two rocks are so close together that the line of junction can be sketched in to within a very short distance.

For about 500 yards above the entrance to the quarry, a nearly continuous section of toadstone is visible in the low bank at the side of the Drive. There is also much rubble, which has evidently come down from the limestone cliffs which stand up boldly above.

At the corner of Cockerspring Wood, the limestone dips at 10° on a bearing of 224°; in other words, in a direction opposed to that observed at a similar point on the opposite side of the river. Hereabouts, there is no sign of toadstone in the side of the track.

The traverse is closed by following the old pack-horse trail (Salter Lane, leading to Hollow Lane) which branches off in a north-easterly direction from point 3467 6249. *En route* to the village, where the track crosses the 600-ft. contour, limestone is observed in each bank, and then for a distance of about 150 yards, to the 500-ft. contour, there are good exposures in toadstone, all of which are marked on the map. Again, the contact can be located within a very few yards.

A little below the bridge over the river, sections about 6 ft. in height are observed. They show buff or yellowy silty material, quite different from the purple-coloured product derived from the weathering of the toadstone. This is evidently alluvium, and is marked on the map by the conventional sign ∾.

Standing on the bridge, map in hand, we observe that the river meanders in a narrow "flat," which is evidently its flood-plain. When followed outwards from the river, the flat ground gradually gives place to a gentle slope, and the colour of the soil changes from pale "earthy" to dark purple. Still further from the river, the slope becomes steeper. It may be inferred that, so far as information at present is available, the geological section is something like that shown in Fig. 28, which represents a sketch made at the time in the notebook. The section is, of course, hypothetical, and the idea is subject to revision in the light of further evidence. A geologist should be continually framing hypotheses to explain what he has observed. In doing so, however, he should avoid so falling in love with his theories that they become obsessions which are difficult to discard if they fail to agree with facts which are ascertained subsequently.

The other numerous observations plotted on the map were made in a series of traverses along roads and footpaths. It has not been considered necessary to give details of how these traverses were carried out; instead, excerpts from field-notes, dealing with a number of the exposures, are given.   One useful general hint may be given on the procedure to be adopted when seeking for information.   Whenever an isolated clump of trees is seen on farm land, it is always worth investigation, even though this may mean a considerable detour.   It will frequently be found that the trees are growing in and around an abandoned surface-working or an old quarry.   When a working is abandoned, the site is either impossible

Fig. 28.   INFERRED SECTION ACROSS THE CENTRAL HUMMOCK, ASHOVER.

or difficult to plough; therefore, if seeds take root, the shoots are not interfered with, and in the course of years a well-grown clump of trees often forms.   Similarly, it will sometimes be noticed that there is an irregular patch of rank grass in a cornfield; this should be investigated, and signs of old workings or possibly a dump of stone will be found.   Therefore, keep a watchful eye open for any abnormality in the vegetation or surface of the ground, and examine it carefully.

The following notes represent entries abstracted from the notebook:—

Road junction at 3532 6315, shallow working showed black shale overlying limestone.   The boundary between the limestone and shale must be not more than a few feet from this point.

At the back of the old mill at 3456 6284, a small exposure in toadstone was noted, and within a few feet of it, limestone.

Cockerspring Wood.   Abandoned quarry, showing about 10 ft. limestone.   There are two well-marked faces, practically at right angles to one another; one is along the strike, the other shows a dip of 13° on a true bearing of 218°.   A diagrammatic sketch of the section is shown in Fig. 29.   A number of fossils, identified as *Dibunophyllum, Lithostrotion, Lonsdaleia, Productus,* and *Pugnax,* were obtained here.   *Vide* pp. 191 to 193 for identifications.

Between *Cockerspring Wood* and *Overton Hall,* numerous shallow pits (trial-pits for fluorspar) were found.   These were all in limestone, and good specimens of *Spirifer*, showing the internal spirals, *Productus*, *Lithostrotion*, and *Dibunophyllum* were collected.

The assemblage of fossils proves the limestone to be of Lower Carboniferous age. The corals *Lithostrotion*, *Lonsdaleia*, and *Dibunophyllum* are restricted to the Carboniferous Limestone, while *Dibunophyllum* is a zone-fossil of the upper portion of that

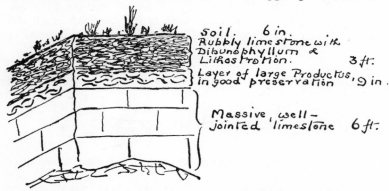

Fig. 29.   SKETCH OF SECTION IN COCKERSPRING WOOD, ASHOVER.

formation. *Productus* and *Spirifer* are longer range forms, but the species, when determined, reinforce the conclusions arrived at from the corals.

THE FRAME

Having examined the inner hummock and found it to consist of limestone resting on toadstone, with a fringe of black shales, we may now turn our attention to the outer frame, formed by the high ground round the hummock.   Maps in Figs. 26, 30, and 31.

A convenient procedure is to make a traverse of the heights on the south-west of the area, starting from the "Lord Nelson" Inn (now closed), which is at point 3340 6300, proceeding from Ashover by the field-path which runs approximately west from point 3462 6311.

Immediately on the north side of this path are a number of exposures of limestone, and at 3420 6317 toadstone is seen underlying the limestone, while a little beyond the river is a patch of shale. From this point the ground rises sharply, and in wet weather the surface is soggy and slippery; the final slope to the road is considerably steeper than the earlier part.

Above the road which runs south-east from the former "Lord Nelson," the ground rises steeply and is clad with a thick growth of gorse, bracken, and wiry grass, distinctly different from the lush grass with sedgy patches which characterises the lower slopes.

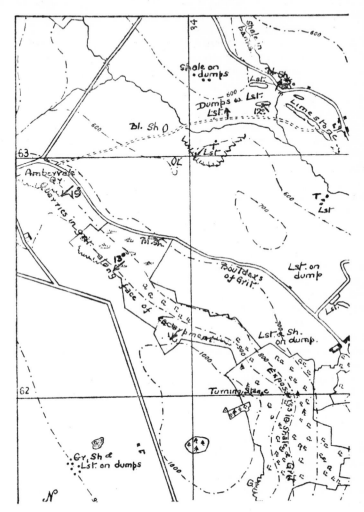

Fig. 30. North-West Area of Ashover Map with Observations Plotted.
Kilometre grid.

Behind the inn is Ambervale Quarry, with a face about
75 ft. high.   The lower 50 ft. shows massive bedding and conspicuous jointing;   above, the rock is much more closely bedded
("flaggy") and contains bands of nodular material and thin layers

of sandy shale. Examination of a number of specimens shows
that the rock is a *Grit* (see p. 170) having a biscuit colour.

The dip, measured at point 3347 6283, is 19° on a true bearing
of 226°. The biscuit-coloured grit was quarried for the manufacture
of millstones and grinding stones for the production of wood-pulp.
At Ambervale Quarry, which has long been abandoned, there are
several millstones and rings from which stones have been cut.
At Robin Quarry, near Cocking Tor farther along the escarpment to
the south-east, the manufacture of pulp-stones has also ceased.

The few fossils are ill-preserved; streaks and patches of car-
bonised plant remains may be found, and in Robin Quarry we have
collected a bifurcating, rather flattened cylinder of grit, marked with
diamond-shaped scars arranged in a series of spirals round it. This
was identified as the internal cast of a branch of *Lepidodendron*,
and provides some evidence that the grit is of Carboniferous age.

By following along the escarpment, we find other old quarries
and numerous exposures in biscuit-coloured grit. Practically on
the 1,000-ft. contour and on the edge of the escarpment, at 3429
6200, is an isolated mass of grit, about 15 ft. high, showing well-
marked current bedding and differential weathering. Since there
is little likelihood that this crag can have come down from a higher
level, when the escarpment was higher and projected farther to the
east, we conclude that the Turning Stone, as the crag is called,
must be a residual mass of grit which has resisted the action
of denuding agents. The thinly-bedded nature of the mass suggests
that it corresponds to the higher part of the grit series which was
observed at Ambervale Quarry.

Continuing along the escarpment, the grit can be traced as far
as the southern edge of the map (Figs. 30 and 31), while in the woods
which line the face, there are also numerous exposures in black
shales resembling those which were seen near Fall Hill (p. 69).

At or about point 3350 6170 are a number of old mine dumps.
These consist of plentiful fragments of grit, with black shale and
pieces of limestone. From this, we conclude that the outcrop
of the biscuit-coloured grit extends at least as far west as the
dumps; its width in this neighbourhood must therefore be about
1,000 yd.

Turning now to the eastern margin of the frame, on Fig. 26, a
belt of steep wooded ground extends northwards from 3600 6200 to
the northern margin of the figure. There are numerous exposures
in the pale grit, exhibiting dips towards the east (at the southern
end) and nearly north-east at the northern end. This ridge evidently
corresponds to that which we have been examining on the western
side of our area.

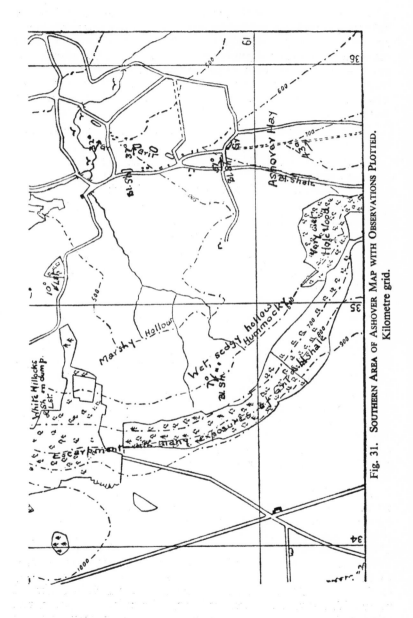

Fig. 31. SOUTHERN AREA OF ASHOVER MAP WITH OBSERVATIONS PLOTTED.
Kilometre grid.

At the sharp bend on the road at 3613 6270, there is an exposure in brown, gritty shale in the side of the road, and a few yards higher up, iron-stained grit is observed. Stratigraphically, the brown shale and the red-brown grit are evidently *above* the biscuit-coloured grit. A hundred yards or so to the north (on the very edge of the map) masses of the red-brown grit are seen near the edge of a field which slopes gently towards the "cliffs of grit" which are marked on the map.

We may therefore conclude that the succession in the Ashover area consists of—

Red-brown Grit (Upper),	Black Shales,
Brown Shales,	Limestone,
Biscuit-coloured Grit (Lower),	Toadstone.

Our knowledge of the succession depends on observations made at the following critical or "key" sections:—

Hockley Quarry, limestone/toadstone.

Road junction at 3532 6315 (p. 71), black shales/limestone.

Ashover Hay, 3563 6115, biscuit-coloured grit/black shales (Fig. 31).

Road section at 3623 6270, brown shales/Lower Grit.

Roadside quarry at 3399 6086 (Fig. 32), red-brown Upper Grit/ brown shales.

The only good section in Upper Grit which appears on our map is that at Poorlots Quarry in the south-west corner of the area (Fig. 32). Here the rock is seen to be thinly bedded, rubbly, very ferruginous, and containing much mica. Both it and the brown shales which intervene between the Upper and the Lower Grits are definite lithological entities and hence can be mapped as individuals. The brown shales are rarely seen; there is a section about 100 yards long and 3 feet high in a stream bank between the points 3330 6137 and 3337 6127, showing brown, gritty shale, passing into dark brown bog iron ore.

Although we must pass a little beyond the limits of our map, we find that near the north-east corner of the area, the frame of Lower Grit bends round from its northerly trend and takes on a roughly north-westerly direction. Above the escarpment, at point 3570 6273, there is a conspicuous mass of Lower Grit, known as the Fabric, corresponding to the Turning Stone, which is about $1\frac{1}{2}$ miles to the south-west and on the other side of the Ashover valley (p. 74). Like the Turning Stone, the Fabric, which is illustrated in Fig. 33, shows the current bedding, differential weathering, and jointing characteristic of the Lower Grit; a noteworthy feature is

the greater abundance of mica.   In fact, the sandy surface of the
path (when dry) leading from the road to the Fabric, glistens by
reason of the abundant scales of muscovite.

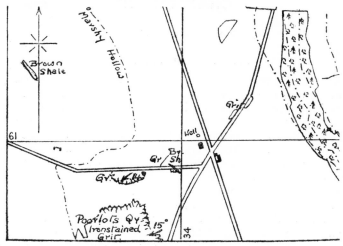

Fig. 32.   SOUTH-WEST CORNER OF ASHOVER MAP.
Kilometre grid.

There is a third conspicuous landmark, the Wirestone, at point
3222 6337 (a little way off the north-western corner of our map),
which rises to a height of 1,038 ft., and consists of a mass of red-
brown, or Upper Grit.   Unlike the Turning Stone and the Fabric,
which are situated on the very edges of steep escarpments, the
Wirestone overlooks the much gentler scarp formed by the Upper

Fig. 33.   THE FABRIC, NEAR ASHOVER.

Grit, and hence is suitable as a permanent triangulation point of the
Ordnance Survey.   The other two landmarks are insufficiently
stable to be used for this purpose.   There is a triangulation point
very close to, but not *on*, the Fabric.

CHAPTER VIII

GEOLOGICAL MAPPING (5)

PLOTTING THE BOUNDARIES

Although in practice the collection of data and the plotting of boundary lines proceed simultaneously, it seems simpler to deal with the two processes separately. In this chapter, we propose to show how the information obtained at the various exposures is utilised in plotting certain of the boundaries which appear on the finished map. We have not attempted to show how *all* the lines are drawn, but have selected certain areas of the map which bring out the principles already developed.

At the outset, we would re-iterate that *plotting of boundaries must be done in the field*, with the evidence at hand. The only work which may be done indoors on the map is inking in, colouring, and drawing of sections. If, at any stage of the indoor work, there is any doubt about the exact location of a boundary line, recourse must be had to the field, where, with the evidence at hand, any necessary rectification can be made.

The relevant sections of the map to which reference will be made when showing how the lines are plotted, are given in Figs. 34 and 35.

THE ALLUVIUM-TOADSTONE JUNCTION

In drawing this line, which is one of the easiest to tackle, three sources of information are employed, namely: (i) the shape of the ground, (ii) the colour of the soil, and (iii) the use of the auger.

As was pointed out on p. 53, the alluvial tract at the sides of a river is almost dead level; at any rate, the slope is inappreciable to the eye, although, of course, there must be a gentle rise when the river is followed upstream. A traverse is therefore made along both sides of the river, and a light pencil line is sketched in where the ground shows signs of changing from a flat to a gentle slope on passing outwards from the stream to the flanks of the valley.

While carrying out these traverses, the colour of the soil is carefully noted, for it has already been pointed out (p. 70) that the alluvium gives a neutral-coloured "earthy" looking soil, while the toadstone breaks down into a soil which has a markedly purple colour. At some places, this is found right down on the flat, but since the sides of the valley are sometimes steep, downwash from the toadstone is suspected. Here the auger is brought into play, and samples are drawn from a depth of (say) three feet. If a sample from the bottom of one of the holes is chocolate- to purple-coloured and contains small fragments of toadstone, it is concluded that toadstone is here *in situ*. If, on the other hand, the auger brings up purplish soil for the first few inches or a foot, and then earthy or neutral-coloured samples, then there must be down-washed toadstone overlying alluvium, and the line must be drawn between the flank of the valley and the position of the hole. The line of junction as adopted on the finished map is shown as a thin, con-tinuous line in Fig. 34.

THE LIMESTONE-TOADSTONE JUNCTION

This line is also comparatively easy to plot, for there are numerous exposures, and at several points the limestone is seen in actual contact with, or very near to, the toadstone. Starting at the north-western end of the outcrop, there are several small diggings, covering a length of about 250 yards, in which the actual contact of limestone with toadstone is seen. Therefore from about 3400 6318 to 3451 6410, a firm line may be drawn. Proceeding in a south-easterly direction, there are several small exposures of limestone following a slight feature near the edge of the alluvial flat. Although not seen, it may be inferred that toadstone cannot be far below the surface.

The next exposures of toadstone are seen by the side of the road to Milltown at 3507 6263 (entrance to Hockley Quarry) and 3521 6247. Careful inspection in the two cuts shows that the limestone-toadstone junction must lie just below the 600-ft. contour between these two points, and a firm line is therefore drawn between them. Still lower down the road, at point 3545 6225, a small excavation between the road and the river shows toadstone; limestone has been seen (p. 69) in the quarry above the road, and in the deepest excavation there, no toadstone has been observed. The line of contact must, therefore, be very close to the small excavation just referred to, and in view of the high, nearly southerly dip of the limestone at point 3552 6228, we conclude that the toadstone must descend well below the surface of the ground only a few feet from the point at which it was last seen. The junction of the limestone with the toadstone is therefore carried roughly south-east to cut the upper boundary of the alluvium, as shown in Fig. 34.

The two ends of the limestone-toadstone junction on the left bank of the river having been drawn with some confidence, there still remains a gap of nearly a thousand yards (from the cut at the

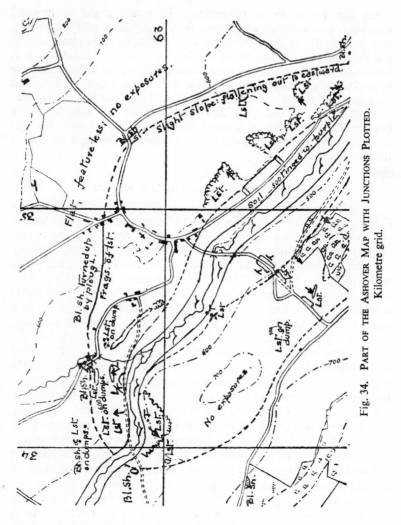

Fig. 34. Part of the Ashover Map with Junctions Plotted.
Kilometre grid.

entrance to Hockley Quarry to 3440 6317) to be filled in. Unfortunately, there are no exposures anywhere between these two points. There is a slight feature below the small exposures of limestone between 3445 6325 and 3465 6306. The best that can be done is to run a *broken line* (inferred boundary) just below this feature, roughly parallel with the river, curving it round to meet the firm line at Hockley Quarry.

A similar procedure is followed on the other side of the river. The "fixed points" are the small digging at the lower end of the Drive (3541 6216), the lower end of the loop on Salter Lane, and the two contiguous exposures behind the old mill at 3456 6284. Furthermore, toadstone was seen in the south bank of the Drive over a distance of about a quarter of a mile. The problem is to convert these observations into a continuous line on the map.

The boundary line along the Drive can be drawn with some confidence as a broken line situated about half-way between the southern bank of the road and the foot of the cliffs of limestone which overhang the track. It is necessary to map well up on the slope, because there is a thick pile of debris which has resulted from weathering of the limestone cliffs, and if the line of contact between limestone and toadstone were drawn at the edge of the road, no allowance would be made for the effect of these slips. From the point where the cliffs die out, the dotted line is continued to the observed contact at Salter Lane, which is a little above the 600-ft. contour.

Thence, taking advantage of a slight step on the hillside, the line is plotted (still discontinuous) so as to run between the exposures at the back of the old mill, and continued as shown on the map (Fig. 34) to the alluvium, the point at which the toadstone disappears being located by augering.

There is a small, but growing, patch of toadstone visible in the floor of the Butts Quarry; this is an artificial inlier which has been brought into being by quarrying operations. This patch of toadstone is isolated and completely surrounded by limestone, which lies *above* the toadstone. The toadstone in the quarry is therefore a true inlier, that is, an outcrop of rock surrounded on all sides by rock of a later date.

THE BLACK SHALE-LIMESTONE BOUNDARY

This line is more difficult to map accurately; there are long stretches over which no exposures are seen, and recourse therefore must be had to feature-mapping.

One section of the line is shown "solid," and this across an area which normally would be very difficult. It so happened, however, that during one of our visits, several fields had recently been ploughed, and we were fortunate enough to be able to plot a line dividing an area over which the plough had turned up innumerable fragments of black shale from one where there were many fragments of lime-stone. As the result of this evidence, the continuous line was drawn.

At the road-fork 3532 6315, black shale was seen overlying lime-stone in an old shallow working, and the point at which the contact crossed the road could be located at 3530 6315. This point is joined by a discontinuous line with the end of the firm line already referred to.

Between the road junction at 3532 6315 and point 3567 6222, where black shales thrown out during the digging-in of a water-tank (p. 69) were observed, there is only one exposure, where there is an overgrown surface scraping for limestone (3548 6267). The surface of the ground slopes very gently down from the line of limestone quarries and flattens out along the line which has been dotted in on the map. This is taken to be the line along which the limestone passes beneath the overlying black shales. Further information can be obtained by the use of the auger.

Turning now to the north-western end of the central hummock, the exposures and dips marked on the map indicate that the black shales-limestone contact should swing round from a general east-west to a north-west-south-east trend.

In the right bank of the small stream (the Marshbrook), at point 3439 6333, an exposure of black shales is observed, and about 50 yards above this is a larger section, showing some 10-15 feet shale dipping at 30° in a north-easterly direction. Numerous fossils, mostly flattened, are found here, including a lamellibranch, *Dunbarella* (p. 230), a univalve which may be a gastropod or a cephalopod, and many remains of plants. Among the latter, pieces bearing diamond-shaped impressions arranged in several spirals (*Lepidodendron*, p. 258) are recognisable. The spiral shell can only be determined by an expert, it is a species of Goniatite (*Reticuloceras*) characteristic of a low zone of the Upper Carboni-ferous. Another lamellibranch which cannot be identified by our schemes, may be *Carbonicola*, a freshwater form which is restricted to the Carboniferous.

On the opposite side of the adjacent road, at about points 3444 6326 and 3432 6328, are trial workings in limestone. There are a number of dumps about 350 yards west of the road, the nearest being at 3410 6335, on which, *inter alia*, many fragments of black shale together with limestone are observed. The line of junction between shale and limestone must run between the dumps on which the shale is found and the trial workings in limestone. Taking into consideration these facts, and the general shape of the ground, an interrupted line is therefore drawn, curving round to end against the alluvium at point 3398 6322.

On the right bank of the River Amber, there are two important small exposures in black shales and limestone respectively at points

3390 6312 and 3393 6295.   The form of the ground indicates that the limestone in this neighbourhood is plunging underground, the general direction of the line of junction between shales and limestone being from north to south.   Between these exposures and the limestone which is seen on Salter Lane, there are no exposures. There is a slight feature to guide us, however, and provisionally, this is taken to mark the boundary between black shales and lime- stone; on the map, it is indicated by a discontinuous line, swinging round to run roughly south-east and running under the centre of Overton Hall (shown on Fig. 26, but not on the slip used to illustrate this chapter).

THE LOWER GRIT-BLACK SHALES JUNCTION

When reading our descriptions of how the limestone-toadstone and the black shales-limestones junctions were mapped, the impres- sion may have been gained that we have been proceeding in an unsystematic manner and jumping from point to point without any good and sufficient reason.   We have, nevertheless, recommended a logical method of attack, namely, to start by establishing as many fixed points and short lengths of line where the junction can be plotted with considerable accuracy, and then to deal with the gaps between the fixed points.   An attempt to "walk" a line which is not visible will lead the beginner to conclude that geological mapping is indeed "vanity and vexation of spirit."

It will be remembered that on first approaching the north-west end of the escarpment of grit (p. 72), we drew attention to the difference between the vegetation on the upper, steeper part of the slope (Lower Grit) and on the lower, gentler slope (black shales). The grit is characterised by a prolific growth of bracken, gorse, and wiry, tussocky grass, in contrast to the lush grass which clothes the black-shale country.   Great assistance is therefore to be expected from a study of the vegetation.   Furthermore, since the line we are about to map is between hard beds overlying soft, it is probable that there will be a distinct change of slope at or about the line of junction.

The relevant section of the map is reproduced in Fig. 35.

When approaching the north-western section of the escarpment by the footpath from the Butts Quarry, it appears at first sight that the grit-black shales line might be mapped from a distance merely by reference to the general appearance of the ground and the change in vegetation.   A profile section along a line from point 3396 6317 to 3363 6259 is shown in Fig. 36.   The lower limit of bracken reaches at least down to the 700-ft. contour, and at about this level the ground steepens appreciably.   On approaching closer, however,

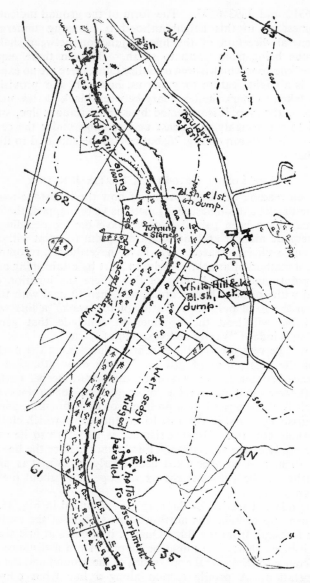

Fig. 35. PART OF THE ASHOVER MAP WITH JUNCTION OF LOWER GRIT/BLACK
SHALES PLOTTED.

Kilometre grid.

these observations are seen to be misleading, for at one point at least (3385 6266) in the side of the road at a level *above* the 700-ft. contour, a sizeable excavation in black shales is found. Further-more, about a quarter of a mile along the road to the south-east, numerous boulders and slabs of grit are found in a field of bright-green grass with numerous patches of sedge, indicative of underlying black shales. The presence of shale can be confirmed by augering. The fact, of course, is that in mapping the grit-shale junction we must work along a steep slope, and the precautions referred to on p. 51 must be borne in mind.

In mapping this contact, it is better to start from the southern section of the escarpment and work northwards. In the woods

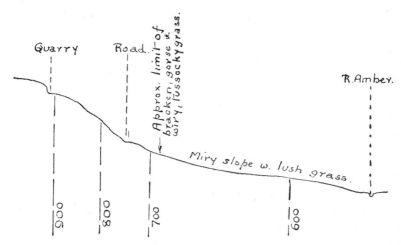

Fig. 36. PROFILE SECTION FROM THE RIVER AMBER TO THE (FORMER) "LORD NELSON" INN.

south of grid line 62, there are numerous exposures of grit and black shale, which is fossiliferous yielding *Reticuloceras,* and by detailed examination of this woodland area, a firm line may be drawn. In locating the line, the position of the junction must be taken as not below the *highest point at which black shales can be observed.* Patches of grit may be misleading, for they may represent slipped masses; the shales, on the other hand, cannot have rolled uphill.

When the line is mapped in this way, it is found that the grit-black shale contact, far from running *below* the 700-ft. contour, is always above it, and near the Turning Stone, at 3429 6217, rises above the 800-ft. contour, while at 3380 6241, the junction nearly touches the 900-ft. contour.

On Fig. 35, two old mine-dumps are marked.   On both of them, plentiful fragments of black shale and limestone are found, with only a sparse scattering of pieces of grit.   This indicates that the shafts from which the debris was derived penetrated black shales and limestone only; the proportion of grit is insufficient to warrant the conclusion that in their upper portions they passed through the grit.

We have not considered it necessary to describe how the other lines which are shown on the finished map have been plotted.   To do so would merely entail repetition of what has gone before.   We can only recommend our readers, armed with the information supplied, to go out into the field and try for themselves to make a geological map, however crude; for more will be learned by a few days on the ground than by months of reading.

When the mapping has been completed, or is approaching completion, it is often instructive to go over the sketches which were made during the preliminary reconnaissance of the ground and fill in the geological detail on them as far as that can be done.   This, of course, necessitates revisiting the points from which the original sketches were made; the time so occupied is by no means wasted, for the geologist finds that he views the scenery with different eyes, and what formerly was a mass of unconnected detail, reveals itself as a connected pattern once the underlying structure is correctly apprehended.

Completing the Map

When the field-work has been completed, there still remain the finishing touches.   As we have already pointed out, inking-in should proceed concurrently with the mapping, but the whole map should be carefully scanned, with the notebook at hand, to make certain that all lines have been properly inked in and that all symbols, such as dip-arrows with the accompanying dip, have been inserted correctly.   After this has been done, the last of the pencil marks should be carefully and completely erased.

Next, a decision must be made on the manner in which the various outcrops are to be distinguished; this may be done by colouring or shading.   Whichever method is chosen, care and thought should be devoted not only to the selection of colours or symbols to be used, but also to their application to the map.   Nature is beautiful, and a geological map, which is an epitome of one aspect of nature, should be pleasing to the eye.   An ill-finished, "messy" map is an indication of bad craftsmanship on the part of the geologist; even though he may have little artistic ability, his finished map should bear evidence to his having put the best work of which he is capable into its preparation.

A very important addition which must, at this stage, be made to the map is the "key to the geological formations." This is drawn up in the form of a number of superposed rectangles which are coloured or shaded in accordance with the scheme of colouring or shading the various outcrops, arranged in descending order. The key is normally situated on the border of published maps, but on a field-map from which the margins have been cut, the key must be inserted in some other convenient place, for example, on the back of the map, or on a separate piece of paper, which is hinged to the edge of the map.

COLOURING

Colouring may be on a lithological or a stratigraphical basis. A satisfactory colour scheme for our map of the Ashover district is—

Limestone, pale blue.

Black shales, grey.

Grits, Lower, light green; Upper, darker green.

"*Grit-shales*," separating the two grits, light brown.

Toadstone, red.

Alluvium, pale yellow, with the appropriate conventional sign ∽.

Water-colours are generally used for colouring field-maps. Each colour should be laid on in the form of a *pale* wash, care being taken to work rapidly over the whole area to be coloured. When the area is large, it is important to take care that the edge of the coloured area is kept wet until colouring is complete; otherwise, there will be a distinct dark line where fresh wash has been laid against the dried margin. If it is considered desirable to produce a darker tint than that resulting from a single wash, a second layer should be applied *after* the first has dried. It is far better to use two pale washes superposed on one another than to attempt to produce the desired tint by means of a single dark wash.

As an alternative to water-colours, good quality coloured pencils may be used. A light scummle of the required colour is applied, and the colour is then carefully spread uniformly over the appropriate area by means of a pledget of cotton wool or a paper stump moistened with benzene or petrol. If this procedure is carefully carried out, very uniform colouring can be obtained, which may be applied piecemeal, without any hard lines where successive additions have been made to the area coloured. Another advantage is that there is no danger of warping or "cockling" the paper as there is when water-colour is used.   Furthermore, the colour can be removed by means of an ordinary eraser; notwithstanding this, the colour does not smear when the map is handled.

The maps issued by the Geological Survey are coloured stratigraphically; each system has its own range of colours and tints. Thus, for example, Cretaceous rocks are coloured in shades of green, Jurassic in yellows and browns.   To appreciate the possibilities of subdivision of outcrops by means of a limited range of colours, Survey maps of the most recent series should be studied.

SHADING

When a map is to be reproduced for publication, it must almost always be shaded, since the cost of colour-printing is too high to justify the expenditure, save in rare circumstances.

To make a workmanlike job of shading a map is tedious and requires much patience.   Unless the lines used to form the patterns are uniformly spaced and end accurately on the boundaries between formations, neither falling short of nor transgressing them, the map will fail to fulfil the requirements that it should be pleasing to the eye.   A disadvantage of shading is that once the map has been completed, it is difficult to make any insertions, because the shading will interfere with the lettering or symbols which are added.

Here we would remark that the *field-map is a unique production*. If a map is to be published, the field-map should be carefully and accurately reproduced, either by tracing, or by transferring the necessary information to a clean base-map, and *the copy* should be sent to the publisher; the precious original should not be committed to the hazards of the post or into the hands of a publisher or printer.

In its original form, our map is lithological, that is, we have mapped *rock types*.   A geological map of stratified rocks, however, is coloured or shaded, and the key is given in terms of *formations* according to their position in the geological column.   In mapping the Ashover area, we have assumed that the work was started without any previous information; therefore, it is necessary for us to decide what to call the various rocks which have been mapped.

The clue must be sought in the fossils.   As pointed out on p. 72, the palaeontological evidence proves that the limestone is Carboniferous Limestone, and that it is the upper part of the formation which is represented at Ashover.   It can be concluded that the two grits are members of the Millstone Grit series; the lower is known as the Ashover and the upper as the Chatsworth Grit.

The black shales which overlie the Carboniferous Limestone are more difficult for the beginner to deal with, for they might be associated with the Carboniferous Limestone and thus taken to be Lower Carboniferous and equivalent to the Yoredale Beds, or, alternatively, they might be more closely assimilated to the Millstone Grit and be Upper Carboniferous in age. On the completed map, we have labelled the black shales "Butts Shale," and have given no verdict as to their precise age.

Careful examination of the shales in the banks of the Marsh-brook (p. 82) has provided evidence that the junction between Lower and Upper Carboniferous lies *in* the shale. At or about point 3439 6333, the palaeontological evidence is that the shales are Lower Carboniferous, while 50 yards farther upstream the fossils prove the shales there to be Upper Carboniferous. We do not suggest that to obtain this information would be within the compass of a beginner; we merely record the fact as an example in which it is necessary, on palaeontological grounds, to introduce a boundary line in what is lithologically a more or less homogeneous group of sediments. In spite of the fact that the black shales should really be subdivided into members belonging respectively to the Lower and Upper Carboniferous, this has not been attempted on the map for the good and sufficient reason that *up to the present* the data are inadequate.

On our completed map (Plate II), we have used the following nomenclature and colouring for the rocks:—

Alluvium, uncoloured.

Chatsworth Grit, green. The Millstone Grit consists of three beds of grit, separated by shales. The uppermost member, the Rough Rock, crops out to the north and east of our area, therefore the upper of the two grits in the immediate neighbourhood of Ash-over is correlated with the Middle or Chatsworth Grit, which is called after Chatsworth, where it is well developed.

Grit Shales, brown.

Ashover Grit, stippled green.

Butts Shales, stippled brown. We have adopted this name because the shales are best exposed in the vicinity of the Butts Quarry and the Butts Chapel; moreover, it is here that they are most fossiliferous.

Carboniferous Limestone, blue.

Toadstone, scarlet.

Although the tyro in field-work can scarcely be expected to identify this rock, we may state here that the *Toadstone* is a tuff or pyroclastic rock, consisting of finely-divided basaltic material, together with bombs or lapilla of basalt or altered dolerite and fragments of limestone and chert.

Elsewhere in Derbyshire, *Toadstone* is the name applied to sheets of basalt, which occur at several horizons in the Carboniferous Limestone.

CHAPTER IX

THE INTERPRETATION OF GEOLOGICAL MAPS

"Map-reading" in the ordinary sense implies the formation of a three-dimensional image or model of a piece of country by the study of a two-dimensional plan. When reading a geological map it is necessary also to form a mental picture of the underground structure of the country.

The faculty of rapidly and accurately interpreting geological maps can be acquired with practice, and is well worth the labour involved, for not only does it facilitate the geological investigation of an area with the aid of some other geologist's map, but it is also of great importance when actually mapping to be able to interpret one's own map as it gradually grows.

The presence of faults and overlaps will often be suspected only when mapping is well under way, while an important break in the succession, such as that in the Butts Shales at Ashover (p. 89) was not detected until the evidence from the fossils had been fully considered.

By carefully scanning his map as it grows in the field, the geologist will be saved from falling into a number of traps. Thus, he will remember that on undulating ground, a boundary line can never be straight unless it is the trace of a vertical contact. He will also be reminded that when the dip of the beds is low and the ground but gently undulating boundary lines are very sinuous, and that, on a dip-slope, a slight difference in the dip or in the inclination of the ground may cause a line to fly off in an unexpected direction; consequently, when mapping on a dip-slope, extra care is required in following lines of junction.

When reading a geological map, the data from which the underground structure is deduced include—

(i) The relief of the country, as shown by the contours and the position and direction of the streams.

(ii) The disposition and shape of the outcrops of the rocks which appear at the surface.

(iii) The sequence of the rocks which, on British maps, is given in the margin in the "Explanation of Colours and Geological Signs." On some maps, the thickness of the various formations is also given.

(iv) The inclination of the beds; on the one-inch geological maps, numerous dip-arrows are shown.

(v) The position and direction of faults, which are shown by white, blue, or, sometimes, red lines.

One of the best ways of acquiring facility in reading geological maps is to draw sections across a number of them, and the method of so doing, follows.

THE CONSTRUCTION OF A SECTION ACROSS A GEOLOGICAL MAP

This may be illustrated by drawing a section across the map of Ashover (Plate II). The first thing is to decide the line along which the section is to be drawn. This is almost always at right angles to the strike; it should be chosen so as to cross the outcrops of most, if not all of the rocks which appear at the surface, and it is therefore often necessary to choose a somewhat zig-zag line. Sometimes, two or more sections may be necessary to bring out the full structure.

Next, a profile-section should be drawn along the chosen line. Exaggeration of the vertical scale should be avoided, otherwise a distorted idea will be formed of the underground structure.

In the Ashover area, the strike in the central hummock is from north-west to south-east; the rocks forming the eastern limb of the frame, however, strike very nearly from north to south. The line of section chosen (see Plate II) runs for the greater part of its length from south-west to north-east, then turns practically due east.

To construct the section, a profile of the ground is first drawn, horizontal and vertical scales being the same. Then, on the base-line, the points at which the various geological boundaries intersect the line of section are carefully marked. These points are projected vertically upwards to fix their positions on the profile. The outcrops on the surface of the ground are thus defined.

Since there are observed dips at various points close to the line of section, it may be assumed that some dips will be found on the chosen line. For example, near the south-west of the section, the grit was observed to dip at 13° and the black shales at 10° south-westwards. Therefore, at point A on the profile, it may be assumed that the junction between them dips at 12°, and a short line, inclined from left to right at 12° to the horizontal, is therefore drawn. The other junctions are similarly drawn in at the correct inclinations. Having delimited the rocks for a short distance underground, their nature is shown by means of the appropriate symbols.

When drawing such a section, the (not unnatural) desire to make a pretty picture and to show the rocks continuing with a constant dip for long distances underground, should be resisted. It is quite evident that a bed cannot continue to dip underground at an angle of even 5° for an indefinite distance. The limestone in the Ashover area dips to the south-west at about 10°. That is, in a horizontal distance of 3 miles, were this dip maintained, the surface would be practically 2,800 ft. below ground-level. In point of fact, the limestone comes to the surface of the ground near Matlock (about 3 miles from Ashover) and forms hills 1,000 ft. above sea-level.

Examination of the section (Fig. 38) shows that at Ashover, the rocks are bent into an arch, or anticline, in which the limestone has been exposed by removal of the overlying rocks by denudation, so that it now forms an *inlier*, or an outcrop of older rock completely surrounded by younger rocks. A study of the map shows, furthermore, that the limestone plunges under the shales both at the north-west and the south-east ends of the inlier; this is evident, not only from the relation between the shale/limestone junction and the contours, but also from the dip-arrows plotted on the map. The dip, in fact, is *quaquaversal*, that is, radially outwards. The structure of the inlier is therefore that of an elongated *dome*.

Anyone who is accustomed to reading geological maps would gather the above information by simple inspection of the map, without having to draw a section. The beginner is advised to draw sections in various directions across a number of maps, for this is the best way to acquire the faculty of translating the two-dimensional representation of the map into a three-dimensional model of nature. He will do well, also, to take a contoured map of a piece of country (real or imaginary) and plot the outcrop of a bed (say, 100 ft. thick), dipping at various angles. He should then investigate what would be the effect of a fault or faults of various hades and throws and trending at different angles to the strike of the bed.

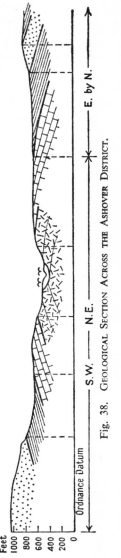

Fig. 38. GEOLOGICAL SECTION ACROSS THE ASHOVER DISTRICT.

SECTIONS OBLIQUE TO THE DIRECTION OF DIP

It is sometimes convenient, or desirable, to draw a section along a line which is inclined to that of the true dip, and it is then necessary to determine the *apparent dip* (which is always less than the true dip) in the line of section. The method of doing so is as follows:—

Given that the true dip is (say) 20° in the direction $A'B'$, it is required to determine the apparent dip in the direction $C'D'$ (Fig. 39).

Draw a straight line AB in the direction of the true dip, making its length 20 units (in general terms, the length of AB is proportional to the angle of dip), and draw BE at right angles to AB. This is the direction of the strike. Through

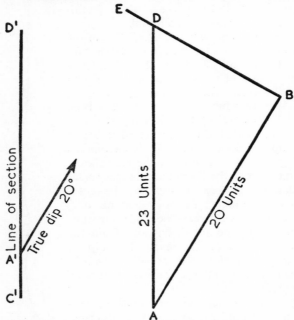

Fig. 39. DETERMINATION OF APPARENT DIP IN A DIRECTION OBLIQUE TO THE TRUE DIP.

A, draw a straight line parallel to $C'D'$ (the direction along which the apparent dip is to be found), and let it intersect BE at D. Measure AD in the chosen units. Then the apparent dip $= \dfrac{\text{Length of } AB \times \text{Degrees of true dip}}{\text{Length of } AD}$.

In the example given, $AB = 20$ units, and $AD = 23$ units, hence the apparent dip along $C'D' = \dfrac{20 \times 20}{23} = 17.4°$.

It is not difficult to show mathematically, that

tan Apparent Dip = Cosine Difference of Bearing × tan True Dip.

If the angle between the bearings be 30°, then

tan Apparent Dip = cos 30° tan 20° = 0·8660 × 0·3640 = 0·3152,

whence,   Apparent Dip = 17° 30′.

In the remainder of this chapter, we give several maps of small areas, each illustrating one or more geological structures, together with brief descriptions. If the reader is to gain the greatest benefit from the study thereof, he should draw sections across each of the maps in more than one direction. He will be well advised, also, to obtain one or more published geological maps and draw sections

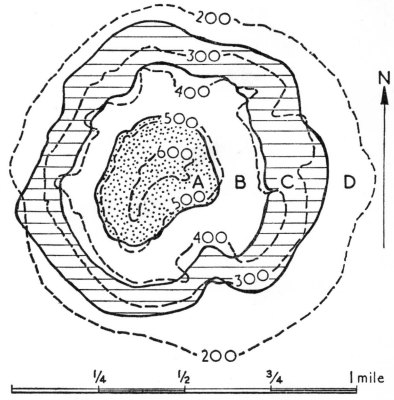

Fig. 40. MAP OF NEARLY HORIZONTAL STRATA.

across them both along the lines adopted by the Geological Survey, and also in other directions.

Although in drawing sections, vertical and horizontal scales should, whenever possible, be the same, it sometimes happens that the relief of the surface may be so low that exaggeration of the vertical scale cannot be avoided. When this is necessary, the least practicable multiplication of the vertical scale should be adopted, and it should always be clearly stated on the legend to the section that the vertical scale is enlarged 'x' times.

The close approximation in shape of the contour-lines and the boundaries in Fig. 40 show that the beds must be very nearly

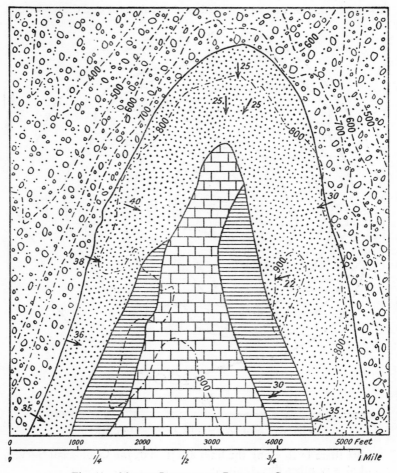

Fig. 41.   Map of Pitching or Plunging Syncline.

horizontal. Readers should prove, either by drawing a section, or by calculation, that the direction of dip is nearly west-south-west, also that the thickness of bed *C* on the west side of the hill is twice the thickness on the east side.

Fig. 41 is a skeleton map of an area in which there are four beds, a limestone, a shale, a sandstone, and a conglomerate cropping out. The map is contoured at intervals of 100 ft., and numerous dips are recorded. No table of strata is given, but it should be easy to

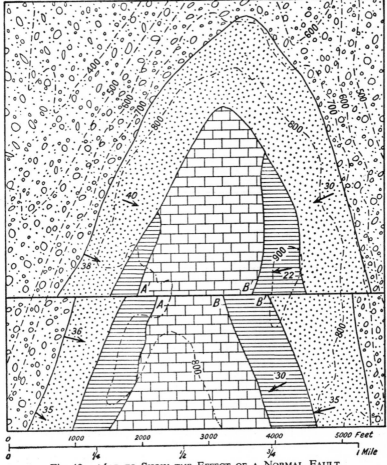

Fig. 42. MAP TO SHOW THE EFFECT OF A NORMAL FAULT.

determine the structure and the geological succession without drawing a section.

Since the dips are inwards, the structure is *centroclinal* and the beds are bent into an elongated basin. The youngest bed must be in the middle of the basin, and in proceeding outwards, older beds must be traversed. The upward succession must therefore be: conglomerate, sandstone, shale, and limestone. Since both the upper and lower boundaries of the sandstone and shale are given, and since the dips are known, the thickness of these beds may be determined by construction (see p. 21). The base of the conglomerate and the top of the limestone do not appear on the map; therefore the thicknesses of these beds cannot be ascertained.

Note that the outcrop of the limestone at its northern end terminates against the sandstone and that the outcrop of the shale is divided into two by the limestone. This is an example of an *overlap*, such as we referred to on p. 62. The limestone gradually creeps across the shale and finally rests on the sandstone.

In Fig. 42, the same area is shown, but a fault has been introduced for the purpose of demonstrating how the downthrow side and the amount of vertical displacement may be determined.

Since the trace of the fault on the map is a straight line, the fault must be vertical or very nearly so, for the intersection of a plane

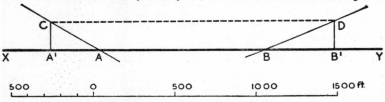

Fig. 43.   DETERMINATION OF THE DOWNTHROW OF A FAULT.

(of faulting or of contact) with an undulating surface can only appear as a straight line on a map when the plane is vertical.

The beds are dipping inwards, approximately along the line of the fault; therefore, corresponding lines of junction must become farther and farther apart in a vertically upward direction. On the downthrow side of the fault, the effect on the boundary lines is exactly the same as an increase in the elevation of the surface of the ground; therefore, corresponding lines must be farther apart than on the upthrow side, when a normal fault affects a syncline.

If a strike-fault intersects an anticline, corresponding lines become closer together on the downthrow side.

In Fig. 42, points A' and B' are farther apart than A and B; therefore, the downthrow side of the fault is towards the north.

The vertical displacement or "throw" of the fault may be determined graphically, as shown in Fig. 43. Draw a straight line XY, representing the line of the fault, and on it mark points A, B, A', and B' in their correct positions. Through A and B draw straight lines inclined to the horizontal at the appropriate angles of dip, and at A' and B' erect perpendiculars to intersect these lines at C and D. The distance between XY and CD, measured on the scale of the diagram, gives the throw of the fault.

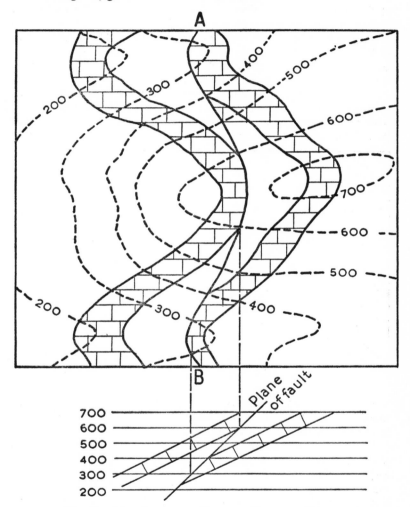

Fig. 44. MAP SHOWING A REVERSED FAULT OR THRUST.

It will be observed that CD and XY are not quite parallel; $A'C$ is 200 ft. and $B'D$ is 170 ft. The throw of the fault is therefore 200 ft. at A', and 170 ft. at B', with an average of 185 ft.

Appropriate methods of construction can be used to determine the throws of faults oblique to the dip, and we strongly advise students to make diagrams for themselves, working out the effects of faults running at various angles to the strike of the rocks and hading at different angles to the vertical.

A small area of hilly country is shown in Fig. 44. A single bed of limestone, with its outcrop interrupted by a fault *AB*, runs in a general direction from north to south across the map. The problem is to deduce the structure of the country.

Since no dips are marked, use will have to be made of the intersections of the boundaries of the limestone and of the line of fault with the contours. By joining points of equal elevation on the boundaries of the limestone, and also on the line of the fault, it is

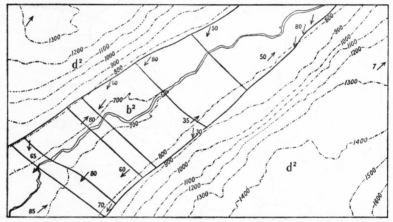

Fig. 45.   GEOLOGICAL MAP OF THE INGLETON UNCONFORMITY.

found that the straight lines are parallel with the side-lines of the map, and are therefore from north to south. The strikes of the limestone and the fault are also from north to south.

To determine the dips, a scale of heights (graduated on the same scale as that of the map) is constructed, its length being at right angles to the strike of the beds and of the fault. Perpendiculars are then dropped from the 600-ft. and the 300-ft. levels on the fault-line to the 600-ft. and 300-ft. lines of the lower scale. The points of intersection are joined, giving the trace of the plane of the fault. The hade of the fault is seen to be from east to west, and its inclination to the vertical, as measured with a protractor, is 45°.

By a similar method of construction, the section of the limestone is plotted. The thickness of the bed is approximately 100 ft., and

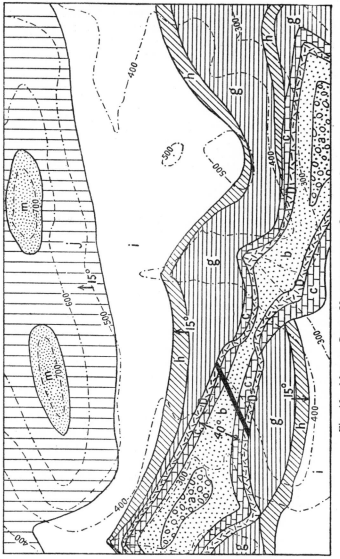

Fig. 46. Map to Show Unconformities, Outliers, Sill, etc.

it dips at 26° towards the west.   We observe also, that on the western side of the fault, the limestone is raised relatively to the part on the eastern side of the fault, and consequently lies much higher than might have been expected.   The dislocation is therefore a *reversed fault* or *thrust*; the vertical displacement of the limestone, or the *throw* of the fault, is 200 ft., the *heave*, or horizontal displacement of the limestone, caused by the fault is 400 ft.

Fig. 45 is a sketch-map of the district near Ingleton, to show the great unconformity which was illustrated in section in Fig. 24. The high ground bordering the valley of the River Greta consists of Carboniferous Limestone (d^2), dipping gently in a direction approximately north-east.   The floor of the valley consists of Pre-Cambrian rocks (b^2) dipping at high angles, and forming a number of strips of highly-compressed grits and slates which extend between the boundary lines of the Carboniferous Limestone.

Our last map (Fig. 46) illustrates a number of features, some of which we have not referred to previously.   Sufficient data are given for the student to verify for himself that the succession, in ascending order, is $a, b, c, \ldots g, h, i, j, \ldots m$.   The missing letters represent periods of time which are not represented by deposits.   There are, therefore, two unconformities, between c and g, and j and m.

The small isolated outcrop of a, at the western edge of the map, is an *inlier*.   The inferior series a to c is traversed by a dyke (shown in black) which, since its trace on the map is straight, must be vertical.   There is a *sill* which, towards the eastern side of the map, lies between b and c, but which ascends towards the west, ascends and overlies c.   The rise from below the limestone c to above it, proves that D must be intrusive, although a cursory glance at the map might suggest that D was a member of the normal succession.

From g to j the succession is straightforward.   The formation m forms two small outliers above approximately the 650-ft contour.

The student would be well advised to draw sections from north to south across the map, with a view to verifying these statements for himself, and also to determine graphically the thicknesses of the beds.   Any convenient scale may be assumed, for, providing the vertical and horizontal scales of the section are the same, the conclusions will be correct.   The scale of the map as reproduced in Fig. 46 is approximately 4 in. to the mile.

CHAPTER X

WATER SUPPLY

Of the many valuable economic substances we derive from our rocks, probably the most important is *water*. Large and additional quantities are constantly being demanded to meet the needs of modern civilisation. With increasing population and the introduction of new and modern industrial works, the problem of finding further supplies for both towns and villages is one which the field geologist is being urgently called upon to solve. It has been estimated that the world will need an increase of four times its present supply for A.D. 2000.

If it were possible, however, to pool all existing supplies, this question might not arise. But in districts where natural storage occurs, they do not always correspond with areas of large population. As early as 1879, W. H. Penning in his book on *Field Geology* wrote—"We do not economise that sources to be derived from the natural founts, and we do not sufficiently avail ourselves of the artificial founts which are at all seasons practically inexhaustible." In many respects these comments could apply to water-supply conditions existing even today.

Water supplies are derived from rainfall. In the British Isles this varies considerably in amount from place to place; for example, the average yearly rainfall in London (Westminster) is 24 in. (600 mm), in Derbyshire (Buxton), 53 in. (1,300 mm), and in the Lake District to well over 100 in. (2,500 mm).

Many hilly or mountainous areas like the Peak District of Derbyshire, Yorkshire, and the Lake District are particularly prone to *orographic rain*. This type of rainfall occurs when certain low heavy clouds reach such lofty points or barriers. Air contained in the upper layers of these clouds or atmosphere is then forced to rise, when the dewpoint is reached and the water vapour quickly falls as precipitation.

Although such hilly areas may receive a heavy rainfall, it does not necessarily follow that they will have good water supplies; in fact they are frequently less well served with water than are those situated on lower ground. Again, most of the areas of greatest rainfall are thinly populated. Thus, although there is plenty of water in the country as a whole, there is not a sufficient quantity of it at the right place and at the right time. With such a variation in water supply, its conservation is therefore essential and urgent. Perhaps one of the main factors in the neglect of water-storage is the indifference of the public to this matter. Waste could be prevented if the regard for water was higher and people were made aware of its great importance.

The spread and extent of rainfall is shown by the following figures: one inch of rain is equivalent to 22,620 gallons of water to an acre, or about 100 tons in weight.

Geological conditions may also give rise to considerable variations from place to place where water is obtainable. The height of an area above sea level, the character, structure, and relation of its strata, all play a very important role.

Where geological mapping has been done on six-inch maps, many minor sub-divisions in addition to the main rock divisions will have been recorded and these will often prove to be of much value to the field geologist in locating small water supplies. Again, from detailed studies of well borings he can often obtain much information regarding the thickness and character of underlying rocks.

A formation of structure that yields water in sufficient amount to supply wells or springs is known as an *aquifer*.

In general, we obtain our water from two sources: (1) from surface deposits such as sands, gravels, and glacial drifts, and (2) from underground accumulations.

Practically all water collected from surface deposits is obtained from *springs*. There are two types: (*a*) normal or gravity, (*b*) artesian.

Normal or Gravity Springs result from water sinking and percolating downwards and laterally until it eventually reaches the water table. Such springs also frequently occur on the upper side of a fault where a pervious bed is faulted against one that is impervious; as a result, water will be checked and diverted on its passage below. The attention of the field geologist is therefore often directed to the sinking or boring of wells where springs occur.

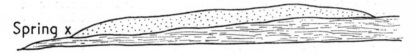

Fig. 47. NORMAL OVERFLOW SPRING.

At times, however, springs become obstructed or choked, thus considerably restricting the supply of water. Under these conditions it can often be increased by clearing any fragmentary rock material, silt, or other debris from the outlet. The conservation of water can be made by constructing a dam or basin at the egress to collect the overflow; but in doing so, great care must be taken to secure that the water so obtained is kept free of all impurities.

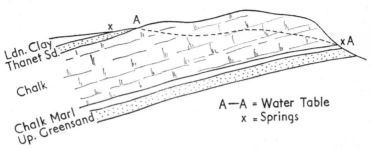

Fig. 48. PLANE OF SATURATION AND WATER TABLE, CHALK DOWNS (*after H. B. Woodward*).

Note: Plane of saturation or water table here is independent of dip and is regulated by the Chalk Marl below.

An *artesian spring* occurs where water is confined or imprisoned in a permeable formation and is overlain by an impermeable cover. If this cover happens to be thin or is fissured it will yield to the underlying pressure, and any water trapped or imprisoned in the formation will be ejected and thrown out at the surface. The chief rocks representing this type of supply are the chalk of Yorkshire and Lincolnshire, and the Carboniferous Limestone.

Fig. 49. ARTESIAN WELLS, FLOWING FROM BED 'A'.

An example of such imprisoned water has been recorded in Litton, N.W. Yorkshire. Here, Boulder Clay lies at the boundary of rising ground in Carboniferous Limestone. At their point of contact, following heavy rain, the underground pressure of water is so great that it is forced to the surface in the form of jet-like eruptions. On one occasion no less than fifteen pressure jets (or *blow-holes* as they are called) were counted; these rose 2-4 in. above ground level. Water flowing from such spots often results in the formation of *dubs* [dub (Scot.), a puddle or pool].

Underground Water. Underground water in this country is derived from rain which has passed downwards from the surface. In distribution, underground water is much more complicated in character than surface supplies. Alternating permeable and impermeable beds may overlie each other and each saturated zone or belt will thereby have a floor or limited shelf. In such cases water-carrying beds (varying in thickness and composition) are enclosed and sandwiched between strata devoid of water. Thus each pervious bed will have its own water table (see p. 104).

Again, underground water usually flows much more slowly, and where movement takes place along well-defined passages or levels these may become underground rivers, as is the case in many limestone areas.

In limestone areas many underground water courses occur in fissures and caves. Following heavy rain, caves and pot-holes in particular are often quickly filled with floodwater. There is usually little warning given of such an influx of water, and to the unwary and inexperienced caver hazardous and dangerous conditions may arise suddenly.

It is, however, from our open textured and consequently extremely porous rocks, such as sandstones and grits, that water at depth is found readily available. For example, the Bunter Sandstone and Pebble Beds provide in themselves excellent underground storage in the form of underground reservoirs.

But it is not only from sedimentary rocks that underground accumulations occur; volcanic and metamorphic rocks will at times yield good supplies of water. Here, however, geological structure plays a very important part in the form of flexuring, faulting, and folding.

In recent years geophysical methods have been used in investigating water at depth, particularly abroad in arid areas.

Water Tables. Rain which has drained or percolated through permeable strata is called groundwater; such zones of saturation, bounded by an upper surface are termed *water tables*. A water table will vary in depth, depending on the intake from the water-bearing bed and the thickness and extent of the permeable strata at outcrop.

Water tables are undulating in form; they are rarely, if ever, flat. In dry periods they may fall even below the valley bottom and prevent springs from flowing. On the other hand, there are occasions following heavy rain when water tables will attain a definite rise or crest.

To obtain a constant and regular supply of water, a well must reach the zone of saturation or water table; in other words, it must be sunk into the standing water level or *rest level*.

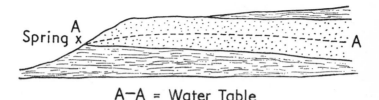

A–A = Water Table

Fig. 50. NORMAL HILL-SIDE SPRING: INCLINED BEDS.

Perched Water Tables. Formations consisting of alternating open-textured rocks with silts or clay, often provide adequate water for domestic use. When impermeable rocks underlie sandstones or limestones, they offer great resistance to downward percolation. Indeed, in some cases where the clay-content is high, percolation may be completely stopped. The effect of these silty or clayey bands is to "split" the water table and enable it to pass downwards from saturated to unsaturated rock. In such instances water becomes shelved or "perched" and results in a *perched water table*. They may occur in long unbroken series, or in detached lense-shaped forms in alignment.

Permeablity or Porosity of Rocks. An important factor governing the accumulation of water is the permeability of the rocks of an area. Some rocks are extremely porous (or permeable) such as the Millstone Grit, The Trias (Bunter Sandstone) and Greensand sandstones, while others like shale, mudstone, and clay are impermeable.

Although a rock may have a high porosity and thus hold a large volume of water, it will not necessarily yield a supply. For example, a clay is extremely porous—holding up to 50% of water—but its pore space is so fine as to make it *impermeable*, and render the passage of water within the rock practically impossible. Other examples of such rocks are silts, porcellanites, and calcitic mud-stones of frequent occurrence in the Carboniferous Limestone.

We can therefore define a *permeable rock* as one which, when kept at saturation point, is able to supply a well to provide sufficient water for a normal-sized house. In some rural districts, however, cess pits or sumps are present and from these serious risk of pollution could arise. But, where there is a protecting cover consisting, say, of clay, shale, or marl, wells dug beneath such deposits may give pure water. Great care, however, must be taken to ensure that cess pits do not penetrate the water-supply bed.

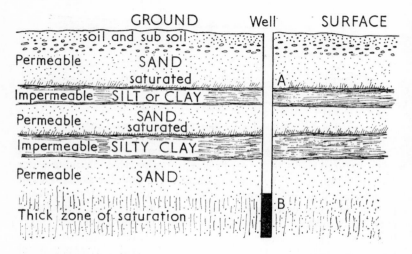

Fig. 51. DIAGRAMMATIC SECTION SHOWING 'SPLITTING' OR PERCHING OF WATER TABLE.

Water that appears clear and sparkling, and good to the taste, may nevertheless be much polluted and contaminated. Water which rises suddenly in a well after heavy rainfall should arouse suspicion, unless the vicinity of the well is absolutely clean. Sudden rises or falls (*i.e.* a foot or more) in the water table of a well, associated with heavy rainfall, implies that water gets into the well without being cleaned or filtered through a good depth of soil. For safety, a well should be placed so that it will strike water at a depth of not less than 15-20 ft.

When the impermeable bands are punctured or bored, water can be drawn off by shallow wells, often giving good yields. During periods of drought, however, a well may tend to dry out, in which case it will require deepening to reach another and thicker zone of saturation.

Perched water tables are common in the Wealden deposits of Kent and Sussex, particularly in the Ashdown Sand and Tunbridge Wells Sandstone series. In many parts of Yorkshire, perched tables also occur in the Carboniferous Limestone, and water obtained from them often constitutes an important source for domestic supply. The village of Litton, in Littondale, has only 60 inhabitants, but no less than four different supplies come from such sources.

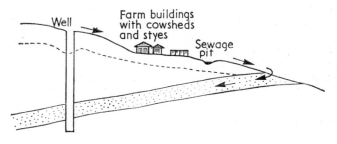

Fig. 52. SHOWING PASSAGE AND ACCESS OF SURFACE DRAINAGE WATERS TO WELL BY PERCOLATION ALONG A PERVIOUS ROCK.

SOME IMPORTANT WATER-YIELDING STRATA

Of the many important rocks or strata yielding water are the following:—

Soils. These are the uppermost layers of the earth's surface in which plants grow. Although varying in thickness they are very porous and readily take up or absorb water from rain. A certain amount of this water is lost by evaporation, some of it is taken up by plant life, and the remainder—on the soil becoming saturated—sinks and percolates downwards into the subsoil and rocks below. When soils consist partly or wholly of *gravel* they provide the best sources for water supply. A coarse clean gravel has a high porosity and will give a high yield. There is, however, a possibility of pollution in gravels.

Sands, Sandstones, and Grits. Owing to their open textures or numerous pore spaces, these rocks are invariably very porous and their water content often high. But, the extent of their porosity is dependent, however, on their grade sizes. A rock consisting of uniform grade will have a porosity higher than one made up of a mixture of grades. Water obtained from all these rocks is said to be *soft*, like rainwater. Examples: Wealden deposits—Ashdown Sand, Tunbridge Wells Sandstones, and Upper and Lower Greensand, Triassic Sandstones, and Millstone Grit of the North of England.

Chalk. The Chalk formation varies considerably in its capacity of supplying water, and it is from the beds which are fissured and which possess great permeability that our chief yields are obtained.

The rock is saturated up to a certain surface or plane which fluctuates according to the undulations of the ground. The level of the plane is therefore determined by the depth of the steepest valleys, and one which is sufficiently deep to reach a saturated plane will give rise to a perennial stream. Many valleys, however, are not deep enough to reach such a zone and they then form that well-known feature of our Chalk country, *dry valleys*.

Into the saturated beds deep wells are sunk and, from these, long headings are constructed so as to intercept the fissures or channels containing water.

The Upper Chalk of the South of England is nodular and flint-bearing and constitutes the best yielding part of the formation. The Middle and Lower Chalk, on the other hand, are often soft and marly, and being mainly impervious give little water. It is from the Chalk that many south coast towns, as Portsmouth, Southampton, and Brighton, rely for practically all their water. In Lincolnshire and Yorkshire, however, the lower parts of the Chalk yield fair supplies, but here the rock is flint-bearing and less marly than their equivalent horizons in Southern England.

Limestones. The problem of finding water in limestones is often speculative, especially so in massive limestones, like the Carboniferous Limestone. At times, limestones yield excellent supplies and are amongst the best aquifers; in other cases they may prove failures.

There are many factors affecting the yield of water from these rocks. In the Carboniferous Limestone the rock is well jointed and fissured, and the openings produced by solution act as traps for rain and become wider and enlarged. Thus, the transmission of water is possible under these conditions even through non-porous rocks. Again, all limestones vary considerably in pore space. In Oolitic Limestones, for example, the open packing of the grains gives the rock a high porosity; in the rocks the movement of water is largely governed by their porosity.

In limestones (as the **Carboniferous**), where the water sinks to great depths, the surface is often dry. But water which becomes trapped or imprisoned is thrown out at the base of the formation, or it may issue from caves or from small underground rivers. Sometimes underground water may be polluted *surface water* which has sunk below and temporarily followed a course in joints or caves. Special heed and attention should therefore be given to areas where contamination of this nature could arise. In Littondale, near Penyghent, two wells were recently sunk—one to over 300 ft., both of which yielded supplies, but on analysis proved to be quite unfit for drinking purposes.

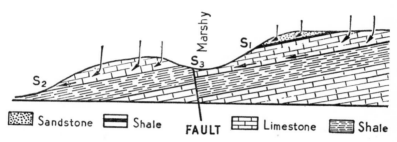

Fig. 52A. THE FORMATION OF SPRINGS.

All water from limestones (like the Chalk) is said to be *hard*, due to being charged with much carbonate of lime, often as much as 240 p.p.m. calcium hardness (compare with 7 p.p.m. calcium hardness in soft waters).

The contact between the pervious and impervious beds may be the result of deposition; thus, in Fig. 52A, rainwater percolating through the sandstone and limestone is prevented from passing downwards indefinitely by the underlying shales and where the contacts intersect the surface of the ground, at S_1 and S_2 the water will issue as springs.

On the downthrow side of the fault, the truncated end of the limestone is brought into contact with the shale on the upthrow side; consequently, the water is forced to the surface as a spring at S_3. The thin limestone in the valley will become waterlogged, and the valley will develop into a marshy strip. A line of springs formed along a fault is likely to be less sinuous than one resulting from a normal sedimentary contact.

PART II

CHAPTER XI

COLLECTING

Collecting fulfils two main functions: *first*, it affords valuable self-instruction to the beginner. By finding and extracting minerals, rocks, and fossils from mine or quarry he will not only learn to recognise them, but he will see them in their natural setting or environment. No amount of reading and studying illustrations or even frequent examination of hand specimens from a cabinet will confer facility in the determination of minerals, rocks, or fossils. In addition, with one's own collection, there is the advantage that specimens can be broken, scratched, or ground, to test for fracture, cleavage, or hardness in minerals, or to look for internal structures in fossils.

Secondly, a collection is essential to the geologist in illustrating the material found in his area: complete identifications are not always possible in the field, therefore it will be necessary to take away representative specimens for more detailed examination. Moreover, if he proposes to publish the results of his field-work, his fossils (at any rate) should be submitted to a specialist so that identifications may be properly checked.

A specimen of a rare or new species or genus, when it has been identified by a specialist, should at once be offered to a national museum, and the finder should retain a record of the registration number which will gladly be furnished by the museum. The beginner should resist the (not unnatural) desire to retain for himself rarities which should be deposited in a public collection.

Some general hints on the collecting, packing, and labelling of specimens in the field are given below.

The exact locality and bed from which every specimen is obtained must be recorded. A specimen whose source is unknown or is inaccurately recorded is valueless, and conclusions based on it may be misleading. Wherever possible, a note should be made of the grid reference of the position.

The specimens from each exposure should be kept separately from those obtained at other exposures. The outside of each package should be marked clearly with the position of the exposure from which the contents were obtained, and a record should be made in the notebook. Time will be saved when unwrapping, for it will be possible to proceed systematically and assemble together the collection from each exposure.

A supply of newspaper should be carried for packing; each individual specimen should be wrapped so that at least one thickness of paper separates it from its neighbours. If this precaution is not taken, irreparable damage may result from one specimen rubbing against another.

Where small and delicate fossils are collected, it is useful to carry a few empty match-boxes or glass tubes (3 in. × ½ in. or ¾ in.) with corks, and a small supply of cotton wool and tissue-paper. Tubes are conveniently carried in a tin box in which they are carefully packed in soft paper. Blank labels may be stuck on the outside of the tubes or match-boxes on which particulars of locality are entered.

ROCKS

Rocks should always be collected *in situ*. Pebbles from beds of streams or sea beaches, and fragments from stone walls, although of little value for scientific study, should not be despised, since they often give an idea of the types of rock which occur in the vicinity.

Before taking a sample, thought should be given to what the specimen is to show; normally, it will be desired to illustrate the typical properties of the rock. Sometimes, however, it may be that certain abnormalities present features of interest. If, for example, an exposure shows a dyke in limestone, the geologist would probably set out to obtain three specimens: (*a*) the limestone, (*b*) the material of the dyke, and (*c*) a composite sample showing the actual contact of the dyke with the limestone. The latter would enable the mutual effect of rock on rock to be studied.

If a number of specimens are taken at one exposure, it is desirable to make a sketch and a plan in the notebook, and to mark thereon the position from which each was taken. The wrapping paper of each should bear cross-references so that the samples may be correctly located with reference to the entries in the notebook.

If the rock is fine-grained and homogeneous, it is easy to take a suitable specimen, for one part of the exposure will serve as well as another. Where there is much variation, the problem is more difficult, and it becomes necessary to take several samples. The Ashover Grit presents difficulties. At the Robin Quarries, for example, the upper part is thinly-bedded and flaggy, while the main body of the rock varies in texture from a grit to a fine-grained conglomerate; in fact, three grades of pulp-stones (coarse, medium, and fine) are made. Four samples would therefore be required.

The size of the specimen will depend on the nature of the rock and the purpose for which it is required. In the interest of economy of effort, it is desirable to keep specimens *small*, say a little larger than an ordinary match-box. The finer the grain of the rock, the smaller the specimen which will illustrate it adequately. Remember, samples have to be carried, and eventually must be stored.

When taking a specimen, make for a projecting edge or corner *where the rock is fresh and unweathered*, and knock off a piece by judicious use of the hammer. The specimen should then be reduced to suitable dimensions by means of the trimming hammer. Deeply weathered specimens should generally be avoided, unless it is desired to illustrate the products of decomposition. On the other hand, weathering sometimes reveals features which would not be apparent on freshly broken surfaces, Thus, a limestone may not disclose the fact that it is fossiliferous, and the spheroidal structure of a dolerite or basalt may become apparent only when it has been exposed for a long period to atmospheric agencies.

Soft or friable rocks are better sampled by means of a pointing trowel or a putty-knife. Slabs of shale can be prised out and trimmed to shape, frequently merely by breaking off the portions which are not required. Clays must generally be dug out, and soft, friable sandstones treated in the same way.

MINERALS

Apart from those minerals which constitute the essential constituents of a rock, there may be others which occur often in veins, fissures, or cavities (p. 40); these should always be looked for, and if found, specimens should be taken and a careful record kept of how they occurred. Thus, for example, we might make a note, "Calcite, found on joint-planes, Fall Hill, point 3545 6323."

When making a record to accompany a mineral specimen, *all* relevant information should be given, including the rock in which the mineral was found and the manner of its occurrence.

There are certain characteristic *mineral associations*. In the quarry at Fall Hill, fluorspar was found (p. 68). Now, where fluorspar occurs, barytes, galena, and blende are often found also. Therefore, it is worth while looking out for these minerals, all of which occur in one or other of the exposures of the limestone in the Ashover district.

When looking for minerals, do not despise iron-stained lumps which often look unpromising. Decomposition and oxidation may give rise to a crust of limonite, perhaps a quarter of an inch thick, and until the lump has been broken open with the hammer, it is impossible to decide whether there is a useful specimen of mineral within.

In *"metalliferous"* *districts*, "heavy" minerals, which are often of economic importance, accumulate in the alluvium of streams and rivers. Those minerals whose specific gravities are upwards of about 3 tend to separate from the lighter materials from the weathering of the rocks and collect to form *heavy mineral assemblages*; these are often to be found on small terrace-like ledges and pockets formed at bends in streams, or on the upstream side of obstructions such as boulders or sand-bars.

Some beach deposits, below the limit of shingle, are often rich in heavy minerals.

The usual method of collecting and separating minerals which occur under the conditions described above, is by the use of the pan, or **panning.**

Panning can be carried out in almost any sort of flat-bottomed dish, soup plate, or pan; the miners' pan, which is used by prospectors, is made of thin steel, and has a diameter of from 12 to 16 in. and a depth of from 3 to 4 in., with sloping sides. The interior must be kept smooth and free from rust.

The art of panning is not difficult to acquire; if the beginner can watch the operation being carried out once or twice by an experienced panner, he will learn the process much more easily than by reading pages of explanatory matter.

The pan is half-filled with sand or gravel and held horizontally under water; it is then rotated backwards and forwards, coupled with a slight rocking motion. This has the effect of bringing the lighter and clayey material to the surface and causing it to slop over the edge of the pan, while the heavier materials, consisting of pebbles and the "heavy" minerals, settle at the bottom. The pebbles are then picked out by hand, and the process is continued until the water in the pan is quite clear, and a residue of clean sand remains.

The next stage requires greater care and skill; the pan is submerged in water, tilted to about 45°, and a similar gyratory motion is imparted to it. The effect is to bring the material of lower specific gravity towards the edge of the pan, while the "heavier" components of the mixture collect nearer to the centre of the pan. This is repeated again and again, until only a small residue remains; this should consist of metallic and other heavy minerals.

Many of the mineral grains recovered by panning are metallic and often possess distinctive colours and lustres, which materially assist in their provisional identification. From their lustrous appearance, the grains are called "colours" by the prospector.

The metallic minerals may include platinum, gold, chalcopyrite, galena, wolframite, chromite, magnetite, hematite. The non-metallic minerals may include diamond, cassiterite, corundum, topaz, barytes.

Magnetite is often abundant in the residue, and, together with other iron-bearing minerals, should be removed by means of a magnet before the examination of the residue is continued.

FOSSILS

Success in collecting is primarily a matter of close observation, but other factors also come into play. It is necessary to have an idea of what to look for, where to look, and how to extract the specimen when found. There is also an element of luck, for although a certain bed or formation may be richly fossiliferous, the fossils may be very unequally distributed, and often tend to be concentrated at particular horizons; sometimes, also, they may be crowded together at a few localities, while at many places the formation is practically barren of organic remains.

Knowing what to look for. Much can be learned by the preliminary study of fossils displayed in the cabinets of a museum and from illustrations in books. Better, still, is the opportunity of handling specimens, for it is then possible to view them from a number of different angles, which is not possible in a museum or in a figure. In the field, of course, fossils look different from museum specimens, because the latter have been cleaned and developed from the matrix in which they were imbedded, while in the quarry-face, a small area of the surface, or perhaps only a projecting corner, may be visible to show that there is something worthy of investigation.

Most people, too, find it necessary, when examining a quarry or exposure, to "get their eye in" before specimens begin to be found. It is, therefore, advisable to give plenty of time to searching a section. Provided that there has not been metamorphism (such as cleavage, induced by pressure), the finer the grain of the rock, the more likely is it to yield good specimens.

Limestones may be richly fossiliferous without showing the fact on fresh fractures; the only indication of a fossil on a clean fracture may be a rather vague line of a different colour to that of the rock generally, or, alternatively, a few cleavage-rhombs of calcite. Under the action of atmospheric weathering, however, the matrix generally tends to decompose faster than the organic remains, with the result that the latter stand out in relief. In limestone quarries, therefore, attention should also be devoted to the spoil-heaps, where nearly perfect specimens may often be obtained.

While, however, the best *specimens* are usually obtained from weathered pieces on screes and tip-heaps, these may have come from any part of the quarry. Therefore, having established that the quarry yields a particular suite of fossils, and having collected a representative set, the face itself should be carefully examined with a view to ascertaining whether particular species are restricted to special zones, or whether they are scattered broadcast throughout the rock.

Clays are often fossiliferous, but specimens may be difficult to find *in situ*. At brickworks, large quantities of clay are often dug and allowed to weather before being worked up, with the result that the fossils are washed out and accumulate at the foot of the heaps. Nodules should be broken, since they may have formed round a fossil.

It is a matter of observation that *mottled* clays are generally unfossiliferous.

Shales should be split along the planes of lamination, and the surfaces thus disclosed should be closely examined.

Sandstones, particularly if unconsolidated, are often very poor in organic remains; the fossils may have been dissolved by percolating water. Nodules of ironstone and compact layers should always be examined and broken open; they often yield casts and moulds of fossils which are identifiable.

Slates should be carefully examined to determine as far as possible the direction of the original bedding; this is sometimes indicated by parallel bands of slightly different texture. It is then necessary to break numerous pieces of the slate along the bedding to ascertain whether there are any fossils.

Attention must here be drawn to the fact that it is not always what appear to be the most perfect specimens which are the most valuable, either as biological or stratigraphical material. Fossils which are incomplete have often provided evidence of details of internal structures which have solved problems in classification, while recognisable fragments are as useful in dating a deposit as more perfect "museum" specimens. When collecting, therefore, every endeavour should be made to obtain a complete fauna from each exposure, regardless of whether the *specimens* are complete or not.

When collecting from "hard" rocks, such as limestones, it is often necessary to use a cold chisel. The chisel should always be directed *away* from the fossil which is being cut out; otherwise, one of two things may happen: either the edge of the chisel may slip and cut into the fossil, or, what is more likely, a chunk of rock may be split off, carrying part of the specimen with it, and leaving the major part still embedded.

Fossils can often be separated from friable rocks, such as soft, ill-cemented sandstones, by scraping the matrix away with the corner of the chisel or with the point of a trowel. In dealing with shelly sands (such as the crags of East Anglia, or the shelly cliffs near John o' Groats), where the proportion of shells to matrix is very high, the specimens may be picked out and are best deposited in a tin which is then packed with the finer matrix.

A certain amount of trimming may be carried out at the exposure in which collecting is proceeding, but this should not be overdone. It is a good plan to leave a little of matrix adhering to specimens that are taken away for, not only does the matrix act as a protection to the specimen during carriage, but it often affords proof of the layer from which it was collected. Final clearance can be deferred until more time is available. Where specimens are covered with mud or clay, they should be cleaned up by being carefully brushed with a nail-brush under water.

Collecting should be carried out systematically; the specimens from different beds and localities should be kept separate. Much confusion can arise if sufficient attention is not paid to this important point. It is not enough to acquire a large collection from (say) the Carboniferous Limestone in the Ashover district. Fossils from each exposure should be kept distinct, and the position (in a vertical sense) should be noted as nearly as possible. It is found, for example, that large productids which were recorded from the quarry in Cockerspring Wood (p. 71) form a distinct layer, about 9 in. thick, underlying about 3 ft. of rubbly limestone. A similar bed of large productids can be traced for a considerable distance round the inner margin of the limestone, and always near the upper parts of the exposures. Unless the specimens were collected *in situ*, and a careful record made, the fact that the large productids are restricted to the upper horizons of the limestone would not be appreciated.

FIELD IDENTIFICATION

Having collected various specimens, it is next necessary to try and identify them; and the remainder of the book is intended to assist the beginner in making provisional determinations in the field. Giving a correct name to a specimen is not an end in itself, it is only one stage in using the specimen to advantage, for a name is not an attribute of a specimen, but merely a conventional term designed

to facilitate reference.   Ideally, the name should give an indication
that the specimen possesses certain observable characteristics which
distinguish it from, or affiliate it to other specimens.   So far as
mapping is concerned, we have seen that it is quite possible to trace
and record the outcrop of a rock without knowing what the rock
was.   The toadstone at Ashover proved this.   As soon, however,
as the rock is identified as a *tuff*, our horizon is widened, for this is
evidence of volcanic activity.

Again, until the fossils from the limestone are identified, the
age of the rock is unknown.   When the corals have been assigned
correctly to their genera, it is possible to date the limestone
accurately.   Similar remarks might be made about the minerals;
once their nature has been determined and names have been correctly
assigned to them, we learn that the neighbourhood of Ashover is a
potential source of lead, zinc, fluorspar, and barytes.

The power of identifying specimens is gained by practice; a
student who takes an elementary course of geology is carefully
drilled so that, at the end of his studies, he can attach correct names
to perhaps eighty minerals, forty rocks, and a hundred fossils.
If, when he confronts his examiners, he can reproduce his knowledge,
he feels satisfied, and often straightway forgets all about the subject.
Given practice, therefore, identification is comparatively easy.   We
therefore recommend our readers to take every possible opportunity
of handling geological specimens and of identifying them as far as
possible with the aid of the tables and schemes which follow.   In
this regard, we would not despise specimens whose source is
unknown.   Once the student can determine samples of galena,
blende, barytes, etc., by means of the analytical tables and schemes,
he really begins to *know* those minerals.   And the same applies to
rocks and fossils; that of which he has had experience he *knows*,
that of which he has only *read* is not the best kind of knowledge.

A name should conjure up associations.   Consider the single
word *Productus*.   The associated ideas include, brachiopod, marine
origin, Upper Palaeozoic; and, to the student who has collected
specimens of *Productus* for himself, his mind should form a picture
of where he had collected these fossils.

Minerals, rocks, and fossils have their own associations, and
appreciation of this fact is very important to the geologist.   At
Hockley Quarry, for example, the rock was found to be a limestone.
The immediate suggestion is that it will be worth while searching
for fossils, and also that the most likely place to find specimens will
be on weathered surfaces.   Therefore, recourse is had to the
scattered pieces of rock which were left by quarrymen when the face
was last worked.

At the same time, a knowledge of associations is useful in that it forms a check against hasty conclusions. There are certain assemblages which do *not* occur in the normal course of events. The presence of two incompatible fossils such as an ammonite and a chain-coral in a quarry may be due to the fact that Secondary or Mesozoic rocks (ammonite) are lying unconformably on Palaeozoic rocks (chain-coral). Alternatively, either of the fossils may be derived from a drift deposit, such as a boulder-clay, which forms a cover or mantle over the rock in the quarry.

The ability to identify a specimen correctly and rapidly is the result of study and experience. Even in the initial stages, however, the observer will probably find that he can identify a few rocks and minerals almost subconsciously, for very few people are entirely without some knowledge of geological facts, even though the information may be unsystematic and unco-ordinated. The beginner will, therefore, do well to obtain specimens to which he can give names, and to study them in the light of the appropriate tables; he will thus see how the tables are intended to be used and acquire experience which will be valuable when he comes to dealing with specimens of unknown materials.

As aids in the determination of the commoner minerals, rocks, and fossils, we have drawn up three separate sets of tables or schemes in which the more obvious properties are set out. In each table, we have endeavoured to group together a limited number of specimens having a number of properties in common, then to break each group down into two or more smaller ones, and so by a continued process of subdivision, to lead to the correct identification of the specimen.

In drawing up the schemes, our object has been to start with the more obvious properties and to lead up to the final identification. We have tried to avoid the common practice of working by definition, that is, naming (say) a genus of fossils and then summarising its characteristics. From the point of view of the field geologist, this is irrational, for he starts with an unknown specimen having various ascertainable properties, from the study of which he arrives at a conclusion as to its nature.

There are three separate sets of tables or schemes, directed to the identification of minerals, rocks, and fossils, respectively. The first step in making a determination is obviously to decide in which category the specimen belongs. So far as fossils are concerned, this is generally simple, for organic structure is usually easy to detect. On the other hand, it is often less easy to decide whether a specimen is that of a mineral or a rock, particularly when the sample is compact or where it has not been found *in situ*, but is picked up in the form of a pebble or a small, isolated fragment. When seen *in situ,* a rock forms a large mass, which is generally continuous over considerable areas, while a mineral usually is found in smaller quantities and sometimes in veins in the country-rock. Having got over the first fence and decided in which category the specimen is to be classed, its determination is fairly straightforward, and the use of the schemes is illustrated on pp. 163 and 191.

It should here be pointed out that the schemes are in no sense intended to be *classifications.* We have tried to do no more than provide what are really mnemonics, by whose aid it is possible to name limited series of minerals, rocks, and fossils.

We have assumed that the observer is provided with no more than the simplest apparatus, such as can readily be carried in the field. This should include a few *brass* pins, a knife, and a piece of quartz for determining hardness of minerals, a small, strong magnet, a carborundum "slip" (fine on one side and coarse on the other), and a small set of blowpipe apparatus and reagents. The latter is useful for carrying out confirmatory tests on minerals in the evenings or when the weather is wet and outdoor work is impossible.

CHAPTER XII

IDENTIFICATION OF MINERALS

Although some thousand mineral species have been described, the majority are comparatively rare, and it is necessary for the beginner to be familiar with only a limited number. These minerals he should be able to identify quickly and with certainty, either as hand-specimens or as they occur in their native habitat as constituents of rocks.

The properties on which identification in the field depend include—

Lustre, hardness, crystalline form, type of fracture, cleavage, colour, "streak," specific gravity (whether "light" or "heavy" when hefted in the hand), mode of occurrence, and associates (this is particularly valuable when dealing with ore-minerals). In addition, a few minerals are sufficiently strongly magnetic to be picked out by means of a magnet; one only—namely, magnetite—shows polarity.

Minerals are commonly classified according to their chemical compositions, which is not particularly useful to the field geologist, for it presupposes a chemical analysis. The most that the worker in the field can do is to make a few tests with the blowpipe to confirm the conclusions he has come to after examining the physical characters of a specimen.

The following tables are designed as *aides memoires* to the properties which are most likely to be of use to the field geologist; they are not intended to be a substitute for books on mineralogy, and full advantage cannot be obtained from them unless the student has handled a good series of minerals and tried the tests for himself.

The eighty-odd minerals included in the tables are, with few exceptions, those most likely to be found in the British Isles. The primary division is *hard* minerals (that is, those which are as hard as, or harder than, quartz) and *soft* minerals, which are softer than quartz. The latter are further subdivided into a number of categories according to the colour of the mineral in mass and as a fine powder (the *streak*).

The streak of a mineral is the mark made when a specimen is drawn across a surface harder than itself. The colour of the streak is that of the powder of the mineral, hence the term *streak* is used to express the colour of the powder.

The streak is conveniently determined when a mineral is being tested for hardness; the scratch is carefully examined under a lens to make sure that the mineral under test has been abraded and that the powder is derived from it and not from the reference mineral. The powder should be shaken on to a piece of white paper and rubbed on it so that the colour may be best appreciated.

Minerals of hardness exceeding seven are conveniently treated in small fragments or grains which may be crushed on the clean blade of a shovel by a grinding motion under the flat end of the head of a geological hammer.

The streak of a mineral is frequently different from the colour of the mineral in bulk—generally it is lighter—and a study of the colour and streak of minerals often supplies useful information in their identification. The contrast between colour and streak may be very marked, as for example, hematite, which is iron-black in mass, with a cherry-red streak. Dark coloured minerals, such as serpentine, hornblende and augite, give nearly white streaks.

A common association consists of cassiterite, ilmenite, and wolfram, all of which are frequently found as water-worn grains which superficially resemble one another. When crushed to powder, however, the streak of cassiterite is white or off-white, that of ilmenite is black to brownish-red, while the powder of wolfram is chocolate-brown. A careful examination of small samples of a concentrate will therefore give a preliminary idea of the relative proportions of the three minerals.

The primary division of minerals in the accompanying tables is based to a considerable extent on the comparison and contrast between the colour of the minerals in bulk and the colours of the streaks.

Since both colour and hardness are variable, a number of minerals appear several times in the tables. This is unavoidable; a certain amount of repetition is inevitable to ensure that the tables are sufficiently complete to enable the "variable" minerals to be identified.

Quartz having been selected as a "reference" mineral to divide the specimens into groups according to hardness, a small piece should be carried in the field.

Determination of hardness. Moh's scale of hardness is as follows:—

HARDNESS	REFERENCE MINERAL	REMARKS
1	Talc	} Can be scratched by the finger-nail.
2	Gypsum	

Hardness	Reference Mineral	Remarks
3	Calcite	Can be scratched by a *brass* pin or copper coin.
4	Fluorspar	Easily scratched by a knife.
5	Apatite	Scratched with difficulty by a knife; hardness equal to that of window-glass.
6	Orthoclase	Easily scratched by a file.
7	Quartz	Scratched with difficulty by a file.
8	Topaz	All minerals harder than 6 will scratch window-glass.
9	Corundum	
10	Diamond	

Before carrying out the test for hardness with the reference mineral, the surface of the unknown material should be cleaned from any powder and examined under the lens. Particular care should be taken to see that no oxidised or other alteration product is present on the surface; a fresh fracture should always be used, or, if necessary, made by the hammer. The effect of weathering on certain metallic minerals—such as, for example, oxides and sulphides of iron and copper—will in a comparatively short time bring about chemical alteration and form a thick coating on the surface, and thus effectively conceal the true and original mineral underneath. In the oxidised portions of mineral lodes this action results in complete alteration taking place.

The reference mineral is drawn across the surface selected, and if a scratch is visible, the "unknown" is the softer of the two. The test should be repeated and the powder examined under the lens and rubbed on a piece of white paper. The colour of the powder (or streak of the mineral) is observed and recorded.

When testing with a pin, knife, or file, care should be taken not to confuse a metallic streak of steel or brass which may be left on the surface with the streak of the mineral itself. When a mineral can be scratched by the knife, the pressure which is necessary to produce a scratch should be noted. With practice, it is possible to judge fairly accurately the hardness of minerals which can be scratched by steel.

When identifying a mineral in the field, the following procedure may be followed:—

(*a*) Note the kind of rock in which the specimen occurs and the *associated minerals*; this often gives valuable clue to its identity.

Galena, for example, is often associated with fluorspar, chromite with serpentine, and wolframite with cassiterite.

(*b*) The *general appearance* may be very informative. Pyrite, for example, is often found in cubes or octahedra; the faces of the cubes are often marked by fine parallel striae, so disposed that those on any face are at right angles to the striae on contiguous faces. Calcite commonly occurs as rhombohedral or prismatic forms, with a perfect cleavage parallel to the unit rhombohedron.

(*c*) The specimen may feel decidedly *heavy*. Most of the ores of the metals, the metallic-looking minerals, and the compounds of barium and strontium feel distinctly "weighty" when hefted in the hand.

(*d*) The mineral may next be tested for hardness by means of a piece of quartz to determine in which section of the tables its identity should be sought.

THE USE OF THE TABLES

Proceed systematically in accordance with the following scheme to decide in which section of the tables the mineral should be sought:—

1. { The mineral is as hard as, or harder than, quartz ..   Table **A**
   { The mineral is softer than quartz .. .. ..   see 2

2. { The streak is strongly coloured .. .. ..   see 3
   { The streak is nearly white .. ..   see 6

3. { The streak is black or nearly so .. .. ..   see 4
   { The streak is not black .. ..   see 5

4. { The lustre is metallic or sub-metallic .. ..   Table **B**
   { Both mineral and streak are black .. .. ..   Table **C**

5. { The streak is lead-grey or silvery .. .. ..   Table **D**
   {   ,,   ,,   yellow to yellowish-brown .. ..   Table **E**
   {   ,,   ,,   red to reddish-brown .. .. ..   Table **F**
   {   ,,   ,,   green or blue .. ..   Table **G**

6. { The mineral is coloured in mass, the streak is very
   {   nearly white .. ..   see 7
   { The mineral is white .. ..   Table **J**

7. { The mineral is violet, purple, grey, or green ..   Table **H**
   { The mineral is yellow, brown, or nearly black ..   Table **I**

TABLES

FOR THE DETERMINATION

OF MINERALS

BY PHYSICAL AND OTHER TESTS

The mineral is as hard as or harder than

Hardness and Specific Gravity	Colour	Appearance	Fracture and Cleavage
6–7. 6·4–7·1.	Usually black or brown. Rarely yellow or colourless.	Tetragonal prisms and pyramids; sometimes fibrous ("Woody"). Granular.	Sub-conchoidal. Brittle.
7. 2·65.	Colourless when pure; often amethyst, pink, yellow to dark brown, orange, or smoky. Vitreous lustre.	Hexagonal prisms and pyramids; also massive and granular.	Irregular. No cleavage.
7. 2·6–2·64.	White, grey, pale blue, bluish-white, brownish.	Wax-like masses; often botryoidal, mammillary, stalactitic.	Irregular. No cleavage.
7.	Grey to dark grey, with white cortex when fresh. Often stained brown in gravels.	Nodules and tabular bands; pebbles.	Conchoidal.
7.	Grey to black when fresh. Weathers honey-coloured to rusty brown.	Nodules; bands or seams.	More or less flat. Never conchoidal. Brecciated.
6·5–7·5. 3·1–4·3.	Shades of red, deep hyacinth, brownish red, emerald, or olive-green, depending on the variety.	Massive; often rounded; crystal faces sometimes seen.	Conchoidal or uneven.
7–7·5. 2·98–3·2.	Black or bluish-black; more rarely blue, green, red. Colours sometimes in zones about the long axis of the crystal (parti-coloured). Vitreous lustre. Opaque to transparent.	Hexagonal prisms differently terminated, striated; acicular, columnar.	Sub-conchoidal or uneven.
7·5. 3·1–3·3.	Pearl-grey, purplish, flesh-red.	Prismatic crystals; as "spots" in slates; cruciform sections in chiastolite.	Uneven.

quartz; the powder is white, or nearly so.

OCCURRENCE, ASSOCIATES. OTHER TESTS	THE MINERAL IS PROBABLY
Veins in acid rocks with topaz, tourmaline, quartz, fluorspar, scheelite, wolfram, ilmenite. *Note.*—Streak of wolfram is chocolate-brown, and of ilmenite, black to brownish-red. Separable from gangue-minerals when in grains by panning.	CASSITERITE (Tinstone), SnO_2.
Essential constituent of the more acid volcanic, intrusive plutonic and metamorphic rocks, where it occurs filling the interstices between other minerals. Constitutes almost the whole of sandstones, grits, and quartzites. Enters into the composition of many other sediments, such as clays, mudstones, and siltstones. An important "vein"-mineral.	QUARTZ (Rock Crystal), SiO_2.
Usually filling cavities in amygdaloidal-rocks; frequently in hollows in flints.	CHALCEDONY, SiO_2.
Nodular or tabular masses in chalk. Important constituent (more or less rolled) of many Tertiary rocks and gravels.	FLINT, SiO_2.
Nodular and tabular bands, especially, but not exclusively, in limestones. Nodules, more or less rounded, and often weathered brown, are common in many gravels.	CHERT, SiO_2.
Common red (Almandine) garnet occurs frequently in mica-schists and gneiss; also, more rarely in granite. Grossularite (pale green, greenish-white, or cinnamon) occurs in altered limestones. Pyrope (deep crimson to mulberry colour) occurs in basic igneous rocks, associated with olivine, serpentine, etc. Melanite is black and dull.	GARNET. 3 R″O, $R_2'''O_3$, 3 SiO_2, where R″ = Ca, Fe″, or Mn. R‴ = Fe, Al, or Cr.
Accessory in many granites, syenites, etc., and the more acid rocks generally. Associated with quartz. May occur in veins with ores of lead, tin, and cobalt. Also in metamorphic rocks, such as mica-schists, clay-slates, and metamorphic limestones. Common as a detrital mineral in sediments. The longitudinal striations, combined with the black colour, are very characteristic.	TOURMALINE. Borosilicate of Al, with alkalies, Mg. and Fe. RUBELLITE. (Pink tourmaline). INDICOLITE. (Blue). SCHORL. (Black).
In metamorphosed argillaceous rocks; chiastolite slate, andalusite slate, etc. Accessory in some granites. Associates, sillimanite, biotite, garnet, corundum, tourmaline.	ANDALUSITE, CHIASTOLITE, $Al_2O_3.SiO_2$.

HARDNESS AND SPECIFIC GRAVITY	COLOUR	APPEARANCE	FRACTURE AND CLEAVAGE
7·5. 4·7.	Colourless, grey, pale yellow, greenish, reddish-brown. Adamantine lustre. Transparent to opaque.	Small to minute tetragonal prisms with pyramids.	Conchoidal.
7·5–8. 2·6–2·8.	Emerald-green and pale green, yellow, white. Vitreous or resinous lustre. Transparent, translucent, to opaque.	Hexagonal prisms resembling apatite, which see; compact, columnar.	Cl. basal.
8. 3·6.	Wine-yellow, straw-yellow, white, greyish, sometimes blue or pink. Vitreous lustre. Transparent to translucent.	Short prisms, or granules; sometimes columnar.	Cl. perfect, basal.
9. 3·9–4·1.	Common varieties grey, greenish, or reddish and dull. Sometimes colourless. Ruby, sapphire, oriental amethyst, oriental emerald, and oriental topaz are transparent varieties.	Hexagonal barrel-shaped crystals; often massive and granular.	Conchoidal or uneven. Separation planes common; parallel to basal plane.
10. 3·52.	White or colourless, sometimes yellow, red, etc. Very rarely blue or black.	Octahedra or cubes; spherical. Crystal faces often curved and striated.	Very perfect, octahedral.

(1) Quartz.   (2) Garnet.   (3) Tourmaline.   (4) Corundum.   (5) Andalusite.
(6) Chiastolite.   (7) Beryl, and Apatite.   (8) Pyrite. *A.* Striated cube. *B.* Pyritohedron.
(9) Marcasite, "spear-head" or "cockscomb" crystal.

—*continued.*

Occurrence, Associates. Other Tests	The Mineral is Probably
Primary constituent in granites, syenites, etc. Also in crystalline limestones, gneisses, and schists. Occurs in alluvial deposits with gem-stones and gold. Coloured varieties become colourless and transparent when heated in blowpipe flame.	Zircon, $ZrO_2.SiO_2$.
Accessory in granites and pegmatites, into the druses of which large crystals sometimes project (Mourne Mountain granite). Also in metamorphic rocks, schists, and crystalline limestones.	Beryl, $3\,BeO.\,Al_2O_3.\,6\,SiO_2$.
Acid igneous and metamorphic rocks. Good crystals sometimes found projecting into druses in granites and cavities in rhyolites. As rolled pebbles and crystals in sediments. Associated with cassiterite in tin-bearing pegmatites and tin-veins generally. Also with fluorspar and tourmaline.	Topaz, $Al_2SiO_4F_2$.
In metamorphic rocks such as crystalline limestones, gneisses, etc., and in certain igneous rocks, such as syenite. Also as grains and pebbles in stream sands, where it has been preserved by its hardness. The gem-stones occur as isolated crystals in limestones or as rounded pebbles in alluvial deposits. Hardness and physical properties are distinctive.	Corundum, Al_2O_3.
In alluvial deposits, with other minerals of high specific gravity and extreme obduracy. Unknown in British Isles. The only mineral of hardness 10.	Diamond (Pure Carbon).

(10) Limonite and Psilomelane, columnar; stalactitic. (11) Hematite; "kidney" iron-ore. (12) Fluorspar. (13) Epidote. (14) Barytes. (15) Augite. (16) Hornblende.

The minerals included in this table all have metallic or sub-metallic
The specific gravity is "high," above 4.

Hardness and Specific Gravity	Colour	Appearance	Fracture and Cleavage
3. 4·9–5·4.	Copper-red or pinchbeck brown. Tarnishes rapidly.	Cubes and octahedra, rare; usually massive.	Conchoidal and uneven. Brittle.
3–3·5. 4·6–5·6.	Brass- to bronze-yellow; often tarnished.	Capillary (hair-like) crystals.	Perfect rhombohedral.
3·5–4. 4·1–4·3.	Brass-yellow when fresh. Tarnishes to an iridescent film.	Cubes; generally massive.	Conchoidal, uneven.
3·5–4·5. 4·4–4·65.	Reddish or brownish bronze, or copper colour.	Generally massive; occasionally in hexagonal prisms.	Uneven or imperfectly conchoidal.
5–5·5. 7·3–7·6.	Pale copper-red. Sometimes tarnished.	Usually massive.	Uneven; brittle.
5·5–6. 6–6·1.	Tin-white inclining to grey. Tarnishes to pale copper colour.	Prisms; striated. Granular masses.	Uneven, brittle. Cleavage prismatic.
5·5–6. 6–6·1.	Tin-white; steel-grey when massive.	As modified cubes and octahedra. Massive or reticulate.	Octahedral.
5·5–6. 6–6·3.	Tin-white.	Usually massive, granular. Occas. as pyritohedra.	Octahedral.
6–6·5. 4·8–5·1.	Bronze-yellow to pale brass-yellow.	Cubes: striated. Also massive; nodules with radiating structure.	Conchoidal; brittle.
6–6·5. 4·6–4·9.	Brassy-yellow to steel-grey. Darkens on exposure.	Crystal-aggregates ("Spear - head," "cocks - comb"). Nodules with radiating structure.	

lustre; they are all opaque and the streak is black, or very nearly so.

Occurrence, Associates. Other Tests	The Mineral is Probably
With copper lodes: associated with chalcopyrite. In open tube, gives fumes of SO_2, but no sublimate. Fuses to brittle magnetic globule.	BORNITE (ERUBESCITE) (Horse-flesh ore), Cu_3FeS_3.
Chiefly in nodules in clay ironstone. Also associated in veins with other ores of nickel.	MILLERITE, NiS.
In veins, associated with quartz, pyrite, etc. Also occurs with galena and blende.	CHALCOPYRITE (Copper Pyrites), $Cu_2S.Fe_2S_3$.
In veins in crystalline schists, near contacts. Rarely in igneous rocks. May contain nickel. Associated with pyrite, millerite, chalcopyrite, galena, apatite, molybdenite. Soluble in HCl, with evolution of H_2S. Magnetic.	PYRRHOTITE (Magnetic Pyrites), Fe_nS_m.
In veins, with cobalt, silver, and copper ores.	NICCOLITE (KUPFERNICKEL). $NiAs$. Sb, Fe, and S sometimes present.
In crystalline schists and serpentine, and in veins. Associates: quartz, cassiterite, galena, gold, chalcopyrite, pyrite. Sparks when struck with hammer.	ARSENOPYRITE (MISPICKEL), $FeAsS$.
In veins associated with calcite, quartz, barytes, silver, nickel, and copper compounds.	SMALTITE, $CoAs$.
Occurrence and association as Smaltite.	COBALTITE, $CoAsS$.
Common as a secondary mineral in igneous rocks; in veins and as concretions and crystals in sediments. Contains variable percentages of arsenic. Associates: magnetite, hematite, chalcopyrite, bornite, blende, galena, etc. Sparks when struck with hammer.	PYRITE, FeS_2.
Sedimentary rocks, such as the Chalk. Readily oxidises to ferrous sulphate.	MARCASITE, FeS_2.

Both mineral and streak are black, or nearly so. With the exception specific gravity is above 4.

HARDNESS AND SPECIFIC GRAVITY	COLOUR	APPEARANCE	FRACTURE AND CLEAVAGE
1–2. 2–2·3.	Iron-black to dark grey. Metallic lustre.	Greasy scales, laminae, or columnar. Sometimes granular.	Cl. perfect into thin laminae. Flexible, sectile.
2–2·5. 4·8.	Iron-grey or dark steel-grey. Metallic lustre.	Massive and reniform; often with fibrous and radiating structure.	Rather brittle.
2. 4·5–4·6.	Lead-grey. Metallic lustre. Liable to tarnish; sometimes iridescent.	Elongated prisms striated longitudinally.	Cl. perfect in one direction.
2·5. 7·2–7·7.	Lead-grey. Metallic lustre on fresh surfaces; tarnishes rapidly.	Cubes and tetrahedra; massive.	Cl. perfect into cubes.
2·5–3. 5·5–5·8.	Blackish lead-grey; often with bluish or greenish tarnish.	Compact masses and disseminated grains.	Conchoidal. Cl. poor.
3–4·5. 4·5–5·1.	Steel-grey to iron-black.	Tetrahedral crystals; often twined. Also massive or compact.	Sub-conchoidal, or uneven. Brittle.
5–5·5. 7·1–7·9.	Chocolate-brown, dark greyish-black, reddish-brown. Submetallic lustre brilliant on cleavage faces, dull on others and on fractures.	Bladed or tabular crystals. Also massive.	Uneven. Cleavage perfect.
5–6. 3·7–4·7.	Iron-black, passing into dark steel-grey.	Amorphous, massive, botryoidal, reniform or stalactitic.	
5–6. 4·5–5.	Iron-black. Sub-metallic lustre.	Thin plates and scales.	Conchoidal.
5·5–6·5. 4·9–5·2.	Iron-black. Metallic or submetallic lustre.	Octahedra; also massive and granular.	Cl. poor; octahedral.

C

of graphite, all the minerals included in this table are "heavy," *i.e.* the

Occurrence, Associates. Other Tests	The Mineral is Probably
Fissure-veins; sometimes as lenticular-bedded masses in gneiss. Also, disseminated through country-rock in the neighbourhood of veins. Feels cold when handled, owing to high conductivity for heat.	GRAPHITE (Carbon).
As beds or nodules, together with iron compounds, either as the result of precipitation, or as a residual deposit from weathering of rocks containing manganese.	PYROLUSITE, MnO_2.
In veins associated with other ores of antimony, and having quartz, dolomite, calcite, or barytes as veinstone.	STIBNITE (ANTIMONITE), Sb_2S_3.
Beds and veins in limestones, associated with barytes, fluorspar, and calcite. Also in quartz veins.	GALENA, PbS.
In beds and veins, associated with other ores of copper, and with pyrite, barytes, and galena	CHALCOCITE (Copper Glance). Cu_2S with traces of Fe.
With other ores of copper, and with pyrite, galena, blende, etc. Very thin splinters are sub-translucent, cherry-red by transmitted light.	TETRAHEDRITE. $4\ Cu_2S.Sb_2S_3$. May contain Fe, Zn, Ag, or Hg. Sb often partly replaced by As.
In pneumatolytic veins surrounding granite masses. Associated with tinstone and quartz. Microcosmic bead reddish; borax bead green. Heated with Na_2CO_3 on charcoal, dissolved in HCl with few grains of tin, gives blue solution. Is also characterised by streak, cleavage, and two lustres.	WOLFRAMITE. Tungstate of iron and manganese.
Occurrence as Pyrolusite. Blowpipe reactions also, as for Pyrolusite, excepting that water is given in closed tube.	PSILOMELANE. Hydrated oxide of manganese. *Earthy variety*—WAD.
Accessory constituent in basic rocks. Heated with Na_2CO_3 on charcoal, dissolved in HCl with few grains of tin, gives violet-coloured solution.	ILMENITE (TITANOFERRITE), $FeO.TiO_2$.
Lenticular masses in metamorphic and igneous rocks, and in sands. Associated with chlorite, pyrite, chalcopyrite, quartz, felspar, hornblende, and many other rock-forming minerals. Magnetic.	MAGNETITE (Lodestone), Fe_3O_4.

135

HARDNESS AND SPECIFIC GRAVITY	COLOUR	APPEARANCE	FRACTURE AND CLEAVAGE
1·5. 4·4–4·8.	Lead-grey. Metallic lustre.	Scales; massive or foliated.	Cl. perfect. Sectile and almost malleable.
2·5–3. 10·1–11·1.	Silver-white. Tarnishes readily. Metallic lustre.	Threads, arborescent forms and massive.	Hackly. Sectile. Malleable.

HARDNESS AND SPECIFIC GRAVITY	COLOUR	APPEARANCE	FRACTURE AND CLEAVAGE
2·5–3. 15·6–19·3.	Golden-yellow; if alloyed with silver, almost white.	Scale-like or in threads. Granular; massive.	Hackly; very ductile, malleable and sectile
3·5–4. 6·5–7·1.	Green, yellow, and brown. Colours may be vivid. Resinous lustre.	Hexagonal prisms with pyramids. Crystal aggregates forming crusts; also reniform and botryoidal.	Sub-conchoidal or uneven.
3·5–4·0. 3·9–4·2.	Brown, black, sometimes yellow; rarely colourless. Resinous lustre.	Tetrahedra and rhomb-dodecahedra common. Also massive and compact.	Conchoidal. Cl. perfect; rhomb-dodecahedral.
5–5·5. 3·6–4·0.	Shades of brown. Earthy varieties yellow. Sub-metallic lustre.	Mammillated or stalactitic forms. Massive with radiate structure. Often with black glazed coating. Also earthy.	
5·5. 4·3–4·5.	Iron-black to brownish-black. Sub-metallic lustre.	Usually massive, compact or granular.	U n e v e n; s o m e t i m e s platey; brittle.

D

lead-grey or silver-white.

OCCURRENCE, ASSOCIATES. OTHER TESTS.	THE MINERAL IS PROBABLY
In pegmatites and quartz veins. Distinguished from graphite by much higher specific gravity, and will not smear hands.	MOLYBDENITE, MoS.
Zone of weathering of lodes of silver sulphide. Strings and veins in eruptive and sedimentary rocks. Associated with native copper and galena.	NATIVE SILVER, Ag.

E

brown. All the minerals are "heavy".

OCCURRENCE, ASSOCIATES. OTHER TESTS	THE MINERAL IS PROBABLY
Associated in alluvial deposits with zircon, ruby, topaz, garnet, and other precious stones. In quartz reefs with pyrite; also in Quartz Conglomerate ("Banket"), South Africa. Colour, malleability, sectility, and specific gravity are distinctive.	NATIVE GOLD, Au.
With other ores of lead. Blowpipe reactions for Pb, Cl, and P.	PYROMORPHITE, $3\ Pb_3P_2O_8 \cdot PbCl_2$.
With galena in veins, and as a metasomatic deposit replacing calcite in limestones, as in Derbyshire.	SPHALERITE (ZINC BLENDE), ZnS.
Alteration product of other iron minerals; hence often contaminated with clay and other impurities. Also in beds of "bog ore." Sometimes pisolitic. Heated in closed tube, gives water. Tests for iron. Form and streak.	LIMONITE, $Fe_2O_3.3\ H_2O$. *Earthy Varieties.* BOG IRON ORE. YELLOW OCHRE.
Primary mineral in ultrabasic rocks and their altered representatives—serpentines, with which it is commonly associated. Usually as grains, but may be concentrated into ore-bodies. Magnetic residue on charcoal. Tests for Cr.	CHROMITE, $FeO.Cr_2O_3$.

HARDNESS AND SPECIFIC GRAVITY	COLOUR	APPEARANCE	FRACTURE AND CLEAVAGE
6–6·5. 4·2.	Reddish-brown, red, yellowish, black. Adamantine lustre.	Tetragonal prisms, terminated by pyramids; geniculate twins common. Also acicular.	Sub-conchoidal or uneven. Brittle. Cl. poor, prismatic.
6·7. 6·4–7·1.	Usually black or brown. Rarely yellow or colourless.	Tetragonal prisms, terminated by pyramids; often twinned. Sometimes shows "woody" structure.	Sub-conchoidal or uneven. Brittle.

TABLE

The streak is red to reddish-

HARDNESS AND SPECIFIC GRAVITY	COLOUR	APPEARANCE	FRACTURE AND CLEAVAGE
2–2·5. 8·1.	Vermillion to dark red.	Usually massive, granular or earthy. Sometimes as rhombohedral crystals.	Uneven. Prismatic.
3·5–4·0. 5·8–6·5.	Shades of red, especially cochineal-red.	Cubes and octahedra. Massive or earthy.	Conchoidal. Cl. octahedral.
5–5·5. 7·1–7·9.	Chocolate-brown, greyish-black; sub-metallic lustre: brilliant on cleavage faces, duller on others and on fractures.	Bladed or tabular crystals. Also massive.	Uneven. Cl. perfect.
5·5–6·5. 4·5–5·3.	Steel-grey or iron-grey. Lustres: splendent (specular), silky (fibrous), earthy (amorphous).	Flat rhombohedra. Reniform and botryoidal masses with radiating structure; micaceous or foliated.	Cl. poor, rhombohedral.

—continued.

Occurrence, Associates. Other Tests	The Mineral is Probably
Primary mineral in acid igneous rocks; also in gneisses, mica-schists, and phyllites. As grains in alluvial deposits. Tests for titanium.	RUTILE, TiO_2.
Veins in acid rocks. Associated with topaz, tourmaline, quartz, fluorspar, scheelite, wolfram, ilmenite, from which it may be distinguished by the colour of the streak. Separable from the gangue minerals, when in grains, by panning.	CASSITERITE (Tinstone), SnO_2.

F

brown. The minerals are all "heavy".

Occurrence, Associates. Other Tests	The Mineral is Probably
Veins and fissures usually in sedimentary rocks. Often as impregnations in limestone or sandstones. Associated with iron-sulphide ores, calcite, barytes, quartz, etc. Heated in closed tube gives black sublimate; this when detached and rubbed on streak plate, becomes red. Heated with Na_2CO_3 and carbon in closed tube, gives metallic mercury.	CINNABAR, HgS.
Zone of weathering of copper lodes. Usually associated with native copper.	CUPRITE, Cu_2O.
In veins surrounding granite masses. Associated with tinstone and quartz. Microcosmic bead reddish; borax bead green. Heated with Na_2CO_3 on charcoal, dissolved in HCl with few grains of tin, gives blue solution. Is also characterised by streak, cleavage, and two lustres.	WOLFRAMITE. Tungstate of iron and manganese.
Pockets and hollows replacing limestone. Associated with magnetite, limonite, siderite, and quartz. When crystallised and showing splendent lustre.	HEMATITE, Fe_2O_3. Specular Iron.

The mineral in mass and

Hardness and Specific Gravity	Colour	Appearance	Fracture and Cleavage
3·5–4·0. 3·7–4·0.	Bright green. Different shades of the colour occurring in concentric bands. Silky lustre in fibrous varieties; otherwise dull.	Crystals rare; usually massive, compact, nodular, mammillary, botryoidal; sometimes fibrous.	Cl. basal.
3·5–4·0. 3·5–3·8.	Deep azure blue.	Blue monoclinic prisms; also massive and earthy.	Conchoidal; brittle.

TABLE

The streak is white: the mineral is

Hardness and Specific Gravity	Colour	Appearance	Fracture and Cleavage
1·0. 2·7–2·8.	White to pale green. Pearly lustre. Greasy feel.	Usually foliated; also massive, granular, compact.	Cleaves into thin plates which are flexible but not elastic.
1·5. 2·6–2·8.	Shades of green. Pearly lustre. Greasy feel.	Usually granular or in scales; sometimes as tabular crystals.	Cleaves into thin plates which are flexible but not elastic.
2–4. (variable). 2·2–2·3.	Bluish-green, sky-blue. Vitreous to enamel-like lustre.	Amorphous. Massive, botryoidal, and as encrustations.	Conchoidal.
3–4. 2·5–2·6.	Shades of green to almost black; sometimes red, yellow, or brown; variegated.	Usually massive; as pseudomorphs after various magnesian silicates.	Conchoidal; sectile; greasy feel.
3–5·4. 6·5–7·1.	Green, yellow, and brown. Resinous lustre.	Hexagonal prisms in aggregates forming crusts; also reniform and botryoidal.	Sub-conchoidal or uneven. Brittle.
4. 3·3–3·25.	Green, purple, blue, yellow, pink; also white or colourless.	In aggregates of cubic crystals; also compact and granular.	Conchoidal to uneven. Cl. perfect octahedral.

G

the streak is green or blue.

OCCURRENCE, ASSOCIATES. OTHER TESTS	THE MINERAL IS PROBABLY
Found in oxidised portions of copper lodes associated with azurite, cuprite, iron oxides, and various copper and iron sulphides.	MALACHITE, $CuCO_3.Cu(OH)_2$.
Occurrence and associations, same as for Malachite. Named in allusion to its colour.	AZURITE, $2\ CuCO_3.Cu(OH)_2$.

H

coloured violet, purple, blue, or green.

OCCURRENCE, ASSOCIATES. OTHER TESTS	THE MINERAL IS PROBABLY
A secondary mineral, resulting from the hydration of magnesium-bearing rocks. Occurs in schists or as beds resulting from the metamorphism of rocks rich in magnesium.	TALC (STEATITE), $3\ MgO.H_2O.4\ SiO_2$.
Never primary. In amygdules and as a product of the alteration of biotite, hornblende, epidote, etc. Distinguished by colour and physical properties. Heated in blowpipe flame, exfoliates and whitens, fusing to an enamel on edges.	CHLORITE. Hydrated silicate of Al, Fe, and Mg.
Occurs in oxidised portions of copper lodes. Decomposed by acids without effervescence (distinction from Malachite, with which it is commonly associated).	CHRYSOCOLLA. Essentially hydrated silicate of copper.
Mainly results from the alteration of rocks rich in magnesium. Also formed by dedolomitisation.	SERPENTINE, $2\ H_2O.3\ MgO.2\ SiO_2$.
Associated with other ores of lead.	PYROMORPHITE, $3\ Pb_3.P_2O_8.PbCl_2$.
Commonly occurs as a gangue mineral in lead and zinc lodes.	FLUORSPAR, CaF_2.

HARDNESS AND SPECIFIC GRAVITY	COLOUR	APPEARANCE	FRACTURE AND CLEAVAGE
(H. = 4–5 parallel to length of crystal, 7 at right angles to this direction.) 3·6–3·7.	Light blue, sometimes white; also grey-green. Crystals may be blue in middle with white margin. Pearly lustre.	Thin prisms or blade-like forms.	Perfect cleavage.
5. 3·17–3·23.	Various shades of green and brown. Variegated. Resinous lustre.	Usually in prisms, pyramid faces prominent. Crystals often large and resembling beryl. Also occurs massive.	Conchoidal and uneven Cl. basal, poor.
5–6. 3·3–3·5.	Grass-green, grey; metallic or brassy lustre.	Lamellar or foliated masses; occasionally fibrous.	Brittle. Cl. similar to Augite.
5–6. 3–3·47.	Green.	Long slender prisms; acicular.	Cl. two directions approx. at 120°.
6–7. 3·25–3·5.	Pistachio green; yellowish to blackish-green.	Elongated crystals; tabular. Sheaf-like aggregates; acicular and granular.	Uneven. Cl. perfect basal.
6–7. 3·2–4·2.	Shades of green; brownish, rarely yellow. Translucent.	Massive; granular; crystals very rare.	Conchoidal. Uneven.

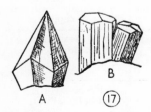

(17) Calcite.   A. Dog-tooth spar.   B. Nailhead spar.   (18) Dolomite.   Crystals with curved faces.   (19) Aragonite.

Occurrence, Associates. Other Tests	The Mineral is Probably
An accessory mineral in mica-schists and gneisses. Often associated with garnet, corundum, etc. Shape and colour of crystals are distinctive.	KYANITE (DISTHENE), $Al_2O_3.SiO_2$.
Widely disseminated as an accessory mineral in all types of rocks: igneous, metamorphic, and sedimentary. Also as dark-brown to brown masses and concretions of indefinite composition (Phosphorite) in sediments, and replacing limestones (Rock Phosphate).	APATITE. $3\ Ca_3.P_2O_8.CaCl_2$ to $3\ Ca_3.P_2O_8.CaF_2$.
Common in Gabbros; also in Diorites.	DIALLAGE (Pyroxene), Comp. as Augite.
Common in crystalline schists; often the chief constituent in green hornblende schists.	ACTINOLITE (Amphibole), $Ca(MgFe)_3(SiO_3)_4$.
Common in metamorphic rocks, schists, and gneisses. Product of contact-metamorphism of limestones. Results from the alteration of many ferromagnesian minerals. Associated with chlorite, garnet, felspar, and pyroxene.	EPIDOTE, $4\ CaO.3\ (AlFe)_2O_3$ $6\ SiO_2.H_2O$.
Essential constituent of ultra-basic rocks: dunite, peridotite, picrite; Dunite consists of almost pure olivine. Occurs also in basic rocks, such as basalt, dolerite, olivine gabbro. Alters to serpentine with separation of magnetite.	OLIVINE, $2\ (MgFe)O.SiO_2$.

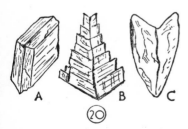
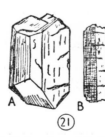

(20) Gypsum. *A*. Single crystal. *B* and *C*. Twinned.   (21) Orthoclase. *A*. Twinned crystal. *B*. Twinned crystal as seen in granite.   (22) Plagioclase, showing repeated twinning.

The mineral is yellow, red, brown to nearly

HARDNESS AND SPECIFIC GRAVITY	COLOUR	APPEARANCE	FRACTURE AND CLEAVAGE
H. variable 2–2·55.	White, grey-white, brown, yellow or reddish.	Amorphous. Clay-like, earthy; may be oolitic.	—
2·5–3. 2·7–3·1.	Dark brown to black; dark green. Splendent lustre.	Dark brown to black flakes; sometimes forming squat pseudo-hexagonal prisms.	Cl. very perfect, basal into thin elastic flakes.
2·5–3·5. 4·5.	Colourless or white; grey; often bluish, yellowish, red, or brown.	Tabular crystals; massive, compact columnar.	Cl. perfect in three directions.
3–4. 2·5–2·6.	Shades of green to almost black; sometimes red, yellow, or brown.	Usually massive; as pseudomorphs after various magnesian silicates.	Conchoidal; sectile; greasy feel.
3·5–4·0. 2·8–2·9.	White, often yellow or brown. Vitreous to pearly lustre; dull when massive.	Rhombohedral crystals; often with curved faces ("Saddle-backs"); also as yellow saccharoidal beds.	Conchoidal or uneven. Cl. perfect, rhombohedral.
3·5–4·4. 3·45–3·6.	Rose-red to dark brown. Vitreous lustre; transparent to translucent.	Rhombohedral crystals; massive, granular to compact.	Brittle. Cl. perfect, rhombohedral.
3·5–4·5.	Yellow or buff, brownish-black or brownish-red. Pearly or vitreous lustre.	Rhombohedral crystals with faces often curved. Also massive.	Uneven Cl. perfect, rhombohedral.
3·5–4·0. 3·9–4·2.	Brown, black, sometimes yellow; rarely colourless. Resinous lustre.	Tetrahedral and rhomb-dodecahedral crystals common. Also massive and compact.	Conchoidal. Cl. perfect, rhomb-dodecahedral.
5–5·5. 3·54.	Usually brown; sometimes grey to black. Adamantine lustre; transparent to opaque.	Wedge-shaped crystals; massive.	Imperfect; conchoidal. Cl. prismatic.

black in mass; the streak is white, or nearly so.

OCCURRENCE, ASSOCIATES. OTHER TESTS	THE MINERAL IS PROBABLY
From the decomposition of rocks, particularly those rich in plagioclase; sometimes, also, as a residual deposit and showing evidences of the original rock structure. Invariably contains iron.	BAUXITE. $Al_2O_3.2 H_2O.$, plus Fe_2O_3 and P_2O_5.
Original constituent of volcanic and plutonic rocks—acid to basic. Also of metamorphic origin in biotite gneiss and schist.	BIOTITE (MICA), $K_2O.4 MgO.2 Al_2O_3$. $6 SiO_2.H_2O$.
Very common as vein-stone in lead veins, where it is associated with galena, fluorspar, calcite, and quartz. Also occurs as nodules in sediments, as in the Lower Greensand of Surrey. Characterised by its weight.	BARYTES ("Heavy Spar"), $BaSO_4$.
Mainly results from the alteration of rocks rich in magnesium. Also formed by dedolomitisation.	SERPENTINE, $2 H_2O.3 MgO.2 SiO_2$.
As a sedimentary rock; often lining cavities in limestones. Also occurs in crystalline schists. Associated with galena and blende. Effervesces only slightly in cold HCl; dissolves readily with effervescence in hot HCl. One of the common Rhombohedral Carbonates.	DOLOMITE, $CaCO_3.MgCO_3$.
Occurs in veins with lead and silver ores; and as a meta-somatic replacement of limestones. One of the common rhombohedral carbonates.	RHODOCHROSITE, $MnCO_3$.
In beds and concretions in shales and clay. Sometimes in crystalline schists and as an associate of pyrite, chalcopyrite, and galena. One of the common rhombohedral carbonates.	SIDERITE, CHALYBITE (Clay-Ironstone), $FeCO_3$.
With galena in veins, and as a metasomatic deposit replacing calcite in limestones, as in Derbyshire.	SPHALERITE (ZINC BLENDE), ZnS.
Original constituent of acid igneous rocks; also in metamorphic rocks rich in calcium, and in crystalline limestones. Blowpipe reactions as for Ilmenite.	SPHENE (TITANITE), $CaO.TiO_2.SiO_2$.

TABLE I

HARDNESS AND SPECIFIC GRAVITY	COLOUR	APPEARANCE	FRACTURE AND CLEAVAGE
6–7. 6·4–7·1.	Usually black or brown; rarely yellow or colourless.	Tetragonal prisms and pyramids; sometimes fibrous ("Woody"); granular.	Sub-conchoidal. Brittle.
5–6. 3·2–3·5.	Greenish-black to black. Vitreous lustre. Translucent to opaque.	Stumpy crystals; section 8-sided. Also massive.	Cleaves in two directions at right angles.
5–6. 3–3·47.	Dark brown and greenish-black. Vitreous lustre. Translucent to opaque.	Prismatic crystals; section 6-sided. Also massive.	Cleaves in two directions approx. at 120°.

TABLE

The mineral and its streak are very

HARDNESS AND SPECIFIC GRAVITY	COLOUR	APPEARANCE	FRACTURE AND CLEAVAGE
1. 2·7–2·8.	White to pale green. Pearly lustre; greasy feel.	Usually foliated; also massive, granular, compact.	Cleaves into thin plates which are flexible but not elastic.
2. 2·3.	Crystals colourless. Massive forms may be grey, pink, or red. Pearly or silky lustre.	Lozenge-shaped crystals, often twinned giving arrowhead shapes. Also compact, granular or fibrous, earthy.	Cl. perfect in one direction giving flakes flexible but not elastic.
2–2·5. 2·85.	Almost colourless in thin sheets; when thicker, yellow, brown, or green. Transparent to translucent. Pearly lustre.	Silvery flakes; sometimes forming squat pseudo-hexagonal prisms.	Cl. very perfect, basal, into thin elastic flakes.
2·5 2·95–3.	Colourless, snow-white, through reddish, brownish to black when contaminated with iron.	Vitreous, usually massive; lamellar.	Cleavable.

Occurrence, Associates. Other Tests	The Mineral is Probably
Veins in acid rocks. Associated with topaz, tourmaline, quartz, fluorspar, scheelite, wolfram, ilmenite. Separable from gangue minerals, when in grains, by panning.	Cassiterite (Tinstone), SnO_2.
In many volcanic rocks, such as andesite, basalt, etc., and in plutonic rocks, as diorite, gabbro. Associated with magnetite, ilmenite, and plagioclase felspars.	Augite (Pyroxene). $CaMg(SiO_3)_2$ with $(MgFe)(AlFe)_2.SiO_6$.
Primary mineral in acid and intermediate volcanic and plutonic rocks. Less common in basic and ultrabasic rocks. Also of metamorphic origin in schists and gneisses. Frequently associated with quartz and orthoclase felspar.	Hornblende (Amphibole). $CaMg_3(SiO_2)_4$ with $Na_2Al_2(SiO_4)_3$ and $Mg_2Al_4(SiO_8)_2$. Ferrous iron is isomorphous with Mg and ferric iron with the Al.

J

pale in colour, white, or nearly so.

Occurrence, Associates. Other Tests	The Mineral is Probably
A secondary mineral, resulting from the hydration of magnesium-bearing rocks. Occurs in schists or as beds resulting from the metamorphism of rocks rich in magnesium.	Talc (Steatite), $3\ MgO.H_2O.4\ SiO_2$.
As a saline residue in beds. As crystals resulting from the action of sulphuric acid, formed by the oxidation of pyrite on $CaCO_3$ in clays and shales. In closed tube, yields water.	Gypsum (Selenite), $CaSO_4.2\ H_2O$.
Original constituent of acid rocks: hence associated with quartz and orthoclase. Also in metamorphic rocks: schists and gneisses. Common as silvery flakes in sediments: sandstones, clays, and shales.	Muscovite (Mica), $(HK)_2(MgFe)_2$, $(AlFe)_2.(SiO_4)_3$.
Occurs as a vein in granite, at Evigtuk in West Greenland, associated with galena, blende, chalybite, and fluorspar. Practically invisible when immersed in water. Reactions for sodium, aluminium, and fluorine. Easily fusible.	Cryolite, $AlF_3.3\ NaF$.

HARDNESS AND SPECIFIC GRAVITY	COLOUR	APPEARANCE	FRACTURE AND CLEAVAGE
2·5–3·5. 4·5.	Colourless or white; often tinged with blue, yellow, red, or brown. Vitreous lustre. Transparent to opaque.	Tabular crystals; massive, compact, columnar.	Cl. perfect in three directions.
3–3·5. 3·96.	Colourless; often has a pale blue tint.	Tabular crystals resembling Barytes; also massive, granular, fibrous.	Imperfectly conchoidal. Brittle. Cl. perfect parallel to base and prisms.
2·75–3. 6·12–6·39.	White; sometimes tinged with blue, green, or yellow. Adamantine to resinous lustre. Transparent to opaque.	Prismatic crystals, often striated. Also massive, granular to compact; earthy.	Conchoidal; brittle. Cl. perfect to base and prism.
3. 2·71.	Colourless, white; may be tinged yellow, blue, red, brown, grey, black. Vitreous to earthy lustre. Transparent to opaque.	Very varied, though crystal rhombs common; massive, fibrous, lamellar, stalactitic, nodular.	Cl. perfect, rhombohedral. Powder consists of tiny rhombs.
3–3·5. 2·89–2·98.	White, often with a grey-bluish or reddish tint. Pearly lustre on cleavage planes. Transparent to translucent.	Prismatic and tabular; commonly fibrous, lamellar, granular, or compact.	Uneven, splintery in lamellar and fibrous forms. Cl. rectangular fragments.
3·5–4. 2·94.	White, grey, yellowish; sometimes green or violet. Vitreous lustre. Transparent to translucent.	Prismatic crystals, often twinned giving 6-sided pseudo-hexagonal forms. Also massive, stalactitic.	Sub-conchoidal; brittle. Cl. poor.
3·5–4·0. 2·8–2·9.	White, often tinged with yellow or brown. Vitreous to pearly lustre; dull when massive.	Rhombohedral crystals; often with curved faces ("Saddle-Backs"). Also as yellow saccharoidal beds.	Conchoidal or uneven. Cl. perfect, rhombohedral.
3·5–4·5. 3·7–3·9.	Pale yellow or buff, brownish-black, or brownish-red. Pearly or vitreous lustre.	Rhombohedral crystals often curved. Also massive.	Uneven. Cl. perfect, rhombohedral.
3·5–4·5. 3–3·1.	White, grey, brown. Vitreous lustre.	Generally chalk-like; very compact, granular. Rhombohedral crystals rare.	Flat, conchoidal. Cl. rhombohedral, but rarely seen.

—continued.

Occurrence, Associates. Other Tests	The Mineral is Probably
Very common as vein-stone in lead veins, where it is associated with galena, fluorspar, calcite, and quartz. Occurs as nodules in sediments, as in the Lower Greensand of Surrey. Characterised by its weight.	BARYTES ("Heavy Spar"), $BaSO_4$.
Occurs in beds of rock-salt, gypsum, and clay, as at Yate, near Bristol. Also as nodular forms in limestones. Blowpipe reactions: distinguished from Barytes by its strontium flame.	CELESTITE, $SrSO_4$.
Occurs in upper oxidised portions of lead veins, associated with galena, cerrusite, and with zinc and iron ores.	ANGLESITE, $PbSO_4$.
Main constituent of limestones. Occurs also in the form of stalactites; in cavities in igneous rocks; and as a product of alteration of other minerals. One of the common Rhombohedral Carbonates.	CALCITE, $CaCO_3$.
Associated with gypsum and rock salt. Distinguished from gypsum by its greater hardness and more massive character; with the blowpipe, by absence of water.	ANHYDRITE, $CaSO_4$.
Occurs in beds of gypsum and iron ores ("flos ferri"). Also deposited from the waters of hot springs. As the pearly layer of many shells. Less stable than calcite, and distinguished from it by the poor cleavage, and by being stained pink when boiled with a solution of cobalt nitrate; calcite is *not* stained.	ARAGONITE, $CaCO_3$.
As a sedimentary rock; often lining cavities in limestones. Also occurs in crystalline schists. Associated with galena and blende. Effervesces only slightly in cold HCl; dissolves readily with effervescence in hot HCl. One of the common Rhombohedral Carbonates.	DOLOMITE, $CaCO_3.MgCO_3$.
In beds and concretions in shales and clay. Sometimes in crystalline schists and as an associate of pyrite, chalcopyrite, and galena. One of the common Rhombohedral Carbonates.	CHALYBITE, SIDERITE (Clay Ironstone), $FeCO_3$.
In irregular veins and fracture zones. Associated with serpentine and talc, as a product of their alteration.	MAGNESITE, $MgCO_3$.

Hardness and Specific Gravity	Colour	Appearance	Fracture and Cleavage
3–3·5. 6·46–6·48.	Colourless, white, or greyish. Adamantine lustre inclining to vitreous.	Prismatic crystals, often in cruciform or radiate forms. Also granular, massive, compact, and sometimes earthy.	Conchoidal; very brittle.
4. 3–3·25.	Colourless, white, also green, purple, blue, yellow.	In aggregates of cubic crystals; also compact and granular.	Conchoidal to uneven. Cl. perfect octahedral.
5. 3·17–3·23.	Light blue, sometimes white; also grey-green. Crystals may be blue in middle with white margin.	Usually in prisms, pyramid faces prominent. Crystals often large and resembling beryl. Also massive.	Conchoidal and uneven. Cl. basal, poor.
5. 4–4·5.	White, greyish, brownish. Vitreous to pearly lustre.	Usually massive, reniform, botryoidal, stalactitic, encrusting granular or earthy. Rarely as modified rhombohedral crystals.	Uneven. Cl. perfect, rhombohedral.
6. 2·57.	White, flesh-coloured, greyish. Pearly lustre.	Prismatic crystals; lath-like forms; due to alteration to kaolin.	Conchoidal; uneven. Cl. at right angles.
5–6·5. 2·62–2·77.	White to greyish-white. Vitreous lustre; pearly on cleavage faces.	Rectangular sections and laths.	Cl. prominent, two at 86°.
5·5–6·0.	White to grey. Translucent to opaque. Vitreous lustre.	In distinct, or rounded crystals; also in disseminated grains.	Conchoidal.
5·5–6·0. 2·55–2·65.	Colourless or yellow. When massive, greenish or brown.	Hexagonal prisms; massive, compact. Oily lustre. Translucent to opaque.	Sub-conchoidal. Brittle. Cl. prismatic, indistinct.

—continued.

Occurrence, Associates. Other Tests	The Mineral is Probably
A mineral of secondary origin; formed by oxidation of galena in waters carrying CO_2.	CERRUSSITE, $PbCO_3$.
Commonly occurs as a gangue mineral in lead and zinc lodes.	FLUORSPAR, CaF_2.
Widely disseminated as an accessory mineral in all types of rocks: igneous, metamorphic, and sedimentary. Also as dark-brown to brown masses and concretions of indefinite composition (Phosphorite) in sediments, and replacing limestones (Rock Phosphate).	APATITE. $3\ Ca_3.P_2O_8.CaCl_2$ to $3\ Ca_3.P_2O_8.CaF_2$.
An ore of secondary origin. Occurs in beds and veins usually associated with blende, hemimorphite, galena, and ores of iron and copper. Results from the replacement of limestones.	SMITHSONITE, $ZnCO_3$. (Sometimes referred to as CALAMINE.)
One of the most common minerals; is the essential constituent of the more acid, volcanic, and plutonic rocks. Often occurs in large porphyritic crystals up to several inches in length. Not common in sediments, except in some felspathic sandstones, resulting from the incomplete alteration and sorting of weathered granites.	ORTHOCLASE FELSPAR, $K_2OAl_2O_3\ 6\ SiO_2$.
A glassy and very fresh variety of Orthoclase is known as	SANIDINE.
Important constituent of many volcanic and plutonic rocks. Not common in sediments. Fine parallel striae, indicative of lamellar twinning, prove that a felspar is *not* Orthoclase; the absence, however, of striae does not prove the felspar to be Orthoclase.	PLAGIOCLASE FELSPAR. Silicates of Al with Ca and/or Na.
Primary constituent in some volcanic rocks, such as leucite phonolites, leucitophyres, leucite basalt, etc.	LEUCITE, $K_2O, Al_2O_3.4\ SiO_2$.
Original constituent of intermediate igneous rocks, such as syenite. Resembles Witherite in lustre and Felspar in colour, hardness and S.G. Before blowpipe fuses to colourless glass. Gelatinises with acids. The variety ELEOLITE may occur as coarse crystals, but usually massive, reddish-brown or grey in colour.	NEPNELINE, $Na_1K_1O.Al_2O_2.2\ SiO_2$.

CHAPTER XIII

BLOWPIPE ANALYSIS

The Apparatus and How to Use It

The apparatus required is neither expensive nor heavy, and should occupy but little space in the geologist's baggage. The necessary articles include a blowpipe, a lamp, several blocks of charcoal, platinum wire, a number of glass tubes, a couple of pieces of dark blue (cobalt) glass, and about a dozen reagents. These will be described seriatim.

THE BLOWPIPE.—There are numerous types; in the best, the body consists of a conical tube, of which the narrow end forms the mouthpiece,* while the other end is closed; this form gives ample room for condensation of moisture from the breath. A small-bore tube, about 2 in. long, is fixed in the main tube, at right angles to it, and near the closed end. The outer end of this tube is furnished with a fine jet, pierced with a small hole, which should be circular and of the diameter of a fine needle.

It is important to acquire the habit of blowing with a continuous and steady blast. To do this, the cheeks should be kept distended and used as bellows, while the operator breathes through the nose.

THE LAMP.—Where gas is available, the ordinary bunsen burner will serve for all purposes of blowpipe analysis, but this method of heating cannot be said to come in the category of apparatus for the field. A portable lamp may burn candle-grease, paraffin wax, methylated spirit, or colza oil; if liquid fuel be used, the lamp should be provided with a well-fitting screw-cap to avoid spillage of fuel when packed.

The simplest form of heating is a *candle flame*; the candle should be stout and thick, and the wick should be bent in the direction in which the flame is blown. Since, however, *grease lamps* are easily obtainable, we recommend that the beginner should provide himself with one, or he can make one for himself. The lamp consists of a cylindrical tin box, about 2½ in. high and 1½ in. diameter,

---

* Some blowpipes are furnished with a trumpet-shaped mouthpiece which is pressed against the lips, thus avoiding the necessity for the end of the blowpipe being held between them.

with a wick-holder about ½ in. wide riveted to the side, through which a flat wick is drawn.   The lamp is three-quarters filled with solid wax or grease, which is melted; the fuel is replenished periodically as required.

Flames.   Two different types of flame are used in blowpipe analysis, *oxidising* and *reducing.*

To obtain an *oxidising flame,* the nozzle of the blowpipe is held

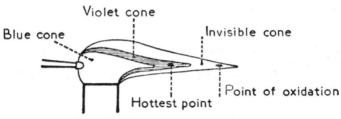

Fig. 53.   OxIDISING FLAME.

inclined to the surface of the wick and introduced into the flame to about one-third of its width.   When the blast of air from the mouth is applied, the flame is pointed and non-luminous, with an inner blue cone (Fig. 53).   The hottest part of the flame is situated just within this cone, and it is here that substances are placed to fuse them.   When it is desired to oxidise a sample, the correct position

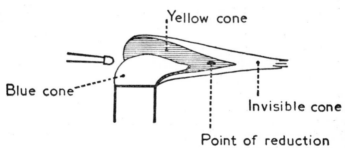

Fig. 54.   REDUCING FLAME.

is just beyond the visible part of the cone, for here the material is heated completely surrounded by air.

The *reducing flame* results when the nozzle of the blowpipe is held a short distance outside the flame (Fig. 54).   When this is done the flame is yellow and luminous, ragged and noisy.   The yellow colour is due to the presence of minute particles of carbon which pass through the flame unconsumed, though at a white heat.   When these particles come into contact with the substance under test, a reducing action takes place.

PLATINUM WIRE.—About six inches should be sufficient, if used with care, to make more than fifty tests. The thickness should not exceed a quarter of a millimetre; thick wire should never be used. It will be found convenient to cut the wire into lengths of 3 in., each of which is fused at one end into a tube or rod of soft glass to serve as a handle. To do this, the end of the handle and the wire are both heated to bright redness (until the end of the tube or rod becomes soft), and the end of the wire is pushed into the softened glass. When cold, it will be found that the wire is firmly anchored into the glass.

Platinum wire serves as a support for the assay when "flame-tests" are carried out, and also for "bead-tests," when using borax, microcosmic salt, or sodium carbonate.

As soon as a test has been completed, the wire should be cleaned *immediately*. A bead should be crushed, and the wire straightened out. The wire should then be heated to bright redness and, while still hot, quenched in a drop of hydrochloric acid in a saucer or a small tube; the wire must *never* be introduced into the acid-bottle, this would cause contamination of the acid. Heating and quenching should be repeated until, on further heating, no yellow colour (due to sodium) is imparted to the flame.

To make the support for a bead-test, the end of the wire is bent round the point of a pencil to make a loop about $\frac{1}{8}$ in. The loop should never be completely closed; a tiny gap should always be left between the end of the wire and the main part, otherwise the wire will become brittle and break off at the contact.

To make a bead, the loop should be heated to bright redness and then dipped into a small quantity of the reagent which is placed *on a clean dry surface*, when a little will adhere to the loop. This is then reheated, and if there is insufficient material to fill the loop, the process is repeated until the loop is filled with the bead. This is then further heated until it becomes clear, free from bubbles, and colourless; coloration is evidence of contamination, indicating that the wire must be cleaned and a fresh bead made.

To carry out a flame-test, the end of the wire is moistened with hydrochloric acid, tested for cleanliness, again moistened, and applied to the powder under examination. The wire, carrying a small amount of mineral powder on the end, is cautiously introduced into a colourless flame, and the colour (if any) imparted to the flame is noted. Certain elements give characteristic colours, as indicated in Table H, p. 161.

COBALT GLASS (which may be in the form of two squares, each 1½ in. side) is used to view the flame whenever the strong orange-yellow of coloration of sodium is observed. The sodium flame is so intense that it masks the violet colour due to potassium; when observed through two thicknesses of cobalt glass, however (if potassium be present), the violet flame will be visible, the yellow caused by sodium being suppressed by the blue glass.

CHARCOAL.—The charcoal block* is the blowpipe analyst's "bench," on which much of his work will lie, especially when examining *metallic* substances. The blocks are obtainable in two forms: (i) sawn out of pieces of wood charcoal, and (ii) compressed, powdered charcoal. Wood charcoal is preferable, since there is less tendency for it to smoulder (with consequent risk of fire) after being withdrawn from the flame.

The charcoal block should be not less than 4 in. long, and 1 in. wide, and have a smooth, flat surface. To support the powder or assay on the charcoal, a small circular cavity is cut into the block about ½ in. from the end. Since some powders (even if moistened) when first subjected to the flame decrepitate and fly, it is advisable to make a slight undercut to the cavity. This has the effect of protecting and retaining light or difficult material.

When holding the block, it should be slightly tilted, and the flame should always be directed *along* the block, and never across it. This is important, since distinctive and confirmatory incrustations may be formed at least two inches, or more, from the assay.

Cautions. Never use a cavity or surface of the charcoal block for more than one powder, until it has been thoroughly scoured and scraped.

Metallic beads are often overlooked; they may be very small, and may require a lens to see them. Whenever possible, the beads should be carefully removed with the point of a knife and tested for malleability on the hammer-head or on a coin. See Table G, p. 160).

If compressed charcoal is used, it should always be allowed to cool off thoroughly before being packed away; a block of this kind has been known to burn itself out and to set fire to other material stored with it.

---

* As an alternative to charcoal blocks, it is possible to use small pastilles of charcoal. The powder of the mineral is heated on the pastille which is supported in a depression at one end of a piece of unglazed porcelain about 3½ in. long, whose surface has been blackened by being held in the smoky flame of the lamp.

GLASS TUBES.—A couple of dozen hard-glass tubes, about 2 in. long and $\frac{1}{4}$ in. external diameter, closed at one end; a similar number of 4-in. lengths of hard-glass tubing of the same diameter as the above and open at both ends; and a dozen soft-glass tubes, 2 in. by $\frac{1}{4}$ in., should form part of the equipment. A tube-holder can be improvised by twisting a strip of paper round the tube when in use.

Test-tubes are of great importance in blowpipe analysis; if a small quantity of a mineral powder be heated in a closed tube, a deposit ("sublimate") will often form on the cooler part of the tube. The nature and colour of the sublimate will generally give an indication of the presence of one or more elements in the assay. Any residue left in the heated end of the tube should be examined and tested for magnetic properties.

Certain minerals give characteristic smells, which are best detected by heating in the closed tube.

In the *open tube*, distinctive colours and indications are also given when a small portion of the sample is heated therein; these depend on the conversion of certain metals to oxides. When using the open tube, the powder under test should rest about an inch from one end of the tube, which is held in a slightly inclined position, and the flame is made to play on the assay. Air currents are thus induced through the tube, and volatile material will become oxidised.

Soft glass tubes are used when liquid reagents are employed, especially when it is necessary to boil the reagent with the sample; if an attempt is made to boil a liquid in a hard-glass tube, the tube is almost certain to break.

Cautions. Many minerals contain small quantities of water, but this does not necessarily imply that they are hydrated. The formation of a faint mist of condensed water should be ignored; water, if present as "water of crystallisation" or of hydration, will condense as numerous droplets or globules and extend over most of the length of the tube.

BEAD TESTS.—When making a bead test, a *very small* amount of the mineral powder should first be picked up on the hot bead, which should then be heated in the flame from the blowpipe. Too much powder frequently results in the final bead being very dark or even opaque, so that it is impossible to distinguish the colour. If this occurs, the process must be started afresh. If too little powder has been picked up initially, it is quite easy to add a further small quantity.

REAGENTS.—It is important that the reagents should be *pure*; when buying them, it is as well to specify A.R. (Analytical Reagent) quality. A complete list of the essential reagents, with quantities suggested, is—

Borax	4 oz.
Sodium carbonate, anhydrous	4 oz.
Microcosmic salt	2 oz.
Cobalt nitrate, as a 10 per cent. solution ..	2 oz.
Magnesium powder	1 oz.
Granulated zinc	1 oz.
Granulated tin	1 oz.
Potassium iodide and sulphur (equal parts)	1 oz.
Copper oxide powder	1 oz.
Manganese dioxide	1 oz.
Potassium hydrogen sulphate, powder ..	2 oz.
Hydrochloric acid (1 : 1)	8 oz.

Although the uses of these reagents are shown in the tables which follow, a few general notes are appended.

Sodium carbonate is used to promote rapid fusion of an assay on charcoal; it is therefore a "flux." The quantity required is about double the bulk of the material under test, and the powder and the flux should be well mixed.

Borax and microcosmic salt are also valuable fluxes; they are used in the form of beads to which certain oxides impart characteristic colours when heated in the blowpipe flame.

Cobalt nitrate plays an important part in the detection of certain metallic oxides and "earths." When cobalt nitrate is added to the fused material after heating on charcoal, and the mixture is reheated, a characteristic colour is produced.

Hydrochloric acid will probably be required more than any other reagent. It is used to clean the platinum wire, in making flame-tests, in detecting carbon dioxide in carbonates, and in the gelatinisation of certain silicates.

It is useful to carry about an ounce of hydrochloric acid in a "dropping" bottle (enclosed in a wooden case) when working in the field to confirm the presence of limestones or carbonates.

Potassium hydrogen sulphate is a convenient substitute for sulphuric acid.

GENERAL PROCEDURE

If the mineral is in the form of a powder, it should first be examined under a lens. Minerals having strong cleavage will show characteristic fragments, *e.g.* galena yields cuboidal, calcite, rhomboidal particles. Metallic lustre may be visible; if it is, there is a likelihood that the mineral will attack platinum when heated; therefore, avoid heating on platinum wire or foil until further tests show that this procedure is likely to be safe.

Tests should be applied systematically, and the results, whether positive or negative, should be noted. At first, it is advisable to go through most, if not all the tests; as experience widens, however, it will be found that after a few tests have been applied, one or two confirmatory experiments will enable the mineral to be identified with certainty.

A. *Heat in closed tube alone.*

SUBLIMATE	INDICATION
(i) Colourless, odourless drops.	Water; if in quantity, a hydrated mineral. Even anhydrous minerals usually give a mist of droplets of water.
(ii) Orange to yellow, or even white in faint reactions. Sublimate melts when heated, giving a dark-yellow liquid.	Sulphur and most sulphides.
(iii) Black-grey and crystalline. Odour of garlic if the tube is crushed and the sublimate is volatilised.	Arsenic.
(iv) Reddish-yellow; deep-red liquid when hot; volatile.	Arsenic in presence of sulphur.
(v) Brown-red; black when hot.	Antimony in presence of sulphur.
(vi) Black; becoming red if rubbed on streak-plate.	Mercury in presence of sulphur.

COLOUR BEFORE HEATING	COLOUR AFTER HEATING	INDICATION
(i) White or colourless.	Yellow.	Some lead and zinc minerals.
(ii) Pink.	Black.	Manganese.
(iii) Red or brown.	Black and magnetic.	Iron.
(iv) Green or blue.	Black.	Copper.

Decrepitation may indicate a strong cleavage or a bad conductor of heat.

B. *Heat in closed tube with reagents.*

	INDICATION
(a) With sodium carbonate and charcoal.	
(i) White metallic mirror, forming globules.	Mercury.
(ii) Grey to black metallic mirror. No globules formed.	Arsenic.
(b) With powdered magnesium; residue moistened with water.	
Smell of rotten fish (phosphine).	Phosphate.

Note.—Phosphates of heavy metals should first be fused with sodium carbonate on charcoal.

C. *Heat in open tube.*

	INDICATION
(i) Sulphur dioxide evolved.	Sulphur or unoxidised compounds thereof.
(ii) White crystalline sublimate, far from assay.	Unoxidised compounds of arsenic.
(iii) Dense white amorphous sublimate; nearer assay than in (ii).	Unoxidised compounds of antimony.

D. *Heat on charcoal alone.*

	INDICATION
Deflagration takes place.	Nitrates.
The substance gives a sublimate, which is:	
(a) White; far from assay. Volatile. Odour of garlic if oxidation is incomplete.	Arsenic.
(b) White; nearer assay than (a). Volatile. Fumes on withdrawing from flame.	Antimony.
(c) White when cold, yellow when hot. Blue when touched with reducing flame. Copper-red round assay.	Molybdenum.
(d) White; canary-yellow when hot.	Zinc.
(e) White or pale yellow; darker when hot.	Tin.
(f) Sulphur-yellow; darker when hot.	Lead.
(g) Orange-yellow; darker when hot.	Bismuth.
(h) No incrustation; smell of sulphur dioxide.	Free sulphur: Sulphides.

E. *Moisten with cobalt nitrate and heat on charcoal.*

COLOUR	INDICATION
(a) Grass-green. ⎫	Zinc.*
(b) Blue-green. ⎬ Incrustation.	Tin.*
(c) Dirty yellowish-green. ⎭	Antimony.
(d) Pale pink.	Magnesium.
(e) Blue; unfused.	Aluminium.
(f) Blue; glassy.	Phosphates.

F. *Heat with potassium iodide and sulphur on charcoal in oxidising flame.*

INCRUSTATION	INDICATION
(a) Brilliant yellow.	Lead.
(b) Crimson, passing into yellow near assay.	Bismuth.
(c) Greenish-yellow fumes, with slight incrustation of the same colour.	Mercury.

G. *Mix substance with powdered charcoal and sodium carbonate and heat on charcoal in reducing flame.*

BEAD	INDICATION
(a) Lead-grey; bright when hot, dull when cold. Sometimes iridescent; soft and malleable; easily fusible. Marks paper with a shining grey streak.	Lead.
(b) Tin-white; bright when hot; dull when cold. Easily fusible. Does not mark paper.	Tin.
(c) Bright when hot or cold; silver-white. Soft and malleable. Does not mark paper.	Silver.
(d) Yellow; bright hot or cold. Soft and malleable.	Gold.
(e) Silver-white; pinkish tinge. Bright when hot, quickly oxidising to dull yellow. Brittle; slightly malleable.	Bismuth.
(f) Copper-red bead or spongy mass. Bright when hot. Tends to blacken by oxidation. Hard and malleable.	Copper.
(g) No bead. Mass exhibits magnetic properties after being crushed.	
(i) Strongly magnetic.	Iron.
(ii) Weakly magnetic.	Cobalt or nickel; traces of iron.

* Assay must be heated with sodium carbonate if oxidised compounds are suspected.

	INDICATION
Transfer residue to a silver coin and moisten with water.	
Brown to black stain.	Sulphates. Sulphides.
Boil residue with hydrochloric acid and tin, and allow to cool.	
Prussian-blue colour.	Tungsten.
Violet colour.	Titanium.

Note.—Molybdenum minerals occasionally give this reaction, but usually a red or green solution.   Tungsten also gives a green colour if excess tin be used.

H. *Heat a little of the powder, moistened with hydrochloric acid, on platinum wire and note colour imparted to flame.*

Note.—When the test fails, and whenever boron and phosphorus are looked for, moisten substance with sulphuric acid and heat again.

Watch the flame at the moment of introducing the assay, since the indications are often slight and transient.

COLOUR OF FLAME		INDICATION
Red.	Brick-red.	Calcium.
	Purple-red.	Lithium.
	Crimson.	Strontium.
Yellow.		Sodium.
Green.	Apple-green.	Barium.
	Yellow-green.	Molybdenum.
	Yellow-green.	Boron.*
	Emerald-green.	Copper.†
	Blue-green.	Zinc.
	Grey-green.	Phosphorus.*
Blue.	Grey-blue.	Antimony.
	Pale sky-blue.	Lead.
	Pale sky-blue.	Arsenic.
	Intense sky-blue.	Copper, as chloride.
Violet.		Potassium.

The intense yellow produced by compounds of sodium masks the violet of potassium.   Whenever sodium is found, the flame should be viewed through one or more thicknesses of cobalt glass.

* With sulphuric acid.   † As oxide, with nitric acid.

I. *Heat a small quantity of the assay in a bead of borax, and note colour of bead after heating in both oxidising and reducing flames.*

Oxidising Flame	Reducing Flame	Indication
Deep blue.	Deep blue.	Cobalt.
Sky-blue; green when hot.	Red, opaque.	Copper.
Green.	Green.	Chromium.
Reddish-violet.	Colourless.	Manganese.
Reddish-brown.	Grey.	Nickel.
Yellow to reddish.	Bottle-green.	Iron.
Yellow.	Pale greenish-yellow.	Uranium.

J. *Heat a small quantity of assay in a bead of microcosmic salt and note colour of bead after heating in oxidising and reducing flames.*

Oxidising Flame		Reducing Flame		Indication
Hot	Cold	Hot	Cold	
Blue.	Blue.	Blue.	Blue.	Cobalt.
Green.	Blue to green.	Dark green.	Copper-red.	Copper.
Red.	Green.	Darker than in O.F.		Chromium.
Yellow to red.	Colourless to brown-red.	Colourless to reddish.		Iron.
Violet.	Red-violet.		Colourless.	Manganese.
Red to brown.	Yellow to orange.	Red to brown.	Yellow to reddish.	Nickel.
Yellow.	Colourless.	Dull green.	Blue to blue-green.	Tungsten.
Yellow-green.	Green to colourless.	Dull green.	Chromium-green.	Molybdenum.
Yellow.	Colourless.	Yellow.	Violet.	Titanium.
Yellow.	Yellow-green.	Green.	Bright green.	Uranium.
Insoluble fragments after long blowing.				Silica.

Saturate a microcosmic bead with CuO, add a small portion of the assay, and heat. A blue-green flame indicates *chlorides* or *bromides*. When heated with $KHSO_4$, bromides give brown fumes, chlorides do not.

K. *Heat a small quantity of the assay in a bead of sodium carbonate.*

Colour in Oxidising Flame	Indication
Opaque blue-green.	Manganese.
Opaque yellow-green.	Chromium.

L. *Tests with acids.*

(i) *Carbonates.*—Most effervesce freely with cold, dilute hydrochloric acid. Dolomite requires to be heated, while chalybite (siderite) requires the use of strong, hot acid.

(ii) *Sulphides.*—Some are decomposed by hydrochloric acid, with evolution of hydrogen sulphide.

(iii) *Fluorides.*—Decomposed on heating with concentrated sulphuric acid. Hydrogen fluoride is evolved in greasy-looking bubbles. Silicon tetrafluoride is formed by the action of HF on glass, and is decomposed by water, depositing white silica. Confirm by holding a drop of water in a loop of platinum wire in the fumes. If SiF_4 be present, the drop will gelatinise.

(iv) *Chlorides*, *Bromides*, *and* *Iodides*, when heated with manganese dioxide and concentrated sulphuric acid, give chlorine, bromine, and iodine, respectively.

(v) *Nitrates* are decomposed by concentrated sulphuric acid, giving brown fumes, which are distinguished from bromine by the smell and by not condensing. Nitrates, moreover, deflagrate when heated on charcoal.

EXAMPLES OF THE DETERMINATION OF MINERALS, USING THE TABLES

The first two samples were obtained in the limestone quarry in the neighbourhood of Point 3546 6235 (Fall Hill) in the Ashover district.

(i) Mineral softer than quartz; colour lead-grey; streak dark lead-grey. Table C, p. 134.

Hardness about 2·5; easily scratched by a brass pin, just marked by the finger-nail. Occurs as cubes, which are dull grey in colour, but brighter when freshly broken. Cleavage perfect and cubical. Feels distinctly heavy. Probably **GALENA** (lead sulphide).

Confirmatory tests with blowpipe

Since the presence of lead is suspected, it is inadvisable to apply a flame-test, since the platinum wire will probably melt.

Heated on charcoal in oxidising flame.

Assay melted, giving a sulphur-yellow sublimate .. .. *Lead*

and a distinct smell of sulphur dioxide .. *Sulphide*

Heated on charcoal with potassium iodide and sulphur.

Brilliant-yellow sublimate .. .. .. *Lead*

Heated on charcoal, mixed with charcoal dust and sodium carbonate.

Lead-grey bead; bright when hot, dull when cold.   Soft and malleable, giving a shining streak when rubbed on paper   ..   ..   *Lead* confirmed

Warmed with hydrochloric acid in test-tube.

Odour of rotten eggs (hydrogen sulphide)   ..   *Sulphide*

Sample dissolved almost completely;   on cooling the solution, white crystals separated; these redissolved when the solution was boiled ..   ..   *Lead*

The mineral was therefore **GALENA** (PbS).

(ii) Mineral softer than quartz;   colour dark brown;   streak dirty white.   Table I, p. 144.

Barely scratched by brass pin, easily by steel needle, hence hardness over 3·5 and less than 5.   Occurs as dark-brown resinous masses.   Quantity too small to enable an idea of the specific gravity to be obtained.   Much resembles **SPHALERITE** (**BLENDE**, ZnS).

Confirmatory tests with blowpipe

Heated on charcoal in oxidising flame.

White sublimate; canary-yellow when hot ..   *Zinc*

and distinct smell of sulphur dioxide   ..   *Sulphide*

Sublimate moistened with cobalt nitrate and reheated.

Colour became grass-green   ..   ..   ..   *Zinc*

Treated with hydrochloric acid in test-tube.

Assay went into solution with evolution of hydrogen sulphide ..   ..   *Sulphide*

The mineral was therefore **SPHALERITE** (ZnS).

EXAMPLES OF THE DETERMINATION OF MINERALS BY MEANS OF BLOWPIPE TESTS

(i) *Mineral consisted of a white, crystalline powder.*

		INDICATION
(a) Flame-test on Pt wire.	Violet colour.	Potassium.
(b) Heated on charcoal.	Deflagration.	Nitrate.
(c) Heated in closed tube with potassium hydrogen sulphate.	Brown fumes with characteristic odour.	Nitrate confirmed.

Mineral was **NITRE** (KNO_3).

These three tests were sufficient to identify the mineral. Only two nitrates, namely those of potassium and sodium, are found as minerals. Soda-nitre or **NITRATINE** would have given a strong orange-yellow flame when heated on platinum wire.

(ii) *Mineral consisted of a dull, black powder.*

			INDICATION
(a)	Flame-test.	No result.	Absence of elements indicated by test.
(b)	Heated on charcoal with sodium carbonate.	No bead or magnetic residue.	Absence of easily reducible metals, iron, cobalt, or nickel.
(c)	Residue treated with hydrochloric acid and tin.	No coloration.	Absence of tungsten titanium.
(d)	Heated in closed tube.	Much water.	Hydrated.
(e)	Borax bead.	Amethyst in oxidising, colourless in reducing flame.	Manganese.

Mineral was **PSILOMELANE** (hydrated MnO_2).

Distinguished from **PYROLUSITE** by the copious evolution of water when heated in closed tube.

CHAPTER XIV

THE IDENTIFICATION OF ROCKS

Although, as has been shown previously, it is possible to map a rock without being able to identify it, the field geologist should never be content to admit that he cannot give a rock a name until he has exhausted all his resources. He should strive to avoid the "laboratory attitude," which would lead him, on meeting an awkward-looking customer, to take a specimen merely for subsequent examination. The geologist who adopts this defeatist attitude is likely to prove a slovenly worker, for, on meeting with further exposures of his difficult rock, he will probably record the fact and pass on without paying careful attention to its field relations, and so miss useful clues which may lead to the identification of the rock.

It would, of course, be possible to construct a geological map in which the rock-types were given arbitrary names, such as Tom, Dick, Harry, etc., without making any attempt to identify them. Such a map, although it might give a picture of the structure of the area, would not be very informative. It might, for a limited period, be useful to the man who constructed it, but after a lapse of years even he would assuredly forget the significance of his arbitrary names, and unless he had the opportunity of revisiting the ground to refresh his memory, or unless he had hand-specimens of the various rocks, the map would be of very little value, and would convey no information to anyone but its maker.

Alternatively, each rock could be referred to by its properties. For example, in the Ashover district, we could describe a rock as being dark grey, compact, of hardness 3 to 3·5, massively bedded, coarsely jointed, effervescing with dilute hydrochloric acid, and containing fossils. All this would merely be a rambling way of saying "limestone."

The beginner in geology should, therefore, from the outset, try to determine his rocks for himself. Not only will much diffuseness of description be avoided, but the geologist will be forced to observe more closely and reason more keenly in order that he may solve the problems which the identification of his rocks present.

The first stage in identifying a rock is to try and determine to which of the three main classes, Sedimentary, Igneous, or Metamorphic, it belongs. On visiting an exposure, it is not advisable to rush up to close quarters and begin hammering before a careful examination of the gross features has been made.

PRELIMINARY EXAMINATION IN MASS

If the rock consists of layers or beds, piled one above the other, and contains broken or rounded particles, and if it contains fossils, it is almost certain to be a *Sediment*.

The individual beds may be from an inch or so to many feet in thickness.   On the other hand, one or more of the beds may consist of thin layers or *laminae*, whose thickness does not exceed that of a sheet of paper (paper-shales).   The planes of separation between the beds may show ripple-marks, sun-cracks, pitting due to rain-drops, and impressions such as those left by worms or the like, or foot-prints.

Furthermore, since the interfaces between the beds of sedimentary rocks approximate to *planes*, there is a definite geometrical relationship between the outcrop of a sediment, its attitude, and the shape of the ground.

If, on the other hand, the rock is not made up of *beds*, but occurs as more or less irregular masses or bosses, from which offshoots (*apophyses*) cut *across* the bedding of sediments, and if the rock consists of crystals arranged in random fashion, or of crystals in a fine-grained or glassy matrix, the rock is probably *Igneous*.   With certain exceptions (sills and dykes), the position of an igneous contact cannot be predicted by geometrical reasoning.

If the rock shows strong cleavage or wave-like bands (folia), and if it consists of crystals showing a determinate direction and not arranged at random, it is probably *Metamorphic*.

Certain metamorphic rocks, notably quartzites and marbles or crystalline limestones and their variants, do not show banding, but are *massive*.

MORE DETAILED STUDY

Having taken a general view of the exposure, and made careful notes and sketches of what has been observed, the geologist should next proceed to a more detailed study.   Now is the time to call the hammer into play and to knock off hand-specimens for careful examination with the naked eye and the lens.

The properties which are of greatest service in identifying rocks in the field are the texture, the mineral composition, the state of aggregation, and the hardness.

Texture.   Although the term *texture* is often used more or less synonymously with *structure*, we prefer to employ *structure* in describing those larger features which are observed in the field, such as the structure or *tectonics* of an area, or of large masses of rock. Thus, we may have bedded structure, flow-structure, columnar structure, etc.

In our use of the word *texture*, we adopt the definition of A. Holmes [*The Nomenclature of Petrology* (1920), p. 224].

"*Texture.* The appearance, megascopic or microscopic, seen on a smooth surface of a homogeneous rock or mineral aggregate, due to the degree of crystallisation, the size of the crystals, and the shapes and inter-relations of of the crystals or other constituents."

Sometimes, one finds a combination of two or more diverse textures or mineral aggregates; when this occurs, we apply the term *structure*. Thus, we may have amygdaloidal, spheroidal, gneissose structure, etc.

The term *hardness*, as applied to rocks, does not necessarily have the same signification as it does when applied to minerals. If a rock consists of a glassy mass, it is correct to say that its hardness is greater than that of steel. If, however, the test is applied to a composite rock consisting of one or more minerals, the result is really an expression of the strength of the coherence between the particles rather than an indication of true hardness, which is a property that the rock does not possess. Nevertheless, provided that the above limitation is kept in mind, the conception of "hardness" of a rock is useful.

Colour is less useful as a diagnostic character for rocks than for minerals, since what is essentially the same rock may vary greatly in colour according as it has greater or less impurity (very frequently oxides of iron) associated with its principal constituents.

The mineral composition is of great importance, but in seeking to identify a rock, this should be considered *after* the texture.

The tables or schemes, together with the notes, should assist the student in identifying a wide range of rocks which he is likely to meet. We have started with the sedimentary rocks, since (*a*) they are generally easier to identify in the field than igneous or metal morphic rocks, and (*b*) they are more widely distributed in those areas of "simple" geology which are most suited to the first efforts of the beginner.

SEDIMENTARY ROCKS

SANDS (unconsolidated) and SANDSTONES (consolidated) consist mainly of grains of quartz associated with small amounts of other minerals. The grains of quartz are usually more or less rounded; fine, well-rounded grains of even size point to the action of wind during the formation of the rock, and therefore suggest sand-dune or desert conditions.

Sandstones vary greatly in colour; yellow and brown hues are due to limonite, red to hematite, and green to glauconite. When there are sufficient grains of glauconite to impart a strong green colour to the rock, it becomes a GLAUCONITIC SANDSTONE. By oxidation, the glauconite is converted to limonite and the sandstone becomes FERRUGINOUS. A red colour is due to the presence of mere films of hematite on the individual grains of quartz.

The cementing materials of sandstones may be ferruginous, calcareous, argillaceous, and sometimes partly siliceous. When the cement is entirely siliceous, the sandstone passes insensibly into QUARTZITE.

When muscovite is present, the rock becomes a MICACEOUS SANDSTONE, and there may be sufficient mica on the planes of lamination to render the rock fissile. A sandstone derived from a rock rich in felspar (such as granite) may contain a high proportion of felspar, giving a FELSPATHIC SANDSTONE, or ARKOSE.

GRIT is composed of coarse and angular grains of quartz; it is usually harder than sandstone, which it otherwise resembles. If the cementing material is calcite, the rock is known as a CALCAREOUS GRIT.

PEBBLE-BEDS (unconsolidated) and CONGLOMERATES consist of well-rounded pebbles in a finer matrix. The pebbles may be of quartz, flint, chert, jasper, granite, limestone; in fact, of practically any rock. When the pebbles are of limestone, the cementing material is usually dolomite, giving a DOLOMITIC CONGLOMERATE. Conglomerates are classified according to the composition of the pebbles or of the cementing material. The cement may be siliceous, calcareous, argillaceous, or ferruginous. The degree of consolidation varies greatly; some conglomerates are so strongly cemented that when broken, the fracture takes place through, rather than round, the pebbles. Others are so fragile that the pebbles fall apart under a light tap from the hammer.

Conglomerates and pebble-beds indicate the sites of old shore-lines or shoals, where wave-action has been active. They are usually only rudely stratified, and in the coarser examples, there may be little evidence of stratification, except in so far as the rock is considered as a whole. The flatter pebbles may show a rough parallelism to the lines of deposit. Careful study of the pebbles may give valuable evidence as to the rocks which were being denuded when the conglomerate was being formed, and also the age of the conglomerate and/or the included pebbles.

BRECCIAS are composed of consolidated masses of angular fragments which, like those in conglomerates, may be very varied. The stratification is very rude. A breccia may consist of cemented

TEXTURE	The rock consists of individual grains, usually quartz: if compact, its hardness is greater than that of steel. SILICEOUS OR SANDY.	The rock effervesces more or less freely with hydrochloric acid. CALCAREOUS.
Pebbles in a finer matrix.	Pebbles angular. BRECCIA. Pebbles rounded. CONGLOMERATE.	
Grains comparatively uniform in size.	Grains more or less rounded. SANDSTONE. Grains angular, poorly sorted. GRIT. Contains felspar. ARKOSE.	Grains round, like fish roe. OOLITIC LIMESTONE. Grains round, about the size of peas or lentils. PISOLITIC LIMESTONE.
Compact: individual grains scarcely visible, even under a lens.	Hardness c.7 Fracture conchoidal. FLINT. Breaks with a flat to hackly fracture. CHERT.	Generally soft and friable. CHALK. Hardness 3 to 3·5. Cleavage-surfaces of calcite often visible. LIMESTONE. Does not effervesce freely with acid. Colour generally buff to pinkish. Often carious. MAGNESIAN DOLOMITIC LIMESTONE The rock contains soft and friable. MARL. As above, but MARL-

Materials including igneous fragments.
TUFFS AND AGGLOMERATES.

170

ROCKS

Earthy smell when breathed on.	Dark brown to black: scratched by a brass pin, giving a brown to black streak. Combustible, leaving more or less ash.
ARGILLACEOUS OR CLAYEY.	CARBONACEOUS.
Pebbles generally sub-angular: often striated. BOULDER-CLAY.	
	Friable and very porous, consisting of a felted mass of vegetable matter. PEAT.
	Earthy to compact: may show vegetable structures. Streak brown to very dark brown. LIGNITE.
Plastic when worked up with water. CLAY. Not plastic in water, but breaks down to mud; unctuous feel. FULLER'S EARTH. Laminated and can be split into thin leaves parallel to the bedding. SHALE.	Black. No vegetable structures seen under the lens: often alternate bright and dull bands; streak black. COAL AND ANTHRACITE.
BITUMINOUS SHALE.	
CARBONACEOUS SHALE.	
Containing quartzose silt. MUDSTONE. much clay and is consolidated. STONE.	Conchoidal fracture; yields oil when heated in closed tube. CANNEL COAL AND OIL SHALE.

scree material, or it may have a different origin. Where masses of rock have been ground against one another, as in movements involving dislocation and crushing, angular fragments are produced which, when cemented, become FAULT-BRECCIAS and CRUSH-BRECCIAS.

Breccias may also be of volcanic origin, consisting of angular blocks of all shapes and sizes which have been discharged through volcanic orifices. The blocks generally consist mainly of volcanic material, but fragments of country-rock, torn from the strata through which the volcano discharged, may form an important constituent. These rocks are called AGGLOMERATES.

TUFF or *Volcanic Tuff* consists of the consolidated material produced by the explosion of superheated steam absorbed in molten lava. Tuffs generally contain angular and vesicular fragments of lava, and also rounded masses (*bombs* or *lapilli*), together with angular or rolled pieces of the country-rock. Tuffs are bedded rocks and often show well-marked lamination resulting from water action. If the whole of the material is fine, the tuff becomes a VOLCANIC ASH. Tuffs and ashes vary greatly in colour, from grey-white to shades of red, purple, green, etc.

FLINT is a form of impure silica associated with chalk, in which it occurs as nodules (often taking the shape of fossils such as sponges or echinoids) and as tabular bands. It is also common as pebbles in sediments of post-Cretaceous age. When fresh, flint is almost always grey to dark grey in colour, and there is generally a well-marked white, porous crust. When weathered (derived from sediments), the colour varies greatly, generally in shades of yellow and brown. Flints in derived deposits usually have little or no porous crust. The fracture is very perfect conchoidal.

CHERT is also an impure form of silica; it is generally associated with limestones older than the Chalk. When fresh, the colour is generally light grey to black; when weathered, various shades of yellow and brown. Weathered pebbles of chert are frequently pierced by tiny holes or pores—*Pin-holed Chert*. The fracture of chert is more splintery and brecciated than that of flint, and the surfaces are generally less smooth.

LIMESTONE.—Hardness averages 3. Colour white, but more frequently bluish-grey, also yellow, brown, and black. Effervesces with and is almost completely soluble in dilute hydrochloric acid. Fossils are often present, and sometimes make up the greater part of the rock; they are generally best observed on weathered surfaces.

Cleavage faces of crystals of calcite may often be observed on fractured surfaces. The presence of impurities gives rise to varieties, such as SILICEOUS LIMESTONE, ARGILLACEOUS LIMESTONE, and BITUMINOUS LIMESTONE, which is often known as *foetid limestone* from the foul smell when the rock is struck with a hammer.

MAGNESIAN (DOLOMITIC) LIMESTONE is rather harder than ordinary limestone (H. 3·5 to 4·5). The colour is yellowish, white, or pale brown. Effervescence with dilute acid is feeble, but becomes brisker when the acid is heated with the powder of the rock. Magnesian limestone is often carious and exhibits complicated concretionary structures which resemble fossils. Ordinary limestones have often suffered *dolomitisation* by introduction of magnesium carbonate in patches, and at the same time the fossils in the dolomitised patches have been destroyed.

OOLITIC AND PISOLITIC limestones consist of rounded grains of substantially pure calcium carbonate; they are almost completely soluble in dilute hydrochloric acid. The distinction between the two rocks is based on the size of the individual grains. In oolites, the grains are generally from 1 to 2 mm. in diameter, while in pisolites, the particles are of the size of peas; they are sometimes known as PEA-GRITS.

CHALK is typically soft, white, meagre to the touch, friable, and consisting principally of a calcareous flour of the remains of *foraminifera*. It also contains echinoderms, molluscs, and other marine organisms. It is generally very pure calcium carbonate and leaves very little residue when dissolved in hydrochloric acid. Unfortunately, the name CHALK is applied in two senses, namely, lithological and stratigraphical. When used in the latter sense, the name may conjure up a soft or hard rock, which may be white, grey, buff-coloured, or red, and the hardness may be up to 4.

MARL is transitional between, and with properties common to both argillaceous and calcareous rocks. Although it has the normal characteristics of clay, it contains considerable amounts of carbonates of lime and magnesia, and is generally regarded as a calcareous rock. MARLSTONE is a consolidated marl.

CLAY.—The characteristic property is that when worked up with water, clay becomes plastic and can be moulded. On subsequent air-drying, the mass becomes *leather-hard*. Clay has a peculiar "earthy" smell when breathed on, and invariably contains a certain amount of finely-divided quartzose silt; where the sandy component is in considerable quantity, the clay becomes a LOAM, which, when hardened, is a MUDSTONE.

The colour varies greatly; *white* implies absence of iron oxides; *red*, the presence of ferric oxide as hematite; *mauve* or *purple*, oxides of manganese; *green*, dissemination of chlorite or glauconite; and *black*, carbonaceous matter. Clays frequently contain crystals of gypsum, calcite, and pyrite.

CHINA-CLAY or KAOLIN is a white, residual clay, derived from the decomposition of felspar *in situ*, and is generally associated with granite.

PIPE-CLAY is white and nearly free from iron. The name is commonly applied to bands of white clay which are sometimes found in sedimentary formations.

FIRE-CLAY contains little iron and is nearly free from lime. It often forms the *under-clay* of coal-seams.

FULLER'S EARTH is very fine-grained, powdery, and earthy; it has marked absorbent properties and adheres to the tongue. It crumbles in water, but will not form a plastic mass.

SHALE, although it has the same composition as clay, is thinly-bedded, and splits easily along its planes of lamination. In some formations, such as the Purbeck, the laminae are so thin and regular, that the rock is known as a PAPER-SHALE.

Black shale, without appreciable gritty component, is probably a BITUMINOUS or CARBONACEOUS SHALE. Shales may become indurated by pressure and show the laminated structure only as bands of different colour; they require to become weathered before the structure is evident. Shales associated with coal-seams frequently fail to show lamination until they have been burned; they then usually leave a pure white to buff residue which splits into thin leaves.

BOULDER CLAY or TILL consists of more or less angular fragments of rock of all sizes, from large boulders down to small pebbles, enclosed in a matrix of finely-divided *rock-flour*, derived from the attrition of the country-rocks over which a glacier has passed. Some of the blocks may show scratches. Boulder-clay is typically unstratified; the included fragments show no signs of having been sorted and are arranged higgledy-piggledy. Where the underlying rock is moderately hard, such as limestone or slate, the surface, when cleared, will generally be found to be smoothed and scored with more or less parallel striations which show the direction in which the ice moved.

The enclosed fragments should be studied, since information may thus be obtained of the direction from which the ice came.

PEAT consists of relatively little altered vegetable matter, generally the remains of mosses or moss-like plants, but sometimes containing reeds and masses of trees.   The vegetable structures can be distinguished by the naked eye or under a lens, and, when freshly dug, the moisture may be as high as 90 per cent. When dried, peat burns readily, leaving (generally) comparatively little ash.

LIGNITE consists of vegetable matter which is more decomposed than that in peat, and is less easily distinguished.   Lignites (or brown coals) may be earthy or compact, and generally contain upwards of 40 per cent. of moisture when freshly dug.   The colour may be from light brown to almost black; the streak is from light brown to dark brown, *never* black.

COAL rarely shows any signs of vegetable structure under the lens.   The colour is black, and the streak very nearly so.   When struck with a hammer, coal breaks down into roughly cuboidal fragments.   It burns freely and leaves only a small proportion of mineral residue.   With increasing contamination with mineral matter, coal passes into BONEY COAL and BITUMINOUS SHALE.

If the specimen breaks down into more or less cuboidal fragments when struck with a hammer, soils the fingers, and, when heated in a closed tube gives tarry vapours and a solid residue which is *caked*, that is, the original separate particles have coalesced to form a coherent mass, the coal is a BITUMINOUS, CAKING COAL.

If the residue is an incoherent powder, but the coal, on heating, gives tarry vapours, it is a BITUMINOUS NON-CAKING COAL.

If practically no tarry vapour is evolved and the residue is incoherent, the coal is ANTHRACITIC.   The anthracitic coals are harder than the bituminous coals and do not soil the hands.

CANNEL COAL is distinguished, in the field, from bituminous coal by the conchoidal fracture.   When burned, it gives a long, smoky flame, and frequently leaves much mineral residue. Generally occurs as lenticular beds associated with bituminous coal.

BITUMINOUS SHALE.—The percentage of organic matter may vary widely.   The colour may be from dark grey to brown, or almost jet black.   Bituminous shales are often resilient when struck with a hammer and can be cut into thin shavings which curl like those from the wood of a pencil.   Small splinters of highly bituminous shales can be ignited by a match and will continue to burn, emitting an "oily" smell.   The fracture is conchoidal or sub-conchoidal.

White, grey, or pink.   Weathering to a pale crust.

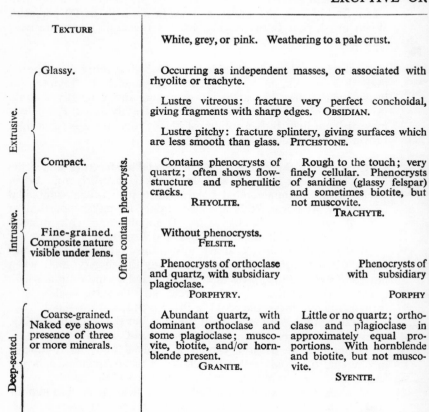

TEXTURE		
Extrusive. Glassy.	Occurring as independent masses, or associated with rhyolite or trachyte. Lustre vitreous: fracture very perfect conchoidal, giving fragments with sharp edges. OBSIDIAN. Lustre pitchy: fracture splintery, giving surfaces which are less smooth than glass. PITCHSTONE.	
Intrusive. Compact.	Contains phenocrysts of quartz; often shows flow-structure and spherulitic cracks. RHYOLITE.	Rough to the touch; very finely cellular. Phenocrysts of sanidine (glassy felspar) and sometimes biotite, but not muscovite. TRACHYTE.
Fine-grained. Composite nature visible under lens.	Without phenocrysts. FELSITE. Phenocrysts of orthoclase and quartz, with subsidiary plagioclase. PORPHYRY.	Phenocrysts of with subsidiary PORPHY
Deep-seated. Coarse-grained. Naked eye shows presence of three or more minerals.	Abundant quartz, with dominant orthoclase and some plagioclase; muscovite, biotite, and/or hornblende present. GRANITE.	Little or no quartz; orthoclase and plagioclase in approximately equal proportions. With hornblende and biotite, but not muscovite. SYENITE.

Often contain phenocrysts.

IGNEOUS ROCKS

Grey to black; deepening.

➤ ————————————————————————→

Green, red, or black: often mottled.

Occurring as selvages on andesite.
ANDESITE GLASS.

Occurring as selvages on basalt or dolerite.
TACHYLITE.

Grey when fresh, weathering to deep red or maroon colour.
ANDESITE.

Generally dark grey to black. Often with patches of olive-green olivine and sometimes black augite.
BASALT.

DOLERITE.

Weather to "rusty" products.

plagioclase, orthoclase.

RITE.

Dominant plagioclase with hornblende and biotite, or augite.
DIORITE.

Coarse and heavy; plagioclase, with olivine, pyroxene, and sometimes hornblende.
GABBRO.

Contains plagioclase; mainly consisting of olivine and augite.
PICRITE.

Without felspar: Mainly olivine.
PERIDOTITE.

Mainly serpentine.
SERPENTINE.

IGNEOUS ROCKS

The scheme for the determination of the igneous rocks is based on a study of (i) their texture, and (ii) the composition. Four types of texture are recognised: (a) *coarse-grained*; rocks falling into this category can be seen by the naked eye to be composite, usually consisting of three or more minerals. The coarse-grained igneous rocks are deep-seated, and form the *holocrystalline* group of the petrologist.

(b) The *fine-grained rocks* disclose their composite nature when examined under a lens; the petrologist classifies them as *microcrystalline*, since, when examined under the microscope, the rocks are found to consist of a felted mass of tiny crystals.

(c) *Compact rocks* include those which, on fresh fractures, have a *lithoidal* or "stony" aspect; so far as the main body of the rock is concerned, individual minerals cannot be distinguished. The petrologist includes these rocks with the *glassy* group, since the microscope proves that there is much glassy material present; for field purposes, however, we have preferred to separate the compact from the glassy rocks, since they do not show vitreous lustre.

Both the fine-grained and compact igneous rocks may contain one or more minerals "floating" as relatively large, recognisable crystals (phenocrysts or porphyritic crystals) in a fine-grained or lithoidal matrix. The nature of the phenocrysts is important as a diagnostic character.

(d) *Glassy rocks*, from our point of view, are those which have a glassy or pitchy appearance. The microscope shows that they consist in the main of a true glass, with a number of feathery incipient crystals (*microlites*) therein.

In the scheme, the coarse-textured, deep-seated rocks are at the bottom, and in passing up the columns, the textures become finer, until the topmost group includes the glassy rocks which are extrusive in origin.

The rocks in the left-hand column consist of the *acid*, or *granite* family, characterised by free silica (quartz), dominant orthoclase felspar, and muscovite. In passing from right to left of the table, the quartz disappears and the orthoclase is gradually replaced by the plagioclase felspars, while muscovite gives place to biotite, when any mica is present. Hornblende is the general ferromagnesian mineral in the *syenite* and *diorite* families, and is gradually replaced by augite and finally by olivine and serpentine in the serpentine or ultra-basic family.

It should be noted that the various classes of rock merge into one another, in texture, mode of occurrence, and composition, and

GROUP & TEXTURE	ACID	INTERMEDIATE	BASIC	ULTRA – BASIC
Volcanic (Glassy)	OBSIDIAN PITCHSTONE RHYOLITE	TRACHYTE ANDESITE	TACHYLITE BASALT	—
Intrusive (Microcrystalline: Porphyritic)	FELSITE PORPHYRY	PORPHYRITE	DOLERITE	—
Plutonic (Holocrystalline)	GRANITE SYENITE	DIORITE	GABBRO	PICRITE PERIDOTITE SERPENTINE
Essential Minerals	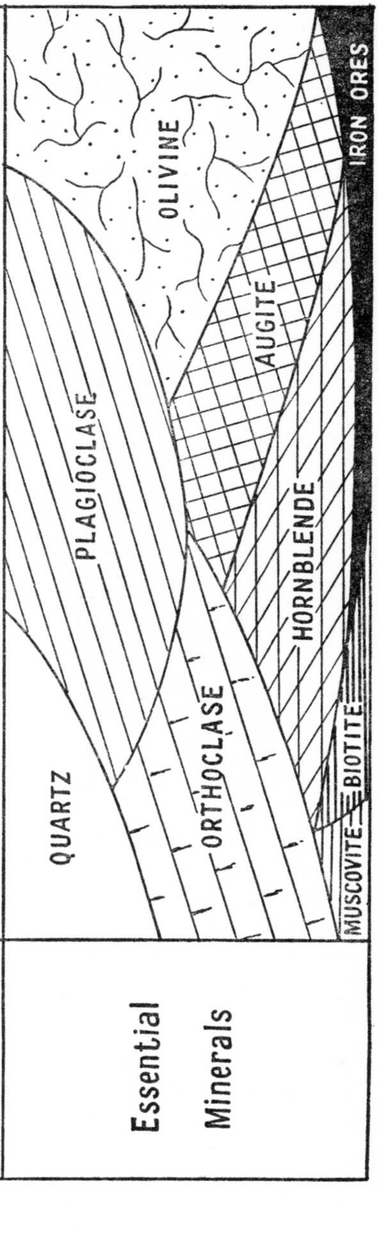 QUARTZ ORTHOCLASE	PLAGIOCLASE HORNBLENDE	AUGITE	OLIVINE IRON ORES

MUSCOVITE BIOTITE

[After Watts.

Fig. 55. TABLE OF COMMON IGNEOUS ROCKS, WITH APPROXIMATE MINERAL COMPOSITIONS.

are by no means clear cut—hence the absence of dividing lines in the scheme. The gradual alteration in composition in passing from left to right is well shown in Fig. 55, which is based on similar diagrams by Professor Watts (*Geology for Beginners*, pp. 178, 183).

The most important *coarse-grained igneous rocks* include—

GRANITE.—This consists of quartz, orthoclase felspar, and either one or both micas, muscovite and biotite. The biotite may be replaced by hornblende, giving HORNBLENDE GRANITE. Plagioclase often occurs, and accessory minerals such as tourmaline, apatite, zircon, and garnet are often present.

The chief minerals occur in approximately equal proportions, and the felspar and mica may be present as porphyritic crystals or phenocrysts. The vitreous lustre, lack of colour, and hardness of the *quartz*; the cleavage, simple twinning, and white or pink colour of the *orthoclase*; the perfect basal cleavage, the low hardness and the silvery-white or brownish-black colour of the *micas* can generally be distinguished in hand-specimens (Fig. 56).

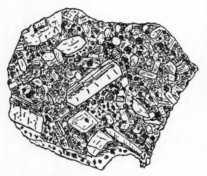

Fig. 56. SMOOTHED SURFACE OF GRANITE. TO SHOW COARSE-GRAINED TEXTURE.

SYENITE is rare in Great Britain; it resembles a granite with little or no quartz, while plagioclase is as abundant as orthoclase. The mica is almost entirely biotite, and with green hornblende represents the chief ferromagnesian constituent. Common and important accessory minerals are sphene, apatite, zircon, and ilmenite. The rock is pink or grey in colour.

DIORITE is closely related to syenite, but differs from it mainly by the fact that plagioclase is the dominant felspar; diorite is also usually coarser in texture and darker than syenite.

GABBRO is a coarse, heavy rock, in which the individual mineral are large and well developed; the colour is usually dark grey to black. The characteristic minerals are olivine and pyroxene and it is the dominance of one or other of the ferromagnesian minerals which gives rise to the varieties of gabbro. Thus, we may have OLIVINE-GABBRO, COMMON GABBRO (with diallage or augite),

HYPERSTHENE-GABBRO (containing rhombic pyroxene), while if hornblende is present as well as pyroxene, the rock is known as HORNBLENDE-GABBRO. The felspar is a basic plagioclase (usually from labradorite to anorthite), and often occurs as large, irregular plates showing coarse lamellar twinning. Apatite is commonly present as an accessory mineral, and iron ores (ilmenite, with leucoxene as a decomposition product, and magnetite) are often abundant.

In the field, the basic rocks, particularly gabbros and diorites, tend to produce a rugged type of landscape. Intersecting joints are widened by weathering, and the rock splits and breaks into large angular fragments, forming rough and jagged ridges, of which the Cuillins of Skye are fine examples.

SERPENTINE AND SERPENTINE-ROCKS are all characterised by olivine, which is their most prominent constituent. The colour is green, red, and black (often mottled); the rocks are heavy, have a soapy feel, and can be scratched by a knife.

When the decomposition product of olivine (serpentine) makes up practically the entire rock, the result is a SERPENTINE. Small amounts of accessory and other secondary minerals, such as iron oxides (including chromite), carbonates (dolomite, etc.), chlorite, and tremolite often occur.

PERIDOTITE consists largely of olivine, often as idiomorphic or rounded crystals. A common ferromagnesian constituent is a rhombic pyroxene, enstatite or bronzite, which also tends to be idiomorphic. The rock is entirely devoid of felspar.

PICRITE is a dark, heavy rock, made up of olivine and augite, with a variable, but always minor quantity of plagioclase; hornblende and biotite are also occasionally present. A characteristic feature seen in hand-specimens is *lustre-mottling*. This is the interrupted sheen on the cleavages of the augite and hornblende, and is caused by the presence thereon of tiny grains of olivine which reflect light at a different angle.

The *lithoidal rocks* include—

FELSITES, which do not contain phenocrysts, and PORPHYRIES, which are distinguished by the presence of well-defined, isolated phenocrysts of certain minerals, such as quartz and orthoclase, "floating" in a fine-grained groundmass. They are very acid and consist essentially of quartz and orthoclase, with accessory minerals such as biotite and hornblende (Fig. 57).

It should be emphasised that it is the combination of a porphyritic mineral or minerals with a fine-texture groundmass that characterises a porphyry. Phenocrysts occur in many types of igneous rocks, but unless the groundmass is microcrystalline, the rock is not a porphyry.

PORPHYRITES are similar to the porphyries, except that quartz is rare or absent and the preponderant felspar is plagioclase. The characteristic repeated or lamellar twinning should therefore be looked for, and if found will assist in distinguishing the rock from a porphyry, in which the felspar is the simply-twinned orthoclase.

DOLERITE is intermediate between the gabbros and the basalts; it frequently shows columnar structure and often weathers into concentric shells like the coats of an onion.

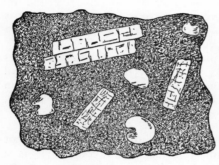

Fig. 57. SMOOTHED SURFACE OF PORPHYRY. PHENOCRYSTS OF FELSPAR AND QUARTZ IN A FINELY-CRYSTALLINE MATRIX.

Among the *compact igneous* rocks are—

RHYOLITE is usually light grey in colour, and frequently shows rather wavy banding which is the result of the flow of the original viscous magma, and spherulitic, and perlitic cracks. Small porphyritic crystals of quartz and orthoclase are common.

TRACHYTES are white to light grey, and noticeably rough to the touch. They contain little quartz, and are characterised by the presence of crystals of *glassy felspar* (Sanidine). The commonest ferromagnesian constituent is biotite, which frequently occurs as idiomorphic crystals.

ANDESITE is a denser rock than trachyte, and is usually darker in colour; it may be vesicular. It weathers to a reddish-brown (not "rusty") colour. Varieties are biotite-andesite, hornblende-andesite, and augite-andesite.

BASALT varies in colour from dark grey to black; the grey varieties often resemble limestones, but are harder. When weathered, the basalts become softer and have a greenish or rusty-brown tinge, especially on the surfaces of joints and cracks. Although for the most part very compact, areas of bottle-green olivine, and black, shining crystals of augite are often found. The jointing is frequently very perfect columnar; the columns may be straight or curved, and may be divided into short sections by ball-and-socket joints. The columnar jointing is an important diagnostic character in the field for basalts and dolerites.

The volcanic glasses may occur as more or less independent masses or be in the form of mere fringes on the edges of lavas or of dykes.

OBSIDIAN is a highly acid glass which occurs in large masses. It resembles bottle-glass, having a perfect conchoidal fracture and breaking into sharp splinters which are transparent on the edges. The colour varies greatly, black, brown, or greyish-green, rarely yellow, blue, or red; often streaked and banded with paler and darker hues.

PITCHSTONE has a more pitchy or resinous lustre than obsidian and the surface of the fracture is not so smooth. It occurs as dykes in Arran.

ANDESITE-GLASS occurs as thin fringes on the edge of some andesite flows.

TACHYLITE is a black glass which is sometimes found as a chilled selvage on the margins of dykes and sills of basalt.

METAMORPHIC ROCKS

Strong cleavage and foliation and/or the presence of certain minerals are the characteristics of METAMORPHIC ROCKS. The cleavage is distinguished from the fissility due to lamination by the fact that it is generally inclined to the direction of the original bedding. Indications of bedding in fine-grained cleaved rocks, such as slates, are given by persistent bands of different colour or shade, or by the presence of layers which are coarser than the main body of the rock.

Minerals which are indicative of metamorphism include *Kyanite, Chiastolite, Staurolite*, and *Garnet*, particularly when present in abundant quantity and as recognisable crystals.

Foliation is a type of banded structure which enables a rock to be split into slabs or sheets which almost always have a rather rough, wavy surface. When examined in a direction at right angles to the direction of the folia, it will be found that minerals having a platy or elongated habit (the micas and felspars) tend to be orientated along the folia, which is in contrast with their random distribution in the igneous rocks. When the foliation is closely spaced, so that almost any part of the rock can be split into flakes or flat lenticles, the rock

FOLIATED OR METAMORPHIC ROCKS

STRONG CLEAVAGE.

Very fine grained, individual minerals indistinguishable under the lens.
SLATE.

Much flaky mica on the cleavage planes.
PHYLLITE.

Smooth surface interrupted by spots or knots.
SPOTTED SLATE.

Spots square or rhombic in shape. Black impurities may be visible in them.
CHIASTOLITE SLATE.

FOLIATION WELL MARKED.

Folia thin, wavy, and continuous.
SCHIST.

Varieties named after the most conspicuous mineral, which may be—
Mica,   Chlorite,
Hornblende,   Talc.
Quartz,
Schists often contain large, well-formed crystals of garnet.

Folia coarse, lenticular, and discontinuous.
GNEISS.

Composition that of granite.
COMMON OR GRANITIC GNEISS.

Large eye-like kernels of felspar or quartz are dispersed through a finer matrix.
AUGEN GNEISS.

Fissility decreasing

MASSIVE AND COMPACT. FOLIATION ABSENT OR OBSCURE.

Texture granular; garnet present.
GRANULITE.

Light-coloured, with much quartz; garnet sparsely distributed.
ACID GRANULITE.

Dark coloured (due to pyroxene, which cannot usually be identified under a lens), with abundant garnet.
BASIC GRANULITE.

Harder than steel, which leaves a metallic streak on the rock. Chief mineral, quartz.
QUARTZITE

Hardness 3 to 3·5: effervesces freely with dilute HCl.
CRYSTALLINE LIMESTONE
(Statuary Marble).

Hardness 3·5 to 4: effervesces feebly with dilute HCl unless the powder is heated with the acid.
DOLOMITE
(Dolomitic Marble).

is called a *schist*. The schistosity is somewhat akin to slaty cleavage, but on a coarser, rougher, and less uniform scale. Schists are often crumpled and contorted; they will not then cleave or split into sheets or fine bands. A rock of this type is shown in Fig. 58.

The scheme divides them into three main groups. The first includes the rocks which exhibit strong cleavage; the second, those which are well foliated; and the third, rocks which are massive and compact, for example, quartzites and crystalline limestones.

SLATE is a very fine-grained rock, having an "earthy" smell when breathed on, and is capable of being cleaved into thin plates.

The colour varies greatly, grey-blue, green, purple, and almost black. The grain is so fine that individual minerals cannot be distinguished even under a lens. When there is much flaky mica developed on the planes of cleavage, the rock is a PHYLLITE. When the smooth surface is interrupted by spots or knots, the rock becomes a SPOTTED SLATE. If the spots are square or rhombic in shape, showing black impurities within them, we have a CHIASTOLITE SLATE.

GNEISS frequently has a mineral composition resembling that of granite, but the constituents are arranged in bands or folia. The bands, which vary in width, are usually coarse and irregular, and seldom consist of a single mineral. Certain constituents, such as quartz and felspar, often occur as *knots* (almond-shaped or eye-like

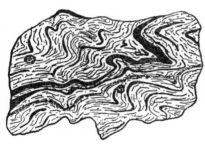

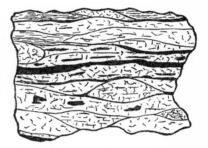

Fig. 58. SMOOTHED SURFACE OF CRUMPLED MICA-SCHIST.

Fig. 59. SMOOTHED SURFACE OF AUGEN GNEISS.

forms), and are enclosed or surrounded by small fragments of other minerals, giving AUGEN GNEISS (Fig. 59).

The SCHISTS are generally distinguished from the gneisses by being more finely foliated, and the bands are usually wavy and very contorted. The mineral constituents are commonly separated and run uninterruptedly throughout the planes of foliation. There are many varieties of schist, which are known by their preponderating minerals.

GRANULITE is composed of small interlocking grains and banded like gneiss. When the rock is light coloured and there is much quartz, with sparse crystals of garnet, it is an ACID GRANULITE; when the rock is dark in colour and contains much garnet, it may be called BASIC GRANULITE.

CHAPTER XV

FOSSILS

"However trivial a rotten shell may appear to some, yet these monuments of nature are more certain tokens of antiquity than coins or medals . . . and though it must be granted that it is very difficult to read them or raise a chronology out of them . . . yet it is not impossible."—ROBERT HOOKE (1699).

Fossils include the remains and *traces* of animals and plants which are found *naturally embedded* in rocks. They comprise not only the actual remains of organisms, such as shells of molluscs, tests of echinoderms, twigs, bark, leaves, and seeds of plants, but moulds and casts thereof, and even impressions left by worms, jelly-fish, and the footprints of birds, reptiles, and other animals.

Fossils are important to the field geologist because they help to throw light on the conditions of formation of the rocks in which they occur, and, of greater importance, they serve to identify the strata in which they are found.

Deductions are based on the principle which is the basis of all geological reasoning, that *the present is the key to the past.* Since many fossils bear a strong resemblance to the corresponding parts of organised beings of the present day, it is concluded that extinct animals and plants can be classified in the same way as their modern representatives; also it is a reasonable deduction that they had similar habits.

A series of limestones, for example, which contain numerous corals and shells belonging to families which at the present day live only in the sea, are therefore considered to have been formed under marine conditions. Prolific growths of organisms which are closely related to modern reef-building corals, suggest that the deposit was formed in comparatively shallow water, because modern reef-building corals all live in the sea at depths not exceeding about 20 fathoms.

Large accumulations of plant remains indicate that the deposits were formed in close proximity to land in a swamp, estuary, or delta. It must be remembered that inferences as to conditions of formation are less certain in the older deposits, for, in general, the older the formation, the more do its contained fossils differ from the remains of modern plants and animals.

THE USE OF FOSSILS FOR THE IDENTIFICATION AND CORRELATION OF STRATA

This depends on the principle enunciated in 1790 by William Smith that *strata can be identified with certainty by means of the fossils which they contain.* It has been ascertained by repeated observations that, *in an undisturbed series of fossiliferous beds,* each bed is characterised by an assemblage of fossils peculiar to it. Furthermore, if, in a vertical section at a particular locality, there are a number of beds containing a sequence of assemblages *A, B, C, D, E,* provided there has been no disturbance, the order elsewhere is always the same; *C* is never found below *B,* nor *D* below *A.* One or more may be absent, showing either that the beds containing them were never deposited, or have been removed by denudation.

The intensive study of fossils has shown that formations can be divided into *zones,* often only a few feet thick, each of which contains its own suite of fossils. Each zone is usually named after a characteristic fossil which attained the height of its development (its *acme*) during the time (*hemera*) occupied by the deposition of the zone. It must, however, be stressed that the zone-fossil is not necessarily restricted to its particular zone; *it is the assemblage of fossils that characterises the zone.* Similarly, in correlating larger stratigraphical units than zones, it is unsafe to rely on the presence of a single species; the character of the assemblage must be taken into account.

The application of the above principles to field geology can be stated as follows:—

(i) If at two exposures the same assemblage of fossils is found, the rocks at the two points, however great the distance between them, must be taken as of the same age.

(ii) If two exposures provide specimens of rocks which, although they are indistinguishable as far as lithological characters are concerned, contain entirely different assemblages of fossils, then, however close the exposures may be to one another, the rocks must be of different ages.

It was seen (p. 72) that the limestone quarries in the Ashover district yielded specimens of *Productus, Spirifer, Dibunophyllum, Syringopora, Lithostrotion,* and *Lonsdaleia.*

This assemblage shows that the limestone is of Lower Carboniferous age; *Dibunophyllum* is found only in the upper beds of the Carboniferous Limestone; therefore, the limestone core of the dome may be taken as dated accurately. *All* the above suite of fossils are not found in *all* the exposures; one or more, however, of the representative species can be collected if careful search is made. It is thus justifiable to correlate all the exposures as being on one out-crop, and there is no suggestion that at any point the Carboniferous Limestone is faulted out against some other lithologically similar rock.

(iii) Complete identity of the assemblages at two exposures is not necessary to prove that the rocks are of the same age. The fossils may be representative of two distinct zoological or botanical provinces, or, alternatively, the conditions under which the rocks were formed may have differed. Different rock-types are being formed simultaneously at different places; near the coast, sand-stones, pass into mudstones and clays, as the water deepens; in deeper water still, limestone may be the prevailing type of deposit. Each of these habitats has its own life-assemblage, and therefore the rocks formed at the same time, but under different conditions, cannot be expected to present either the same facies or the same faunal assemblage. When followed laterally, limestones may be found to grade insensibly into clays and shales by gradual inter-mixture with increasing proportions of muddy matter; in turn, clays and shales pass insensibly into sandstones. The extremes of the series will, therefore, not contain identical suites of fossils. There will, however, probably be some common genera, if not species, which enable correlations to be made. It must always be remembered that superposition affords the fundamental test of age; every endeavour should be made to ascertain the nature and age of the rocks immediately above and below those whose age is doubtful. If *A* is found below, and *C* above the doubtful rock, *its* age is probably that of *B*, even though the lithological character may be very different from that at the type-locality.

Negative Evidence. If, after careful search, no fossils are found in a particular exposure, it should not be pronounced "unfossili-ferous"; a note should be made to the effect that "no fossils were found." This is the truth, the whole truth, and nothing but the truth. The history of geology shows numerous examples of much harm having been done by sweeping statements based on negative evidence; this has retarded research and led to wrong conclusions. Not infrequently, a deposit which has been pronounced unfossili-ferous has been found, in fact, to be locally teeming with organic remains.

It has sometimes been concluded, from the absence of fossils, that a particular deposit was accumulated under conditions which were inimical to life. Fossils are often destroyed chemically and as a result of metamorphism. This applies particularly to the more ancient rocks.

Arguments from negative evidence are, therefore, liable to be untrustworthy; where there is no evidence, the observer should keep an open mind and be prepared (perhaps at a later stage in his work) to re-open the investigation in the hope that he may be able, as the result of further experience, to throw more light on some of his unsolved problems.

DETERMINATION OF FOSSILS IN THE FIELD

The geologist, from the start of his career, should do his best to determine his fossils for himself while he is in the field. His identifications will, of course, be provisional and subject to revision when he is able to make comparisons in a museum or to consult the literature. We strongly deprecate the practice, which is sometimes followed, of collecting such fossils as are available and immediately packing them up to be sent home for later examination. Every scrap of information that is to be had should be made use of *in the field*, and fossils should be made to yield all the information that can be extracted from them at the earliest possible moment.

Even though it may not be possible at first to do more than relegate a specimen to what we have called its *group*, something has been accomplished. With practice, the beginner will soon find that he can recognise a number of the important genera of animals and plants, and if he is working for a considerable time on one or more fossiliferous formations, he will acquire the habit of recognising a number of the commoner species. These will form bases for comparison with other species, so that his powers of discrimination will increase in geometrical ratio with the increase in "known" species.

Since an ounce of practice is worth a ton of theory, we recommend the reader to set about using the tables for himself, even though he has no specimens of fossils available. In fact, he will be well advised to start with the examination of a number of modern mollusca, such as may be obtained at the fishmongers or picked up on a beach. Obtain specimens of the following:—the common cockle (*Cardium*), the mussel (*Mytilus*), the scallop (*Pecten*), the oyster (*Ostrea*), and, with the aid of the scheme for the *Lamellibranchia* see how to identify them. Then, obtain specimens of the whelk (*Buccinum*) and the periwinkle (*Littorina*); verify how the former may be identified by the key for the *Gastropoda*, make sections of both with the aid of the carborundum slip and examine the interiors. By following the above procedure, the student will find that he gains confidence in using the schemes, not only for the two most important classes of the modern mollusca, but also when he consults the schemes for other classes of fossils.

Preliminary Examination

This key should prove useful to the beginner, but it will quickly be found that a specimen can generally be relegated to its appropriate group without reference to the key.

The specimen consists of a single rod-like body, or of a number of similar bodies, each of which is serrated on at least one edge; or it consists of delicate moss-like markings or of a mesh-work of branches which are interconnected at intervals by cross-branches .. .. **Graptolithina**

The specimen in cross-section shows a number of more or less well-marked radiating partitions or septa. There may be a single individual, or a large number of similar individuals forming a colony .. .. **Actinozoa** (Corals)

A definite five-rayed arrangement can be detected **Echinoderma**

The specimen consists of a bivalved shell; the valves are dissimilar and each is symmetrical .. .. .. **Brachiopoda**

The specimen consists of a bivalved shell; each valve is almost always a mirror-image of the other, and each is unsymmetrical
Lamellibranchia

The specimen consists of a univalve shell, in the form of a cone or a simple spiral, which is generally coiled right-handed **Gastropoda**

The specimen consists of a univalve shell, which is divided by partitions into a number of chambers .. .. **Cephalopoda**

The specimen is more or less shield-shaped; it shows bilateral symmetry, and three parts, *head*, *body*, and *tail* can be recognised. The body and tail are segmented and are *trilobed*, into an *axis*, with a segmented area on either side .. .. .. **Trilobita**

Having determined the group to which the fossil belongs, next turn to the scheme for the identification of selected members of the group. Each key is divided into a set of numbered sections. Section 1 splits the group into two sub-groups, each of which is characterised by easily recognisable contrasted properties, and directs the reader to proceed to other numbered sections of the key, in which further subdivision takes place, until finally, the name of a genus is found.

The idea is based on the *floras* drawn up by botanists for the identification of plants. We have, however, introduced an additional feature, which we believe will be found useful. Following the section-number, there is a figure in brackets; this gives the number of the division of the key which immediately led to the section under consideration. Each key can therefore be easily read in either direction, and the student can refer back to the more general properties of the specimen which he is examining.

Each scheme is prefaced by a short note on the morphological characters of the group to which it refers.   These prefatory remarks are merely intended to explain such technical terms as are necessarily used in the keys.

Since the range of sizes of fossils is large, it was not possible to draw all the figures to the same scale.   We have, therefore, indicated the degree of enlargement or reduction adopted, so that the dimensions of each specimen which is illustrated can be determined. It must be clearly understood, however, that there may be a great difference between individuals of a single species;   similarly, the average size of members of one species of a genus may be much greater than those of another species of the same genus.

To illustrate how the keys are intended to be used, we give a few examples applied to fossils found in the Ashover district (*vide* Chapter VII).

1. *Locality.* Hockley Quarry and Cockerspring Wood (pp. 65 and 71).   Bivalved shell;   the two valves are dissimilar and each is symmetrical, *Brachiopod.*   Turning now to the key on p. 214, we find that the two valves are connected at a hinge, indicating section 4. The hinge-line is long, s. 5.   One valve is slightly concave, the other is strongly convex, s. 8.   On examining the surface of the shell with a lens, a number of tiny projections (spine-bases) are found scattered irregularly over the surface of the convex valve, s. 10.

In this section of the key, two genera are included.   The specimen under consideration differs from *Chonetes,* in that there is no cardinal area, the spines are not confined to the margin of the pedicle-valve, but are distributed over its surface.   The fossil does conform with the description of *Productus* in the convexity of the pedicle-valve and the slight concavity of the brachial valve.   Furthermore, the beak is curved over, and there is no foramen.   The surface is ornamented by radial costae which are crossed by fine concentric ribs, particularly in the neighbourhood of the beak and on the brachial valve.   The result is that the surface of the shell is marked by a definite reticulate pattern.   The dimensions of the specimen described are:—extreme width parallel with the hinge, $1\frac{1}{2}$ in., length from anterior to posterior margin $1\frac{3}{8}$ in.   We conclude, therefore, that the specimen is a **Productus.**

2. *Locality.* Cockerspring Wood and Hockley Quarry.   Bivalved shells, valves dissimilar and showing signs of being symmetrical, although generally more or less imperfect, *Brachiopods.*   At Cockerspring Wood there is a bed consisting of little else but these shells,

towards the top of the section, while at Hockley Quarry, occasional specimens are to be found.

The valves are connected at a hinge, and the hinge-line is long, in fact the hinge is the longest dimension of the shells, ss. 4 and 5. The surface of the shell bears a number of tiny projections which are the stumps of spines, s. 10.

Again, the convexity of the pedicle-valve, the decided concavity of the brachial valve, the great curvature of the beak, the absence of any cardinal area and foramen lead to the conclusion that the shells are specimens of **Productus**. The outline of the shells is very different from that of the *Productus* dealt with previously; moreover, the size is much greater, the leading dimensions being 5 to 6 in. along the line of the hinge, and only about 3 in. at right angles thereto. This large *Productus* has the hinge-line prolonged laterally into "wings," one or both being frequently broken off in the specimens found; still, by examining a number of specimens, the winged nature of the shell can be clearly made out. Since there are many specimens available at Cockerspring Wood, it is worth breaking one or two across, as nearly as may be, at right angles to the line of the hinge. It is then found that the brachial valve is fitted so closely within the pedicle-valve that the wonder is that there was room for the animal within the heavy shell!

3. *Locality.* Cockerspring Wood, from the layer of rubbly limestone at the top of the section, immediately below the soil, also in Hockley Quarry. The specimen consists of a squat, oblique cone, with a more or less circular section, which is slightly etched out by weathering, so that a number of radiating partitions stand up slightly above the surface. These are the marks of a coral—scheme *Actinozoa*. To enable the structure to be more easily seen, the specimen is rubbed down on the coarse side of a carborundum slip, and then smoothed on the fine side; the smoothed surface is then examined under a lens, after wetting with water. The septa are then seen to consist of long and short groups, *Madreporaria*, s. 7.

The coral has bilateral symmetry, being divided into two nearly equal parts by a median plate, s. 8, *Rugosa*. The coral is simple, that is, it occurs as an individual and not attached to a number of others as a colony, s. 9. The shape is conical, s. 11. There is a distinct axial structure (s. 14), which is made up of a number of elements (s. 15), and has a well-marked median plate. The septa are numerous, as are the dissepiments. The coral is therefore identified as **Dibunophyllum**.

4. *Locality.* Small excavation west of Cockerspring Wood. Bivalved shell, valves unequal, each valve symmetrical, *Brachiopod.*

The hinge-line is long, ss. 4 and 5. Both valves are convex; the brachial valve is partly broken, and the shell can be seen to contain a well-marked spiral, which the lens reveals to consist of crystals. The pedicle-valve bears a flat area which is expanded laterally, s. 7. The beak of the pedicle-valve is sharp and bent over; both valves show a cardinal area and both are radially plicated. There is a median fold on the brachial and a corresponding furrow on the pedicle-valve. The hinge-line is produced into ear-like expansions of the valves below it. The fossil is therefore a **Spirifer.**

GRAPTOLITES

Graptolites are sometimes considered to be colonial hydrozoa; each colony consists of a number of cups or *thecae* attached to a horny rod. The cups may be arranged on one or both sides of the supporting rod or axis. A complete colony may consist of from one to many conjoined branches. Growth started from a conical or dagger-shaped body known as the *sicula* (marked "S" on a number of the figures), and this marks the *proximal* end of the colony. The end remote from the sicula is the *distal*.

The skeletons are composed of horny material; they are usually preserved as carbonaceous films, and are generally most prolific in argillaceous rocks. Less commonly, the organic material has been replaced by pyrite and is then uncrushed; occasionally, unaltered graptolites may be extracted from limestone by treatment with acid.

The graptolites are valuable stratigraphically, since they have a short range in time and wide geographical distribution. Their presence is an indication of a Palaeozoic horizon; the many-branched types are restricted to the Upper Cambrian, the less-branched Tetragraptids and Didymograptids to the Lower and Middle Ordovician, the Diplograptids to the Middle and Upper Ordovician, while the single-branched, uniserial Monograptids are Silurian and Devonian.

1. A mat-like form, consisting of many branches, forming a delicate net-like structure. Branches connected by cross-tubes   . .   . .**Dictyonema** Cambrian to Carboniferous, but common only in one zone of the Tremadoc.

    Note.—*Dictyonema* is not a true graptolite; it is a member of the *Dendroidea*, which belongs to the class *Graptolithina* as is also *Clonograptus*.

    Branches not connected by cross-tubes.   2

2. (*1*) Branches subdivide repeatedly, giving a form having as many as 32, or even 64 terminal branches   . .   . .   **Clonograptus** Upper Tremadoc and Arenig.

    Terminal branches not more than eight   3

3. (*2*) Eight uniserial branches; a central disc is frequently present   **Dichograptus** Lower Arenig.

    Not more than four branches   4

4. (*3*) The four branches are united back to back; in section, the shape is a cross. Form leaf-like; thecae in contact with one another and provided with spines   . .   . .   **Phyllograptus** Lower Arenig.

    Four diverging branches . .   . .   **Tetragraptus** Arenig.

    One or two branches   5

Dictyonema, x1.

Clonograptus, x1.

Dichograptus, x 1/2.

Phyllograptus, x1.

Tetragraptus, x1.

5. (*4*) Two branches   6
One branch   7

6. (*5*) Thecae are simple cylinders, and therefore give rectangular outlines when crushed; in contact for a considerable portion of their length
Didymograptus
Lower Arenig to Upper Llandeilo.

Thecae with strong sigmoidal curvature   ..   ..   **Dicellograptus**
Upper Arenig to Upper Bala.

Initially one branch with thecae back to back; then bifurcating, forming a **Y**, each branch bearing a single row of sigmoidally curved thecae on the outer side ..   ..   **Dicranograptus**
Upper Llandeilo to Lower Bala.

7. (*5*) Thecae biserial, *i.e.* on both sides of branch   8
Thecae uniserial   9

8. (*7*) Thecae sub-prismatic, or sub-cylindrical tubes, overlapping and arranged obliquely. Axis prolonged distally. Sicula imbedded .. **Diplograptus**
Arenig to Upper Llandovery.

Thecae sigmoidally curved and separated by deep excavations. Axis prolonged beyond both extremities   ..   ..   ..   **Climacograptus**
Upper Arenig to Llandovery.

9. (*7*) Thecae very variable in form in different species; not widely separated ..   ..   **Monograptus**
Characteristic of Silurian.

Thecae long, tubular, and widely separated ..   ..   ..   **Rastrites**
Upper Llandovery.

CORALS

The skeleton of an individual fossil coral is called a *corallite*. At the top, is the cup or *calice* which, during the life of the animal, contained the digestive apparatus. The calice is bounded by a thin wall. The corallite is usually divided into sectors by vertical partitions, or *septa*, which are directed towards the centre of the cup, where there is often a *central column*. This may either be a solid rod (*columella*), or formed of numerous parts, and it may project above the floor of the calice. Below this floor are a number of horizontal or curved partitions crossing the corallite; these are the *tabulae*, and represent successive positions of the base of the calice as the animal grew and added to its skeleton. Sometimes, adjacent septa are connected by small, curved, calcareous plates or *dissepiments*, which may be many or few, depending on the type of coral. Some corals show a well-marked groove or *cardinal fossula* in the floor of the calice; this causes the cup to show well-marked bilateral

Didymograptus,
"extensiform" type x1.

Didymograptus
"tuning-fork" type, x1.

Dicellograptus, x1.

Dicranograptus, x1.

Diplograptus, x2.

Climacograptus, x1.

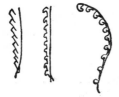

Monograptus, x2.

Rastrites, x3.

197

symmetry, although at first sight, the inpointing septa may give an impression of radial symmetry.

Corals may exist as single individuals, when they are *simple*, or they may be *compound*, when a number of corals are aggregated to form a colony. A colony of corals may (and often does) consist of a very large number of individuals; alternatively, there may be but few individuals and the colony may consist of a simple coral with a number of buds attached to it. The corallite of a simple coral, and the massed corallites of a compound coral form the *corallum*.

The external form is not of great assistance in determining corals; it is necessary to pry deeper into their structure, and here a small double-faced carborundum slip is useful (p. 11), for, by its means, it is easy to make a smooth surface so that both the cross-section and vertical section can be examined by the lens.

Corals at the present day live in salt water; therefore, it may be assumed that beds containing fossil corals in the position of growth are of marine origin.

1.   Coral compound; corallites usually small, tube-like; tabulae numerous; septa absent or few, and represented by spines or ridges .. **Tabulata**   2
       Palaeozoic only.
       Coral, simple or compound; septa plate-like, of two or more sizes
                                        Rugosa or **Scleractinia**   7

2. (*1*) Corallites polygonal, in contact, with mural pores   3
      Corallites rounded, with or without intervening, smaller, polygonal tubes   5

3. (*2*) Corallum discoidal or hemispherical, with a basal *epitheca* (calcareous coating) which frequently develops root-like processes. Corallites rather large; septa represented by peripheral ridges; tabulae irregular and subvesicular   ..   ..   **Michelinia**
      Devonian to Carboniferous, in Britain.
      Corallites small, prismatic; tabulae numerous and horizontal   ..   4

4. (*3*) Corallum generally discoidal or hemispherical; walls thin or only slightly thickened; septa absent or represented by spines   ..   **Favosites**
      Ordovician to Carboniferous (very abundant in Silurian and Devonian).
      Corallum generally branching; walls much thickened near the calices, and hence appearing rounded   ..   ..   **Pachyporinae**
      Silurian to Permian.

5. (*2*) Corallites separated by smaller, polygonal tubes; septa absent or only in the rounded corallites and very short or ridge-like   ..   ..   **Heliolites**
      Abundant from Silurian to Devonian.
      Corallites long, tubular, without smaller, intervening tubes   6

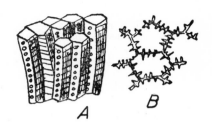

Favosites,

A. Group of corallites to show
   tabulae and mural pores, X2.
B. Section showing spiniform
   septa, X4.

Michelinia,

A. Corallum from above, X1.
B. Corallum from below showing
   epithecal processes, X 2/3.

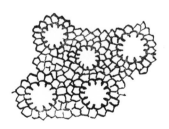

Pachyporinid, X1.

Heliolites, X 3.

6. (*5*) Corallites somewhat sinuous and connected by hollow, tubular
    processes   ..   ..   **Syringopora**
    Llandovery to Carboniferous.

    Corallites laterally compressed and united along their compressed edges
    in single rows (like a tiny string of sausages)   ..   ..   **Halysites**
    Llandeilo to Wenlock Limestone.

7. (*1*) Septa of not more than two alternating sizes, and showing bilateral
    symmetry owing to the presence of a cardinal fossula, which may be
    obscured when the septa are very numerous   ..   ..   **Rugosa**   8
    Palaeozoic only.

    Septa of two or more sizes, with a radial symmetry; no cardinal
    fossula ..   ..   **Scleractinia**   17
    Mesozoic to Recent.

8. (*7*) Coral simple   9
    Coral compound; branched or massive   16

9. (*8*) Shape distinctive; triangular or square   10
    Shape variable; more or less conical or cylindrical   11

10. (*9*) Shape, like the toe of a slipper. Calice deep, extending nearly to the
    apex. Septa feebly developed. Provided with an operculum, which
    is more or less semicircular, easily detached, very thick, and marked
    underneath with a prominent median furrow and fainter lateral septal
    ridges. Root-like processes absent ..   ..   **Calceola**
    Common in Middle Devonian.

    With root-processes   ..   ..   **Rhizophyllum**
    Silurian to Devonian.

    Shape, a four-sided pyramid. Calice deep; septa numerous, thick,
    and very short. Provided with an operculum of four triangular
    pieces which often bear buds ..   ..   **Goniophyllum**
    Silurian.

11. (*9*) No central axial structure   12
    Central axial structure present   14

12. (*11*) Septa do not reach the centre, which is occupied only by tabulae;
    dissepiments present   ..   ..   **Caninia**
    Carboniferous to Permian.

    Septa reach the centre   13

13. (*12*) Shape, cornute or sub-cylindrical; septa numerous, with a well-marked
    cardinal fossula. Dissepiments few or absent   ..   **Cyathaxoniicae**
    Permian.

    Shape generally cylindrical; septa very numerous and long; bilateral
    symmetry not easily seen. Dissepiments very numerous in wide outer
    zone. Sometimes compound, massive   ..   ..   **Palaeosmilia**
    Lower Carboniferous.

Halysites, ✗2.

Syringopora, ✗1.

Calceola, ✗1.

Goniophyllum, ✗1.

Caninia, section, ✗1.

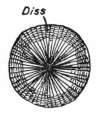

Diss

Palaeosmilia, section, ✗1.

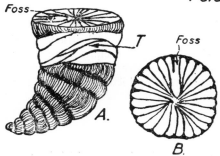

Foss

T

Foss

A.

B.

A. Partly broken to
   show tabulae.

B. Cross section.

Cyathaxoniicae ✗ ⁴/₃

14. (*11*) Central axial structure a tall, solid, styliform columella. Numerous septa and thin tabulae ..   ..   **Cyathaxonia**
Lower Carboniferous.

     Central axial structure not solid, formed of numerous elements ..   15

15. (*14*) Axial column slightly prolonged into the fossula; numerous septa and dissepiments   ..   ..   **Aulophyllum**
Lower Carboniferous.

     Axial column with a median plate; numerous septa and dissepiments   ..   ..   **Dibunophyllum**
Lower Carboniferous.

16. (*8*) A solid, central, laterally-compressed columella in the corallites, which are either rounded, tubular, and not in contact, or polygonal and in contact ..   ..   **Lithostrotion**
Abundant in Carboniferous Limestone.

     Axial column with a structure resembling a spider's web; corallites not in contact and cylindrical, or in contact and polygonal .. **Lonsdaleia**
Common in Carboniferous Limestone.

17. (*7*) Coral simple; shape variable, discoidal, cornute, and cylindrical; septa with granulated sides and upper edges; dissepiments numerous. Well-marked epitheca, which may be lost in weathering .. **Montlivaltia**
Inferior Oolite to Corallian (in England).

     Colony compound   18

18. (*17*) Colony branching, formed of a few individuals, developing out of one. Septa and dissepiments numerous (like those of *Montlivaltia*)
Thecosmilia
Lias to Corallian (in England).

     Corallum massive or branched; corallites contiguous, with polygonal walls. Septa and dissepiments abundant ..   ..   ..   **Isastrea**
Inferior Oolite to Lower Greensand (in England).

ECHINODERMATA

    The Echinodermata include the starfishes and brittle-stars, the crinoids or sea-lilies, and the echinoids or sea-urchins; they are all marine. The great majority of the Echinodermata are characterised by a five-rayed or pentamerous symmetry, which may have bilateral symmetry imposed on it. Only the echinoids and crinoids are referred to in what follows.

ECHINOIDEA

    The hard parts of an echinoid comprise the *test*, which is usually globular, heart-shaped, or discoidal, and the *spines* which, during life, cover the test. After the death of the animal, the spines tend to drop off (since they are held in position by rings of muscles) and

Cyathaxonia
X 2.

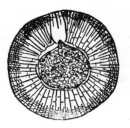

Aulophyllum,
Cross section, X 1.

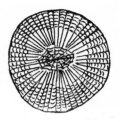

Dibunophyllum,
Cross section, X 1.

B.

A.

Lithostrotion,

C.

A. Group of
  corallites, X 2.

B. Cross section of
  a single corallite,
  X 6.

C. Corallum of the.
  "basaltiform" type
  X 2.

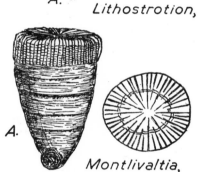

A.

Montlivaltia,
A. Complete corallite, X 1.

Lonsdaleia,
Single corallite,
cross section, X 2.

Thecosmilia, X 1.

Isastrea.
Cross section, X 1½.

therefore seldom remain in contact with the test. Isolated spines are, however, frequently found.

In the great majority of echinoids, the test is made up of five sets of double columns of plates, the plates of one set being pierced near the lateral margins by pairs of pores through which the tube-feet of the animal were connected to the rest of the water-vascular system. These sets are the *ambulacra*; they radiate from the *apical system* of plates, which is situated on the upper (*aboral*) surface of the test, and converge again on the inferior, or *adoral* surface.

The rows of pores on each ambulacrum may diverge rapidly when leaving the apical system and afterwards converge, giving a closed loop; when this occurs, the ambulacra are said to be *petaloid*. If the rows of pores diverge only slightly, the ambulacra are *sub-petaloid*. In the petaloid and sub-petaloid part, the ambulacral plates are low and numerous. The remainder of the ambulacral

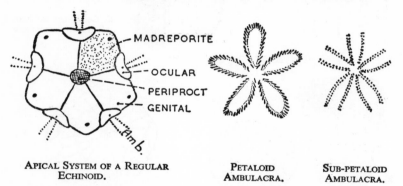

APICAL SYSTEM OF A REGULAR   PETALOID   SUB-PETALOID
            ECHINOID.   AMBULACRA.   AMBULACRA.

areas (mainly on the lower surface of the test) consists of tall plates, few in number, with the pores irregularly developed, or even absent. When the distance between the rows of pores increases uniformly and slowly, in passing from the apical system to the periphery of the test, and when the pores are as well developed on the under as on the upper surface of the test, the ambulacra are *simple*.

Between the ambulacra are the *interambulacra*. Both sets of plates may bear *tubercles* and spines; those of the interambulacra are commonly, though not invariably larger than those of the ambulacra.

There are two apertures in the test. Beneath, is the mouth, which is surrounded by a muscular membrane which decays after death, leaving an opening, the *peristome*. The peristome is always situated at the point of convergence of the ambulacra. The other orifice is the *periproct*; during life, this was occupied by the anus which is surrounded by a ring of tiny plates, supported by a

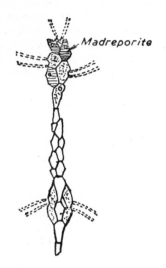

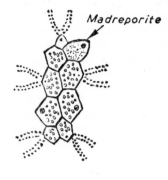

Echinocorys

Collyrites

Apical Systems of Two Irregular Echinoids.
Much Enlarged.

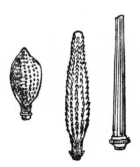

Types of Echinoid Spines.

membrane which, when removed by decay, leaves an opening larger than the anus itself. The periproct may be on the upper or the under surface of the test. It may be within the apical system, when the echinoid is one of the *Regularia*. If not within the apical system, the periproct is behind it, and the echinoid belongs to the *Irregularia*.

In the Regularia, the apical system is relatively large and consists generally of ten plates; five of these are comparatively large and are termed *genitals*, since each is perforated by a genital pore. The anterior right genital plate is pierced by numerous pores; this is the *madreporite* and serves as an inlet for water to the internal system of canals which supply the tube-feet. The smaller plates are known as *oculars*, and each has a perforation which contains an organ sensitive to light. The oculars are at the ends of the ambulacra, while the genitals stand at the heads of the interambs.

In the Irregularia, the apical system is usually smaller and more compact than in the Regularia; furthermore, the plates may be drawn out into a lineal series, as a result of which the three anterior ambulacra (*trivium*) are separated from the point of origin of the two posterior ambulacra (or *bivium*).

1. Periproct situated within the apical disc; peristome central. Spines and spine-bases (tubercles) generally large ..   ..   ..   **Regularia**   2

    Symmetry bilateral, imposed on pentamerous. Periproct outside the apical system; peristome may or may not be central ..   **Irregularia**   7

2. (*1*) Tubercles large on interambulacra; small on ambulacra   3

    Tubercles on ambulacra and interambulacra approximately equal in size   6

3. (*2*) Apical system has a large extra sur-anal plate; thus there are 11 plates instead of the usual 10   4

    Apical system with the normal 10 plates   5

4. (*3*) Test small, globose or depressed. Periproct on the right of a median line joining the anterior and posterior margins of the test. Tubercles imperforate   ..   ..   **Salenia**
    Cretaceous

    Test depressed. Genital plates large, the posterior smaller than the anterior. Periproct situated on the median line. Tubercles perforate ..   ..   **Acrosalenia**
    Lias to Lower Cretaceous.

5. (*3*) Test spheroidal, with flattened base. Ambulacra widen on passing downwards from the apical system. Interambs wider than the ambs on the upper surface, where the interambulacral tubercles are specially large; two rows of tubercles on the interambs. Peristome large, with ten notches round the periphery   ..   ..   **Hemicidaris**
    Inferior Oolite to Upper Cretaceous.

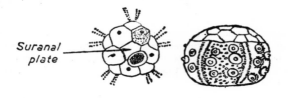

Suranal
plate

Salenia, ✗1.

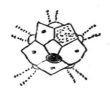

Acrosalenia, apical system, ✗1.

Hemicidaris, ✗2/3.

Cidaris, ✗2/3.

Test spheroidal, summit and base equally flattened. Apical disc large, hence rarely preserved. Ambulacra narrow and uniform in width; more or less undulating. Two rows of large, perforated tubercles on interambs. Peristome large, without notches .. **Cidaris** (*Sensu lato*) Jurassic and Cretaceous.

6. (2) Ambulacra considerably narrower than interambs. Ambulacral pores biserial near apical system, becoming uniserial towards the circumference. Ambulacra bear two convergent columns of perforate tubercles. On the interambs, the columns of tubercles are nearly parallel .. **Diplopodia** Rhaetic to Lower Chalk.

Test depressed. In each ambulacral or interambulacral area there are two principal series of sub-equal, imperforate tubercles, while there are sometimes series of secondary tubercles in the interambs. Each ambulacral plate may consist of 4, 5, or 6 fused plates, with the same number of pores .. .. **Phymosoma** [*Cyphosoma*] Upper Jurassic to Chalk.

7. (1) Peristome approaches a central position 8
Mouth towards anterior border 14

8. (7) Test lofty 9
Test depressed 10

9. (8) Test conical or almost hemispherical; inferior surface flat; outline pentagonal or oval. Ambulacra narrow and straight. Interambs with broad plates. Tubercles very small. Peristome small; periproct marginal or sub-marginal .. .. .. **Conulus** [*Echinoconus*] Upper Greensand to Upper Chalk.

Test hemispherical; inferior surface flat. Interambs with distinct median sutures and small perforate and crenulate tubercles. On the base of the interior are ten vertical plates extending from the margin of the test to the peristome, places on each side of the interambs. On casts the traces of these plates appear as deep grooves .. **Discoides** Cretaceous.

10. (8) The two posterior ambulacra are separated by a long chain of apical plates from the three anterior ambulacra. Periproct on the posterior end, or at the posterior margin of the test .. .. **Collyrites** Middle and Upper Jurassic.

Apical system compact; anterior trivium not separated from posterior bivium 11

11. (10) The periproct is marginal or beneath the test, which is hemispherical with a concave base. The ambs are narrow; widest at margin of test. Interambs or rather large plates, bearing perforate tubercles. Peristome notched .. .. **Holectypus** Upper Lias to Cretaceous.

Periproct on upper surface of test 12

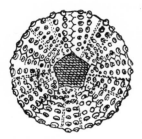

Diplopodia, x 2/3.

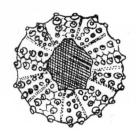

Phymosoma, x 2/3.

Conulus, x 2/3.

Discoides, x 2/3.

Collyrites, x1.

Holectypus, x 2/3.

210 THE ELEMENTS OF FIELD GEOLOGY

12. (*11*) Test sub-circular or sub-quadrangular, truncated and broadest posteriorly; inferior surface concave. Ambulacra petaloid, all the petals being the same shape. Ambulacral pores in two series; the outer slits, the inner round. Periproct not in contact with the apical system, but lies in a posterior groove that extends from the apical system to the margin of the test   ..   **Nucleolites** [*Echinobrissus*] Inferior Oolite to Lower Chalk.

Test large or moderate, with circular or pentagonal outline   ..   13

13. (*12*) Test has a slight posterior notch; base flat or concave. Ambulacra sub-petaloid and, on the upper surface, all similar; on the lower surface, the ambulacra form grooves. Ambulacral pores biserial, those in the outer rows are slits, the inner are circular. Periproct close to the apical system, and lies at the top of a narrow posterior groove ..   **Clypeus** Inferior Oolite to Corallian.

Shape tends to pentagonal. Ambulacra wide at margin of test. Interambs with perforate tubercles. Periproct immediately in rear of apical system; broad in front, narrower in rear   ..   ..   **Pygaster** Jurassic and Cretaceous.

14. (*7*) Test generally lofty; outline oval; base flattened. Apical system elongated, resulting in a tendency to separate the three anterior ambs from the two posterior. Each pair of ambulacral pores is almost in the middle of an ambulacral plate. Periproct oval, just below the posterior margin of the test. Peristome oval, broader than long   ..   ..   **Echinocorys** Abundant in Upper Chalk.

Test somewhat depressed; outline more or less heart-shaped, having an anterior groove on the upper surface   15

15. (*14*) Ambulacra sub-petaloid, situated in sunken areas, the sub-petaloid parts of the two anterior lateral being longer than those of the posterior. Anterior ambulacrum in a deep groove, with its pores circular. Interambs with large plates; tubercles small, perforate, and crenulate; on the inferior surface, the posterior interamb bulges, forming a *plastron*. Beneath the periproct is a narrow ring, which, although it appears smooth, is covered with very fine granules, the *fasciole*. Peristome near anterior border, with a projecting lip   ..   ..   ..   **Micraster** Middle and Upper Chalk.

Ambulacra large, simple; not in sunken areas   16

16. (*15*) Anterior groove on superior surface broad and shallow, containing the anterior ambulacrum. Peristome near anterior margin, elliptical. Periproct supra-marginal. Apical disc elongate, the two pairs of genital plates separated by two oculars   ..   ..   **Holaster** Upper Greensand and Chalk.

Anterior groove deeper than in *Holaster*, with an angular margin. Apical disc similar to that of *Holaster*. Periproct oval, in a depression in the truncated posterior face. A more or less complete fasciole beneath the periproct ..   ..   **Cardiaster** Upper Cretaceous.

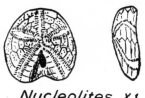

Nucleolites. x1.

Clypeus, x1/3.

Pygaster, x2/3.

Fasciole

Micraster, x1/2.

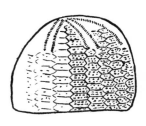 

Echinocorys, x1/2.

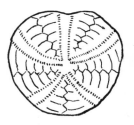 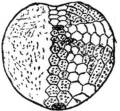

Holaster x2/3.

CRINOIDEA

Crinoids are almost invariably fixed forms; they include the sea-lilies and feather-stars. A crinoid generally consists of a *stem*, a *calyx*, and movable *arms*, which proceed from the margin of the calyx. In those few crinoids which are free-swimming, there is no stem. The stem, calyx, and arms are all made up of a number of pieces, with the result that fossil crinoids are generally found in a fragmentary condition. Crinoids and their remains are frequently found in such profusion that whole beds of limestone may consist of but little else (*crinoidal limestone*).

The stem consists of a number of bead-like *ossicles* or *columnals* which are round, oval, pentagonal, or squarish in plan; the articular surfaces are generally marked by radial grooves. The columnals are pierced by a central hole which is generally filled with the matrix in which the remains occur.

The calyx is formed of rings of hexagonal or pentagonal plates, usually five per ring. The arms consist of ossicles which resemble those of the stem; the arms may be simple or they may branch repeatedly.

The portions most commonly found are the more or less cylindrical ossicles* of the stem, sometimes singly, but often a number are in contact with one another, forming continuous lengths of six inches or a foot. Lengths of fossil crinoid stems are sometimes described by quarrymen as *fossil screws*. Pentagonal and hexagonal plates of the stemless crinoid *Marsupites* are not uncommon in the appropriate zone of the Upper Chalk.

BRACHIOPODA

The brachiopoda are sessile, marine animals, enclosed in a shell of two unequal valves, each of which is bilaterally symmetrical. The animal usually attaches itself by a muscular *pedicle*, which passes through an opening in the larger (or *pedicle*) valve, which is ventral, or, more rarely the shell is supported by spines which grow on its exterior.

Within the shell of the living animal are the fleshy *brachia*, often spirally coiled, which act as a food-collecting apparatus. These may be supported by calcareous *spiralia*, or by a short or long shelly loop which is attached to the posterior part of the *brachial* (dorsal) valve. The internal structure of a brachiopod is of great importance as a means of classification; it can sometimes be seen when the shell is broken open, or preserved as an internal cast. The presence of internal structures can be established by treating the shell with dilute hydrochloric acid or by grinding it down on a carborundum slip.

---

* The ossicles are sometimes pentagonal, as in *Isocrinus*.

x 2

A Derbyshire 'Screw.' Five Stem-Ossicles of a Crinoid.
Carboniferous Limestone, Ashover, Derbyshire.

Isocrinus, x4.   *Bourgueticrinus,* x4.

Stem-Ossicles of Crinoidea.

x 1.   *x 2/3.*

Upper Part of Stem and   **Calyx of Marsupites.**
Calyx of Apiocrinus.   **Chalk.**
Jurassic.

The valves of most brachiopods open and close by means of a hinge consisting of teeth in the pedicle-valve, which fit into sockets in the brachial valve.   The teeth may be supported by *dental lamellae*, often seen through the shell as two more or less diverging plates. Muscles which assist in opening and closing the shell, usually leave scars in the interior of the two valves, and show on internal casts.

Between the beaks or *umbones* of the two valves and the hinge-line there is often a flat or concave area on each valve, known as the *inter area*.

1.   Valves not connected by a hinge   2

   Valves connected by a hinge   4

2. (*1*) Pedicle passes out between the two valves. Shell thin, nearly equivalve, elongated oval, or quadrilateral. Horny; generally black and shining. Surface generally smooth, or with fine concentric or radial lines   ..   ..   **Lingula**
Silurian to Recent.

   Note.—Lingulella (Cambrian to Ordovician) is practically indistinguishable from *Lingula*, but has a furrow in the pedicle-valve for the pedicle.

   Shell somewhat rounded in plan.   Pedicle (if any) passes out through a slit in one valve   3

3. (*2*) Pedicle-valve flattened; pedicle passes out through a narrow slit. Brachial valve conical, with eccentric apex. Both valves horny and phosphatic, and marked with concentric lines of growth   **Orbiculoidea**
Ordovician to Permian.

   Shell calcareous; quadrangular or sub-circular, smooth or with radiating costae. Attachment by cementation of the lower valve; no pedicle. Upper valve conical. Both valves with two large muscle-scars posteriorly ..   ..   **Crania**
Cretaceous to Recent.

4. (*1*) Hinge-line long   5

   Hinge-line short   11

5. (*4*) Both valves convex; calcareous spiralia in interior of shell   6

   One valve convex, the other concave; without spiralia   8

6. (*5*) Pedicle-valve has a lofty cardinal area, in which there is a narrow triangular area perforated by a foramen for the emission of the pedicle. Apices of spiralia directed laterally.   In the pedicle-valve, there are two well-marked dental plates which remain separate   ..   ..   **Cyrtia**
Silurian to Devonian.

   Very similar to *Cyrtia*, but the dental plates in the pedicle-valve unite with the internal septum. Shell punctate   ..   ..   ..   **Cyrtinid**
Silurian to Carboniferous.

   Flat area on pedicle-valve expanded laterally   7

Orbiculoidea,
X 1.

Lingula, X 1.

Crania, X 1½.

Cyrtia, X 1½.

Cyrtinid, X 2/3

Spirifer,
(Partly broken to show spiralia)
X 1.

Orthis, X 2/3.

Resserella, X1.

7. (6) Pedicle-valve with prominent sharp beak, very commonly bent over. Cardinal area on both valves. Shell striated or plicated radially, with concentric lines of growth crossing the striations. Commonly with a median fold in brachial valve, with a corresponding furrow on pedicle-valve. Hinge-line often produced into ear-like expansions of the valves just below it. Apices of spiralia, directed laterally. Dental plates developed. Shell usually impunctate .. .. **Spiriferacea** Silurian to Permian.

   As above: shell punctate. High median septum in pedicle-valve
   Trias to Lias. **Spiriferina**

8. (5) Shell with spine-bases along edge, or scattered over shell 10

    Shell not spinose 9

9. (8) Shell sub-quadrate to sub-circular, ornamented by strong, sharp ribs which may bifurcate. Hinge usually slightly shorter than maximum width of shell. Pedicle valve convex; brachial valve may be flat or slightly concave. Impunctate .. .. **Orthacea**

    Similar to above, but costation delicate. Shell punctate **Resserella** Silurian.

    Similar to above, but convexity of valves reversed .. **Schizophoria** Silurian to Permian.

    Shell small, bilobed, coarsely punctate. Pedicle-valve much more convex than brachial, both with a deep median fold and ornamented with fine ribs .. .. **Dicoelosia** Upper Ordovician to Middle Devonian.

    Shell semi-oval or nearly quadrangular; marked with rather prominent, concentric ribs and radial costae. Where the ribs cease, the valves bend over abruptly, almost at right angles, the brachial valve being within the bend. Two strong, peg-like divergent teeth in pedicle-valve. **Leptaena** Ordovician to Devonian, with similar forms in the Carboniferous.

    In *Strophomena* (Ordovician and Silurian) and *Strophonella* (Silurian and Devonian), the pedicle-valve is concave, and the brachial valve convex. *Strophonella* has a denticulate hinge internally.

10. (8) Shell often small and delicate, transversely elongate or semicircular; ornamented by fine radial striations. Well-marked cardinal areas, that of the pedicle valve carrying long spines, which are generally broken off but whose bases can be seen with the aid of a lens. Pseudo-punctate .. .. **Chonetidae** Silurian to Carboniferous

    Shell quadrate; sometimes prolonged laterally into "wings". Pedicle-valve strongly convex; brachial valve concave or flat. Beak curved over; no foramen. Surface generally marked by more or less prominent radial costae and concentric ribs. Spines irregularly scattered or in concentric rows; usually preserved as spine-bases only. May attain large dimensions .. .. **Productacea** Devonian to Permian.

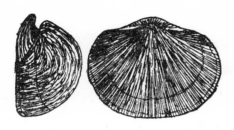

Schizophoria, x 1.

Dicoelosia, x 2.

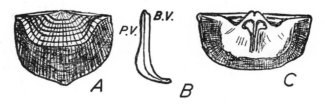

Leptaena, x 1.

A. *Pedicle valve.*   B. *Section.*
C. *Interior of brachial valve to show muscle scars.*

Chonetid x 1½.
(Rugosochonetes)

Reticulariacea, x 1.

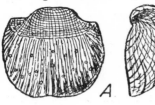

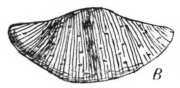

Dictyoclostus Productaceans
semireticulatus x ⅔

Semiplanus latissimus
B. x 1/4

11. (*4*) Shell lamellose or with concentric rows of spines; calcareous spirals internally 12

Shell with radial costae or plications; brachial valve more convex than pedicle-valve 13

Shell smooth or anteriorly plicated 14

Shell biconvex, smooth or costate, with internal septa and plates in each valve, along which the shell tends to split 15

12. (*11*) Shell biconvex, sub-circular, ornamented with concentric rows of spines, which are often double-barrelled. Calcareous spirals directed laterally. Dental plates developed; often a median septum in pedicle-valve .. .. **Reticulariacea** Devonian to Permian.

Brachial valve more convex than pedicle-valve. Spiralia with apices directed towards centre of brachial valve. Ornament of radiating costae and concentric lamellae .. .. **Atrypa** Silurian and Devonian.

Shell ornamented with concentric lamellae or spines born on lamellae; spirals directed laterally .. .. **Athyris** Devonian to Trias.

13. (*11*) Shell usually with well-marked radial costation, impunctate. Anterior margin arched by a well-defined dorsal fold and ventral sinus and notched. Brachial valve more convex than pedicle-valve. No spiralia. Dental plates developed, and sometime a median septum .. .. **Rhynchonellacea** Silurian to Recent. Common in Jurassic and Cretaceous.

Some *Terebratellaceans* may, on account of their radiating costae and plicated margin, be confused with *Rhynchonella*. The shell, however, is punctate, and internally a (sometimes complex) long loop, occurs in the brachial valve, and two dental plates are found in the pedicle-valve.

14. (*11*) Shape like *Rhynchonella*; surface sometimes smooth, with anterior plications. Frontal margin much elevated, and often pointed (acuminate). Dental plates present, but no dorsal median septum .. **Pugnax** Devonian and Carboniferous.

Side-view of shell resembles that of a Roman lamp. Beak of pedicle-valve well-marked and pierced at apex by a foramen. No dental lamellae; internal calcareous loop. Punctate **Terebratulidina** Devonian to Recent.

Shape resembles a wide *Terebratula*, but with a smaller foramen, and impunctate. Internal calcareous spiralia, a dorsal median plate and dental plates present .. .. **Meristina** Silurian and Devonian.

15. (*11*) Both valves convex, shallow; no fold or sinus. Shape elongate oval; smooth. Transverse sections show two divergent plates and low median septum in brachial valve. Two plates fused together, supported by a high septum in pedicle-valve .. .. .. **Pentamerus** Silurian.

Atrypa, x *1.*

Athyris,
(*Partly broken
to show spiralia.*)
x 2/3.

Rhynchonellid. x *1.*

Pugnax, x *1.*

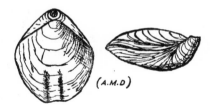

(A.M.D)

Terebratulid, x *1.*

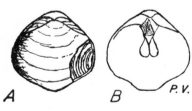

A   *B*   P.V.

A.   *Partly broken to
     show spiralia.*

B.   *Interior of pedicle
     valve, to show
     muscle scars.*

Meristina, x 2/3.

Both valves inflated; beaks incurved; no fold or sinus. Ornament of radiating costae. Arrangement of internal plates as in *Pentamerus* .. .. **Conchidium** Silurian.

Median fold and sinus developed. Shell smooth, becoming costate. Two plates in brachial valve, forming a V-shaped figure; no septum. Septum supporting fused plates near beak only in pedicle-valve .. .. **Sieberella** Silurian and Devonian.

BIVALVIA

The Bivalvia are marine and freshwater molluscs enclosed in two-valve shells; externally, the valves are usually mirror images of each other, and joined along a hinge-line, and they are generally (though not always) inequilateral. The valves are left and right, and the beak or *umbo* above the hinge usually points forward.

Along the hinge are usually a number of projections known as *teeth*; the teeth alternate in the two valves, those of one valve fitting into depressions between those in the other valve. When the whole hinge-margin has a number of short transverse teeth, the shell is said to be *taxodont*. Sometimes, just below the umbo, there are from one to three diverging teeth which are known as *cardinal teeth*. In addition, there may be other teeth more distant from the umbo and nearly parallel with the line of the hinge; these are the *laterals*.

In some genera in which the hinge-line is straight (e.g. *Arca*), there is a flattened triangular part of the shell between the hinge-line and the umbo of each valve; this is the *area*, and when present, the umbones are widely separated. Sometimes there is an oval, depressed area (the *lunule*) bounded by a groove in front of the umbones. A similar but larger area may occur behind the umbones; this is known as the *escutcheon*.

If the interior of a valve be examined, a curved line will be observed parallel with the lower edge of the shell; this is the *pallial line*. At the posterior end, the pallial line is sometimes indented, forming a *pallial sinus*, and the shell is said to be *sinupalliate*; if there is no sinus, the shell is *integripalliate*.

At the ends of the pallial line will be found two round, oval, or elongated depressions; these are the scars of the *adductor* muscles which serve to close the shell during life. Sometimes there is only one scar; this is always that of the posterior adductor. Shells are *monomyarian* or *dimyarian*, according as there are one or two scars.

The shell was opened by means of a *ligament* which was sometimes external and at other times internal. When the animal died, the

Pentamerus, x 1/2.

Conchidium, x 2/3.

Sieberella, x 2/3.

tension on the adductor muscles was relaxed, the springy ligament took control, and the shell opened. When the ligament decayed, the two valves generally became separated; therefore, bivalves are often found fossil as separate valves, in contrast to the brachiopods where the valves are often found together and tightly closed.

The number and arrangement of the teeth, the number of muscle scars, the presence or absence of a pallial sinus, and the pits which held the ligament are important diagnostic characters in identifying bivalves.

1.   The hinge is produced at one or both ends into *wings* or *ears* 23

       Hinge without wings or ears   2

2. (*1*) Shell markedly inequivalve   29

       Shell nearly or quite equivalve   3

3. (*2*) Taxodont teeth   4

       Teeth not taxodont, or absent   6

4. (*3*) Hinge-line long and straight, with numerous small, similar transverse teeth. Umbones prominent and widely separated by extensive areas which carry numerous grooves in the shape of inverted **V**'s. Surface with radiating ribs and concentric striae. Pallial line without sinus   **Arca** Jurassic to Recent.

       Hinge not straight   5

5. (*4*) Shell rounded, thick, and solid. Surface smooth or radially striated. Hinge-line arched or semicircular with numerous small, strong transverse teeth which, towards the ends of the rows tend to become horizontal. Umbones separated by areas with a number of ligament-pits like inverted **V**'s. Margins of shell crenulate inside..   .. **Glycymeris** [*Pectunculus*] Cretaceous to Recent.

       Shell small; oval or triangular. Posterior end very short; umbones directed towards the rear. Surface smooth or with fine radial lines. Hinge-line angular, with a median internal triangular ligament-pit between the two sets of numerous, sharp teeth. Interior nacreous. Surface smooth or with fine radial lines. Pallial line simple..   **Nuculid** Ordovician to Recent.

       Similar, but with a slight pallial sinus. Posterior end produced and pointed, giving a more central umbo than in *Nucula* ..   **Nuculanid** Devonian to Recent.

6. (*3*) The shell is integripalliate   7

       The shell is sinupalliate   19

7. (*6*) The surface of the shell is ornamented with radial ribs or with tubercles   8

       Ornament of concentric ribs or folds, or surface is smooth 10

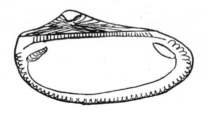

Arca, ×1.

Glycymeris, ×1.

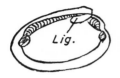

Nuculid, ×1.

Nuculanid, ×1.

Lig.

8. (*7*) Shell is only slightly inequilateral, heart-shaped or oval. Ribs are often spiny. Margins of valves crenulated. Right valve has one or two peg-like cardinal teeth; left valve has two similar cardinals. Lateral teeth are short and well separated from the prominent umbones   ..   ..   **Cardium** Miocene to Recent.

Similar to above, but with radial ribbing only on posterior part of shell; the remainder with concentric ribbing   ..   ..   **Protocardia** Trias to Cretaceous.

Shell highly inequilateral   9

9. (*8*) Shell thick and heavy; trigonally ovate; inner border notched. Umbones far forward. Right valve with two oblique cardinal teeth; left valve with diverging cardinal teeth   ..   ..   ..   **Cardita** Paleocene to Recent.

Shell thick, usually ornamented with concentric rows or tubercles or with ribs. Anterior margin rounded; posterior produced and angular. Generally, there is a ridge, extending from the umbones to the posterior border, cutting off a portion which is differently ornamented. Teeth strong and grooved; in the right valve, two teeth diverge from beneath the umbo; in the left, three teeth, the central being bifid, the posterior (near the hinge-margin) very thin. Muscle-scars deep, the anterior smaller than the posterior, and placed near the umbones ..   **Trigonia** Trias to Cretaceous; abundant and widely distributed in Jurassic and Cretaceous.

10. (*7*) Shell obliquely elongated; umbones terminal, or nearly so. Scar of posterior adductor large; that of anterior adductor small or absent   11

Shape not obliquely elongated. Muscle-scars more or less equal..   15

11. (*10*) Shape acutely triangular; valves keeled, truncated, and gaping posteriorly. Shell thin, with nacreous inner layer. Umbones sharp and terminal. Hinge-line long, without teeth. Ligament long and narrow, in a groove. Posterior adductor nearly central; anterior adductor close to the umbo   ..   ..   **Pinna** Carboniferous to Recent.

The shell is not triangular in shape   12

12. (*11*) Numerous ligament-pits, perpendicular to the line of the hinge ..   13

Ligament lies parallel to the line of the hinge   14

13. (*12*) Shell rhomboidal, sub-quadrate, or sub-circular. No teeth. Ligament-pits closely spaced   ..   ..   **Isognomon [*Perna*]** Triassic to Recent.

Ligament-pits widely separated. Two or more oblique ridge-like teeth. Slightly inequivalve   ..   ..   **Gervillia** Triassic to Eocene.

14. (*12*) Shape sub-triangular; posterior border rounded. Umbones sharp, pointed, terminal. Teeth small or absent. Small anterior muscle-scar near umbo   ..   ..   **Mytilus** Jurassic to Recent.

Cardium, × 2/3.

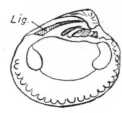

Cardita, × 1/2.

Trigonia, × 2/3.

Pinna, × 1/4.

Isognomon, × 1/3.

Gervillia, × 1/3.

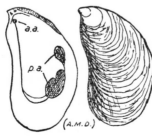

Mytilus, × 1/3.

Shell oblong; inflated in front. Umbones obtuse, anterior, but not terminal. There is often a broad depression running from the umbones to the posterior margin. Anterior muscle-scar near umbo .. .. **Modiolus**
Devonian to Recent; maximum in Jurassic.

15. (*10*) Outline of shell circular to sub-circular 16

Outline not circular or sub-circular 18

16. (*15*) Umbones not prominent; distinct lunule. An oblique furrow extends from the umbo to the posterior border. Hinge usually with two cardinal and one or two lateral teeth in each valve; the lateral or the cardinal may be absent. Ligament elongated, external, sometimes sunk in a groove. Anterior adductor impression elongated, and situated *mainly within the pallial line*; posterior scar oval.. **Lucina**
Cretaceous to Recent.

Umbones prominent 17

17. (*16*) Margins of valves always smooth. Umbones curved forward; lunule seldom present. Prominent external ligament. Right valve with a very small anterior lateral tooth, two triangular cardinals, an oblique posterior cardinal, and a posterior lateral. Left valve with a small anterior lateral, a vertical cardinal, and a long oblique posterior cardinal. Adductor impressions oval .. .. .. **Arctica**
Cretaceous to Recent.

Umbones prominent, triangular. Shell thick. Lunule distinct; escutcheon elongated. Ligament external. Right valve with a stout vertical cardinal, and a very small cardinal on each side; anterior lateral small. Left valve with two diverging cardinals, and a small posterior lateral. Adductor impressions strongly marked; above the anterior one is a pedal impression .. .. .. **Astarte**
Jurassic to Recent.

18. (*15*) Shell solid, oblong, or sub-trigonal, truncated behind; distinct lunule and escutcheon. Margins of valves may be crenulated. Umbones small and close together. Two (sometimes three) cardinal teeth and some small laterals. Well-marked internal ligament-pit beneath the umbo, and pedal scar above anterior adductor .. .. **Crassatella**
Cretaceous to Miocene.

Shell trigonal, oval, or oblong; thick and compressed; surface with rather widely-spaced overlapping folds. Umbones small, sharp, and closely set. Cardinal teeth small or absent; one anterior lateral in right valve; one posterior lateral in left valve. Anterior muscle-scar very deep .. .. **Cardinia**
Trias and Lias.

Shell heart-shaped, oval, or trigonal; umbones often corroded. Usually three cardinal teeth, one anterior and one posterior lateral in each valve. Ligament prominent, external. Margins of valves smooth. Pallial line sometimes shows a very shallow sinus .. .. .. **Corbicula**
Cretaceous to Recent. Lives in fresh and brackish water.

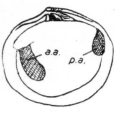

Lucina, x1.

Modiolus, x1.

Arctica, x 1/3.

Astarte, x1.

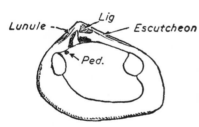

Crassatella, x 2/3.

Cardinia, x 1/2.

19. (*6*) Umbones nearly central; shell is therefore nearly equilateral   ..   20

Umbones far forward; shell markedly inequilateral   21

20. (*19*) Shell oval, trigonal; surface smooth or with concentric striae. Pallial sinus round or angular, rather shallow. One cardinal tooth, which is bifid, in each valve; behind it, and under the umbo, a triangular pit which marks the position of the internal ligament. A second lamellar cardinal tooth is sometimes present. Anterior and posterior laterals well marked; those of the right valve consist of two parallel ridges running along the hinge-line ..   ..   **Mactra**
Eocene to Recent.

Shape, a rather long oval; compressed; concentrically marked. Pallial sinus very broad and deep. Two cardinal teeth (one bifid) in each valve, and one anterior and one posterior lateral. Ligament external, prominent   ..   ..   **Tellina**
Cretaceous to Recent.

21. (*19*) Shell very thin; nacreous internally; gaping at posterior end. Internal casts common; owing to the thinness of the shell, the ornament is shown by the cast. Shape oblong or oval, inflated. Surface ornamented with numerous oblique, slightly-curved, radiating ribs, which are often absent from the posterior region, and with more delicate concentric lines   ..   ..   **Pholadomya**
Trias to Recent; widespread and abundant in the Mesozoic.

Similar to the above, but surface smooth or ornamented with fine granules   ..   ..   **Homomya**
Triassic to Jurassic.

Shell thick   22

22. (*21*) Oval, convex, ornamented with concentric lamellae, sometimes with radial ribs. Lunule distinct. Margins of valves finely crenulate. Hinge-plate wide. Three cardinal teeth in each valve; no laterals. Pallial sinus short and angular   ..   ..   **Venus**
Oligocene to Recent.

Ovate, sub-trigonal, convex. Surface smooth or with concentric ornament. Lunule well marked. Margins of valves not crenulate. Hinge thick, with three cardinal teeth in each valve, two anterior lateral in right and one in left valve. Pallial sinus angular   **Meretricinae**
Cretaceous to Recent.

23. (*1*) The shell is nearly equilateral   24

Shell markedly inequilateral   26

24. (*23*) The ears are small, the surface of the shell is marked by radial ribs which bear spines on the right valve. Form fairly regular, rounded ventrally; more acute towards umbones, which are separated somewhat. Two cardinal teeth in each valve, with cartilage-pit between them   ..   ..   **Spondylus**
Jurassic to Recent.

Ears well marked   25

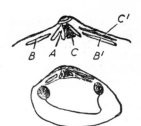

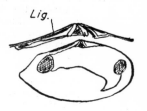

Corbicula,
x 1.

Mactra, x 2/3.

A. Bifid cardinal.
B,B! Anterior and
posterior lateral teeth.
C,C! Interior and
exterior ligaments.

Tellina,
x 1.

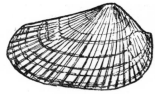

x 1.   **Pholadomya,**   x 2/3.

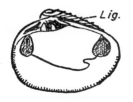

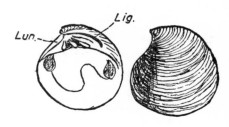

Meretricinae, x 2/3.

Venus, x 2/3.

25. (24) Right valve very convex; left flattened. Almost semicircular ventrally, the border becoming straighter towards the pointed umbones. Generally radially ribbed, sometimes very delicately, but commonly on a bold and regular scale. Triangular cartilage-pit beneath each umbo, and three or four lamellar teeth on each side of the pit .. .. **Pecten**
Eocene to Recent.

Shell ovate or trigonal, nearly equivalve. Surface with radial ribs. The anterior ear larger than the posterior, with a deep notch under that of the right valve .. .. **Chlamys**
Triassic to Recent.

26. (23) The hinge-line is short. Ears small. Shell thin, equivalve, obliquely oval, with pointed umbones, which are separated from each other. Hinge-line without teeth. On each valve, there is a triangular area with a central ligament-pit .. .. **Lima**
Jurassic to Recent: maximum in Mesozoic.

Hinge long 27

27. (26) Both ears are well marked, the posterior longer than the anterior. Beneath the right anterior ear there is a notch. Shell oblique; inequivalve. One small tooth in each valve, and a long lamellar posterior tooth in the right valve. Commonly with concentric ornament
Pteria [*Avicula*]
Trias to Recent.

One of the ears is not well marked 28

28. (27) Shell ovate; right valve less convex than the left. Posterior ear not well marked. Hinge margin with narrow, nearly parallel grooves and a median pit for the internal ligament. Surface with radial ribs and concentric lines, the ornament being the same on both valves .. .. **Dunbarella**
Carboniferous.

Shell oval, left valve large and very convex; right valve flattened. Anterior ear small or rudimentary .. .. .. **Meleagrinella**
Trias to Jurassic.

29. (2) The shell is dimyarian, and the hinge-line carries teeth 30

Shell monomyarian; without teeth, with ligament-pits 31

30. (29) Shell irregular, thick, and nearly circular. Umbones twisted. Surface with concentric lamellae or spines. Pallial line without sinus. During life the shell was attached by the larger and deeper valve. One stout cardinal tooth, the other teeth small .. .. **Chama**
Paleocene to Recent.

Shell small, rounded anteriorly, somewhat angular and contracted posteriorly. Right valve much larger and more convex than the left. Surface generally ornamented by concentric grooves. Strong cardinal tooth in right valve, and behind it, a notch. Left valve has a spoon-like process for the attachment of a ligament. Slightly sinupalliate .. .. **Corbula**
Cretaceous to Recent; especially Cainozoic.

Spondylus, x 2/3.

Pecten, x 1/2.

Chlamys, x 2/3

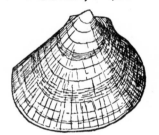

Lima, x 2/3.

Pteria, x 1½.

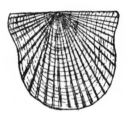

Dunbarella,
x 1.

Meleagrinella
x 2.

Left valve.

Right valve,
Exterior.

Chama, x 1.

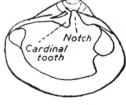

Corbula, x 3.

31. (*29*) Hinge-line usually long, with numerous, parallel, closely-spaced ligament-pits. Umbones frequently prominent. Form very variable. Surface with concentric or (rarely) radiating furrows. Outer layer of shell thick and formed of large prisms of calcite ..   **Inoceramus** Lias to Chalk; common in Upper Cretaceous.

Hinge-line short; a triangular ligament-pit beneath the umbo .. 32

32. (*31*) Left valve large and convex, with a prominent incurved umbo; right valve flattened or concave ..   .. **Gryphaea** Mainly Jurassic; occasionally Cretaceous and Eocene.

Shell with lamellar structure, shape irregular. Left valve convex, often with radiating ribs or striae; umbo neither incurved nor twisted. Right valve flat or concave, often smooth ..   ..   .. **Ostrea** Triassic to Recent.

Similar to above; umbones twisted, directed posteriorly .. **Exogyra** Middle Jurassic to Chalk.

GASTROPODA

The gastropoda are mollusca, characterised by univalve shells, generally coiled in a spiral, which is generally right-handed (*i.e.* when the apex is uppermost, and the mouth towards the observer, the mouth is to the right), but occasionally a simple cone, with no evident indication of coiling. Whereas the other classes of mollusca inhabit salt and fresh water, the gastropoda also live on dry land.

Although gastropods are known from all geological systems, they became abundant only in the Cainozoic; and from the Eocene to the present day, the gastropods and bivalves form the main constituents of the fossil invertebrate fauna.

The shell of a gastropod generally consists of a number of *whorls*, which are in contact with one another at the *suture-line*, and which increase in size from the *apex* of the shell (at the posterior end) to the *aperture*, which is anterior. All the whorls, except the last, make up the *spire* of the shell.

The shape of the spire varies greatly; it may be made up of many or few whorls; it may be elongated, short, or depressed. The *apical angle* may be acute or obtuse. The inner parts of the whorls may coalesce and form an axial pillar, or *columella* which extends from the apex to the base of the shell. Sometimes there is a hole extending from the base of the shell towards the apex, this is the *umbilicus*.

The shape of the aperture varies considerably; the margin may be uninterrupted (*holostomatous*), or it may be interrupted by a notch, or prolonged anteriorly or posteriorly into a canal or canals; the aperture is then said to be *siphonostomatous*.

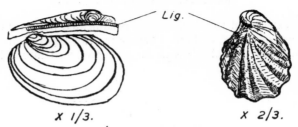

Inoceramus.

x 1/3.　　　　x 2/3.

Gryphaea, x 2/3.

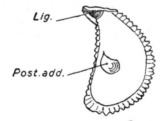

Ostrea, x 2/3.

Exogyra, x 1/3.

The exterior of the shell may be ornamented by spiral or transverse lines or ridges, or both. Where the two types of ornamentation intersect, tubercles, which may be produced into spines, are

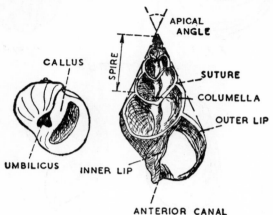

THE PARTS OF A GASTROPOD.

often developed. Smooth, enamel-like layers of calcium carbonate, *callus*, are sometimes developed round the aperture; this shows that part of the shell has become internal, the callus providing a smooth surface of contact between the soft body of the animal and the shell.

1.   The shell shows no signs of being coiled   2
        The shell is coiled   4

2. (*1*) The shell is a wide-angled cone with an oval or sub-circular base; the apex is nearly central and nearer to the anterior border. Surface ornamented with radiating ribs or striae; rarely smooth. Internally, there is a horseshoe shaped muscular impression, which is open in front   ..   ..   **Patella**
Jurassic to Recent.

        The shell is perforated 3

3. (*2*) There is a well-marked slit in the anterior border; during growth, this becomes filled up, leaving a raised band. Surface generally ornamented with a trellis-work of longitudinal and transverse ribs. The apex is curved towards the rear ..   ..   **Emarginula**
Coralline Crag to Recent.

        The apex of the shell is perforated, and nearer the anterior than the posterior border; otherwise, similar to *Emarginula*. Muscular impression as in *Patella*   ..   ..   **Fissurella**
Jurassic to Recent.

Patella, x 1.

(A. M. D.)

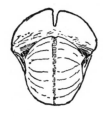

Emarginula, x 1⅓.   *Bellerophon, x 2/3.*

235

4. (*1*) The whorls are coiled symmetrically, or discoidally 5

The shell is not discoidal 7

5. (*4*) Shell globular, smooth or with lines of growth. Whorls few, the outer embracing the inner. The aperture has a deep marginal slit, which, during growth, is filled in by a band or keel, dividing the shell into two similar parts   ..   ..   **Bellerophon**
Silurian to Permian; maximum in Carboniferous.

The shell is flat 6

6. (*5*) Whorls convex, with a ridge on the upper surface. Aperture polygonal, surface smooth   ..   ..   **Euomphalus**
Silurian to Triassic; maximum in Carboniferous.

Shell thin; surface smooth; whorls numerous; left-handed coiling. Margin of mouth sharp, entire ..   ..   **Planorbis**
Jurassic to Recent. A freshwater form.

7. (*4*) The shell is turreted; the apical angle is small, and the size of the whorls increases steadily from the apex of the spire to the mouth 8

The shell does not conform with the above   9

8. (*7*) The aperture is entire, that is neither notched nor furnished with a canal or canals. The whorls are flat or slightly convex, ornamented with spiral ribs and lines of growth. Aperture oval or subquadrate, outer lip thin, sinuous, slightly produced in front ..   ..   ..   **Turritella**
Cretaceous to Recent.

Outline step-like; vertical ornament stronger than in the above, tending to become tuberculous or spinous. Aperture oval, entire, narrow behind, rounded in front   ..   ..   **Melania**
Wealden to Recent. A freshwater form.

Aperture oblong or semi-oval, with a short posterior canal and a well-marked recurved anterior canal. Outer lip thickened and often somewhat recurved. Ornament much bolder than in *Turritella*
Cretaceous to Recent.   **Cerithium**

9. (*7*) The shell is conical, with a flattish base   10

The shell is not conical   11

10. (*9*) The aperture has a slit which, as the shell grows, becomes filled up, leaving a band on the whorls. The lines of growth bend obliquely backwards at the band   ..   ..   **Pleurotomaria**
Triassic to Recent; common and widespread in Jurassic. Rare in Tertiary.

Mouth entire. Whorls numerous and flat or slightly convex; spire sharp. Base flat or nearly so; angular at periphery. Outer lip sharp. Columella twisted, with a prominent anterior tooth-like protuberance or a fold   ..   ..   **Trochus**
Triassic to Recent.

Euomphalus, x 2/3.

(A.M.D.)

Planorbis, x1.

(A.M.D.)

Turritella, x2/3.

Melania, x2/3.

Cerithium, x1.

Pleurotomaria, x2/3.

Trochus, x1.

Shell conical, depressed, angular at periphery. Aperture entire, sub-quadrate; lip sharp. Ornamented with spiral ridges. Base flat. Umbilicus wide and deep, limited by a sharp edge, which is generally crenulated   ..   ..   **Architectonica** [*Solarium*] Jurassic to Recent.

11.   (*9*) The final whorl only is seen 12

         Whorls all visible   13

12.   (*11*) Aperture as long as the shell; oblong and narrow, with a short canal at either end. Outer lip inflected, both lips crenulated. Surface covered with shining enamel; smooth   ..   ..   ..   **Cypraea** Eocene to Recent.

         Smaller than above, with transverse ribs   ..   ..   ..   **Trivia** Eocene to Recent.

13.   (*11*) The mouth is entire   14

         The mouth is notched, or has a canal or canals   17

14.   (*13*) The spire is low   15

         The spire is well marked   16

15.   (*14*) Shell thick; globular; last whorl very large. Aperture semicircular or approaching oval. Outer lip sharp, oblique; inner thickened, not crenulate. Umbilicus almost or entirely filled   ..   .. **Ampullina** Triassic to Recent.

         As above, but umbilicus open   ..   ..   **Natica** Jurassic to Recent.

16.   (*14*) Shell thin; shape, elongated oval. Aperture large, rounded in front, elongated. Columella more or less twisted. Right-handed spiral   ..   ..   **Limnea** Purbeck to Recent.   Freshwater form.

         As above, but left-handed   ..   ..   **Physa** Upper Jurassic to Recent.

         Shell thin; much "fatter" than above; whorls strongly convex; smooth or with faint ribs. Umbilicus very small or absent. Aperture oval; slightly angular behind ..   ..   ..   **Viviparus** [*Paludina*] Great Oolite to Recent.   Freshwater form.

17.   (*13*) The shell resembles two cones, base to base..   18

         The shape is not bi-conical   19

18.   (*17*) Angle of spire wide; last whorl enveloping the greater part of the preceding whorls. Spire with many whorls. Surface generally smooth. Aperture long, narrow, and straight; borders almost or quite parallel. Anterior canal truncated. Outer lip thin, without folds or teeth, notched at suture. Outer shell thick, but inner parts of whorls become very thin, owing to resorption   ..   ..   **Conus** Upper Cretaceous to Recent.

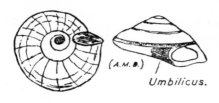

(A.M.B.)

Umbilicus.

Architectonica, x 1⅓.

Trivia, x 1.

Natica, x 1.

Limnea, x 2/3.

Viviparus, x 2/3

Conus, x 1/3.

Small form, with elevated spire. Outer lip arched, with a notch near the suture. Surface ornamented .. .. .. **Conorbis** Eocene and Oligocene.

19. (*17*) The mouth has a long anterior canal 20

The mouth has a short anterior canal or is notched 22

20. (*19*) Shell typically fusiform; *i.e.* tapering towards both ends .. 21

Shell thick, oval, or elongated; whorls convex; surface very rugged and spiny or tuberculated. Aperture ovate; anterior canal straight or curved. No posterior canal. Outer lip thick; inner lip smooth .. .. **Murex** Eocene to Recent.

Resembling above, but with anterior canal *short* and completely closed .. .. **Typhis** Eocene to Recent.

21. (*20*) Aperture has a deep slit in the outer lip, at a short distance from the suture. The lines of growth are bent backwards at the fold which forms as the notch becomes filled in during the growth of the shell .. .. **Turris** [*Pleurotoma*] Upper Cretaceous to Recent.

Aperture oval, with long anterior canal and no notch in outer lip. Shell narrow, elongated; spire sharp, with many rounded whorls. Ornament of spiral ribs and transverse folds or ribs.. .. **Fusinus** Cretaceous to Recent.

22. (*19*) Anterior canal well marked 23

No definite anterior canal; aperture notched 27

23. (*20*) Surface smooth, with little ornament 24

Surface highly ornamented 25

24. (*23*) Spire short and sharp. Last whorl large. Indications of a posterior canal. Surface marked by spiral striae crossed by lines of growth
Sycostoma
Common in Eocene, rare in Miocene.

Shell solid; fusiform; spire somewhat elongated. Frequently coiled left-handed. Aperture pear-shaped. Whorls rounded, smooth or with spiral lines. Anterior canal slightly twisted .. .. **Neptunea** Eocene to Recent.

25. Inner surface of outer lip crenulated; inner lip reflected (bent back) on columella; enamel-like surface. Aperture oval, pointed behind. Anterior canal very short, reflected. Columella with an oblique fold in front .. .. **Nassa** Upper Cretaceous to Recent.

Inner surface of outer lip smooth 26

26. Anterior canal in line with long axis of mouth. Outer lip thin; inner, a little sinuous with callus. Whorls convex; ornamented with small spiral ribs crossed by transverse folds .. .. .. **Buccinum** Pliocene to Recent.

Conorbis, x1.

Murex, x 1/4.

Typhis, x1.

Turris, x1.

Fusinus, x 2/3.

Sycostoma, x 2/3.

Neptunea, x1/4.

Nassa, x 2/3.

Buccinum, x 1/2.

Surface tuberculate, striated, or lamellar. Ornament or spiral ridges which are more prominent than the transverse lines of growth. Outer lip thin; columella flattened with callus. Mouth has a posterior notch or groove ..   .. **Purpura** Miocene to Recent.

27. Spire long, consisting of many whorls, which are smooth or faintly ribbed. At intervals, there are strong vertical ribs on the spire (varices), which mark the positions of earlier reflections of the outer lip, which is reflected. Anterior canal represented by a wide notch; posterior canal reaches nearly to the apex of the spire ..   ..   .. **Rimella** Eocene to Recent.

Spire rather short and conical; apex sharp. Last whorl very large, tapering to the front. Whorls step-like; at the angle of the whorls there is a row of spines which are generally prominent, which are prolonged anteriorly as transverse ribs; the latter are usually crossed by spiral ridges. Aperture elongated; anterior slightly notched. Outer lip generally thin; inner with thin callus. Columella with four or five very oblique folds, the anterior being stronger than the posterior ..   .. **Volutospina** Upper Cretaceous to Recent.

Cephalopoda

Univalve shells which are divided internally by partitions or *septa* into a series of chambers. The traces of the septa on the wall of the shell are known as *sutures*, and the type of suture is important in deciding the group to which a specimen belongs.

1. The shell is coiled spirally, either completely or at one end 2
The shell is not coiled spirally 9

2. (*1*) The spiral is coiled in one plane 3
The spiral is not coiled in one plane 8

3. (*2*) The sutures are simple curves; they do not show saddles (forward-directed curves) or lobes (curves directed backwards); the shell is involute, that is, the outer whorls overlap the inner ..   ..   .. **Nautilus** Triassic to Recent.

The sutures show definite saddles and lobes 4

4. (*3*) The sutures are simple; the saddles and lobes are not "frilled"
Goniatites Lower Devonian to Permian.

The lobes show crenulations ..   .. **Ceratites** Triassic.

The sutures show complicated frilling 5

5. (*4*) The spiral is simple and continuous; the whorls are in contact with one another ..   .. **Ammonitina** 10
Jurassic and Cretaceous.

Purpura, x 1/2.   Rimella, x 2/3.

Volutospina, x 1/2.

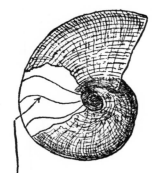

Septal suture

Nautilus, x 2/3.

Goniatites. x 1 ¾.

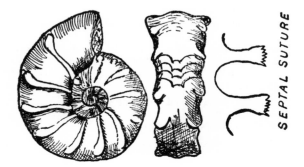

SEPTAL SUTURE

Ceratites. x 1/5.

The shell is not a simple spiral; either the whorls are not in contact, or part of the shell is straight **6**

6. (5) One end of the shell is spirally coiled, the coils being in contact, then follows a straight portion, which is bent back on itself   ..   **Scaphites** Gault to Middle Chalk.

The whorls of the spiral are not in contact with one another   ..   **7**

7. (6) The shell consists of a spiral portion, followed by a straight length which is bent back on itself, like *Scaphites* ..   ..   ..   **Ancyloceras** Lower Greensand.

The spiral is continuous, but the whorls are not in contact with one another ..   ..   **Crioceras** Lower Cretaceous.

8. (2) The shell is turreted, superficially resembling a gastropod, but distinguished by being chambered. Coiling is left-handed ..   **Turrilites** Gault to Chalk.

9. (1) The shell is straight for part of its length, but curved in a hook-like manner at one or both ends, so as to bend back more or less parallel to the straight portion; sutures frilled   ..   ..   ..   **Hamites** Gault.

The shell consists of a cigar-shaped tube consisting of crystals of calcite arranged radially; in the blunt end is a conical hollow which contains a conical, segmented "phragmacone" **Belemnites** (*Sensu lato*) Lower Lias to top of Cretaceous.

The shell is nearly cylindrical; the narrower end is truncated and segmented; the wider end has a hollow in it   ..   .. **Orthoceras** Tremadoc to Triassic.

10. (5) The ammonite is ornamented with ribs which extend across the outer margin or *venter* **11**

The venter of the shell is flat or is marked by a groove or depression   **16**

There is a well-marked ridge or keel along the venter **18**

11. (10) The shell is closely coiled, with only a small umbilicus. The whorls are compressed and ornamented with closely-spaced simple ribs without tubercles   ..   ..   **Macrocephalites** Upper Cornbrash.

The shell is loosely coiled with wide umbilicus **12**

12. (11) The ribs do not bear tubercles **13**

The ribs are tuberculated **14**

13. (12) The whorls are nearly circular in cross-section. Ribs very numerous, rather delicate and straight, sweeping straight across the well-rounded venter   ..   ..   **Dactylioceras** Upper Lias.

Scaphites, x 1.

Ancyloceras, x 1/4.

Crioceras, x 1/6

Turrilites, x 1/2.

Hamites, x 2/3.

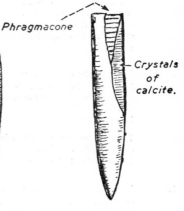

Phragmacone

Crystals of calcite.

Belemnites, x 1.

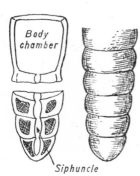

Body chamber

Siphuncle

Orthoceras, x 1.

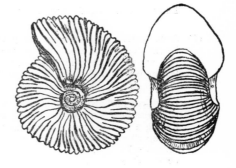

Macrocephalites, x 2/3.

Ribs rather coarse, closely spaced, and straight; usually bifurcating near the shoulder and continuing over the rounded venter
Perisphinctes
Oxfordian to Portlandian.

In the Portland Beds, "Perisphinctids" are often more than 2 ft. in diameter. It is then difficult to realise that such heavy specimens once floated in the sea; remember that the chambers are now filled with mineral matter and not with gas, as they were in life.

14. (*12*) The ribs are simple 15

The ribs bifurcate. Whorls broader than high (depressed), and with the shell increasing rapidly in size along the whorl. On the inner margin there are widely-spaced simple ribs, then comes a row of tubercles and many of the ribs bifurcate. On the shoulder is a second row of turbercles and renewed bifurcation, so that a large number of simple ribs sweep straight across the wide, flat venter ..**Liparoceras**
Lower Lias.

15. (*14*) The prominent, simple ribs are ornamented on the margins, shoulders, and venter by rows of rather flat tubercles. Specimens sometimes of considerable size and usually preserved in pale-grey chalk .. .. **Acanthoceras**
Lower Chalk.

The prominent, simple ribs carry fairly closely-spaced tubercles on the shoulders and venter .. .. **Douvilleiceras**
Basal Beds of the Gault.

16. (*10*) Umbilicus wide; whorls nearly circular in cross-section. Ribs very numerous, rather delicate and straight, interrupted at venter by a smooth area, or even a slight depression. Cf. *Dactylioceras*
Parkinsonia
Inferior Oolite. Often preserved in a matrix of iron-shot Oolite.

Laterally compressed; ribs curved or bifurcating 17

17. (*16*) Small umbilicus. A varied group with numerous curved ribs, often bearing tubercles, especially on the shoulder. In some forms, the ribs are quite faint, in others they are prominent. The distinctive feature is a flattened area, or even a deep groove, along the venter
Gault. **Hoplitidae**

Umbilicus fairly wide. Numerous bifurcating, slightly bent (flexuous) ribs, with one or more rows of very small tubercles. Along the venter there is a smooth area. Specimens flattened on shale often show that the aperture is partly closed by a long forward projection on the ventral side .. .. **Kosmoceras**
Oxford Clay.

18. (*10*) The keel is "frilled" or notched 19

The keel is simple 21

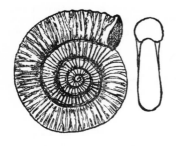

Dactylioceras, x 2/3.

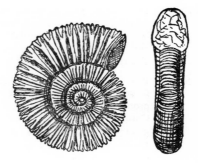

Perisphinctes, x 1/3.

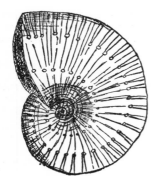

Liparoceras, x 1.

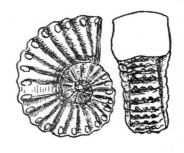

Acanthoceras, x 1/5.

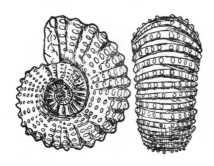

Douvilleiceras, x 2/3.

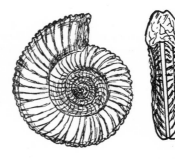

Parkinsonia, x 1/2.

19. (*18*) The ribs are simple, widely spaced, and carry large tubercles at the shoulder and less marked ones at the inner margin. Ventral region broad and rather flat, with a prominent frilled keel ..   **Pleuroceras** Middle Lias.

The ribs are not tuberculated   20

20. (*19*) Ribs fairly widely spaced and strong; bifurcating and sweeping forward at the shoulder, to continue across the venter and produce a prominent frilled keel ..   ..   **Cardioceras** Oxford Clay and Corallian.

Shell compressed laterally; outer whorl embraces about half the inner. Umbilicus small. Ribs generally rather faint, slightly flexuous, widely spaced, and simple. In some forms, the surface is almost smooth. Prominent toothed or frilled keel along the venter ..   .. **Amaltheus** Middle Lias.

21. (*18*) The shell is compressed laterally, with a very small umbilicus. External margin very narrow, rather than having a separate keel. Surface either smooth or with very faint traces of ribs   **Oxynoticeras** Lower Lias.

The ribs are well marked   22

22. (*21*) The ribs bifurcate, and usually bear tubercles at the point of bifurcation. Shell laterally compressed, with a small umbilicus. Distinct keel. Usually preserved in pale-grey chalk   ..   ..   **Schloenbachia** Lower Chalk.

The ribs are simple   23

23. (*22*) There is a more or less well-marked groove on either side of the keel   24

The surface of the shell is ornamented by very numerous, rather delicate, sickle-shaped ribs. Keel prominent, but only fragments may be preserved ..   .. **Harpoceras** Upper Lias.

24. (*23*) Whorls only just in contact. On the inner side of the whorl, the ribs are very faint, then on the outer side, beyond a faint line following the whorl-shape, the ribs become much broader and more prominent, bending forwards on the shoulder ..   .. **Hildoceras** Upper Lias.

Loosely-coiled shell with wide umbilicus. Margins and shoulders ornamented with widely-spaced, strong, simple ribs   **Arietitidae** Lower Lias.

The *ammonites* are valuable as zonal fossils throughout the Mesozoic Period; they may also be found as derived fossils in boulder clays. Their identification is usually a matter for specialists; nevertheless, we give a key for some of the commonest genera, which have also been selected to give an idea of the variation within the group. It must be emphasised that some hundreds of genera

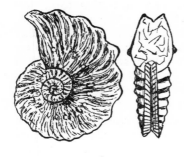

Euhoplites, × 1.

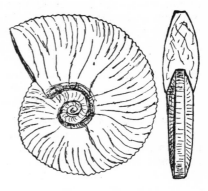

Anahoplites, × 1.

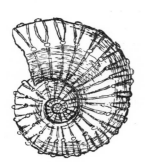

Kosmoceras, × 1.

Pleuroceras, × 2/3.

Cardioceras, × 1.

Amaltheus, × 3/4.

of ammonites are known, so that it is very likely that forms will be found which cannot be named from the key. When this happens, reference must be made to a more advanced work, or, if the locality and horizon from which the specimen was obtained are accurately known, a specialist may be called in to help in settling any problem of correlation which may have arisen.

TRILOBITA

The trilobites comprise an extinct class of crustacea which first appear in the Lower Cambrian, reach their maximum development in the Ordovician, are still abundant in the Silurian, became less important in the Devonian, and, in Europe, died out in the Carboniferous. They are thus characteristic of the Palaeozoic era.

Trilobites are provided with an external skeleton which is roughly oval or shield-shaped, and this is divided by two longi-

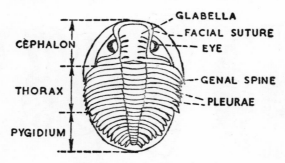

THE PARTS OF A TRILOBITE.

tudinal grooves into three parts, and also transversely into three areas, the head or *cephalon*, the body or *thorax*, and the tail or *pygidium*.

The head generally consists of a more or less semicircular shield, having two longitudinal grooves enclosing a raised area, the *glabella*, which usually shows signs of transverse grooves or furrows, and at the rear a complete transverse furrow. Surrounding the glabella are the *cheeks*, which carry the eyes (when present). The cheeks are divided into *free* and *fixed cheeks* by a line of weakness, the *facial suture*, running from the front of the cephalon, immediately behind the eyes, and then either sideways or backwards. During life, when the moulting period arrived, the free cheeks broke away, and thus assisted in the escape of the animal from its crust. The posterior corners of the cephalon are the *genal angles*, and they may be rounded, sharp, or produced into spines.

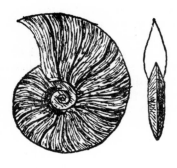

Oxynoticeras, x 2/3.

Schloenbachia, x 2/3

Harpoceras, x 2/3.

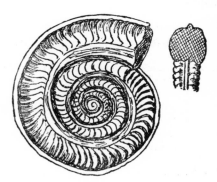

Hildoceras, x 2/3.

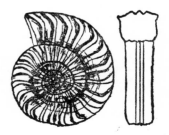

Arietites, x 1/8.

The *thorax* consists of a number of articulated segments (2 to 14, or even, sometimes 29), each made up of a central portion or *axis*, and two lateral members or *pleurae*.

The *pygidium* varies greatly in size; it may consist of from 1 to 15 segments. The segments of the pygidium were fused into one piece, and the front of the pygidium may be distinguished in a fossil by the fact that the segments remain always strictly parallel, whereas those of the thorax, being movable, almost always are slightly askew.

Owing to the unfortunate habit (which is common to all the Arthropoda) of moulting during growth, the head, body, and tail portions of a trilobite are frequently found separately. This renders identification difficult. In the criteria given in the scheme which follows, we have assumed that complete specimens are available. Since the trilobites are confined to the Palaeozoic, and since these rocks in Great Britain have often suffered alteration as the result of earth-movement, trilobites are not infrequently found distorted.

1. Thorax consists of not more than 4 segments   2

      More than 4 segments in thorax   3

2. (*1*) Thoracic segments, 2. Head and tail very nearly the same size and very much alike. Tail not segmented   ..   ..   **Agnostus** Cambrian and Ordovician.

      2 to 4 body-segments. Axis of pygidium shows numerous segments Cambrian.   **Eodiscus**

         Note.—Both *Agnostus* and *Eodiscus* are very small, the overall length is generally less than half a centimetre.

3. (*1*) Head-shield has a well-marked flattened border or "brim"   4

      Head-shield without brim   5

4. (*3*) Body-segments, 6. Head-shield with a broad, flat, ornamented border. Genal spines long. Glabella pear-shaped, swollen and broader in front. Cheeks convex and smooth. Pygidium small   ..   **Trinucleidae** Arenig to Bala Beds.

      Body-segments, 12 to 29. Head-shield with a broad, finely-pitted brim, which is prolonged backwards nearly to the end of the thorax. Glabella short and convex; not expanded in front. Pygidium very small **Harpes** Ordovician to Devonian.

5. (*3*) Head-shield much larger than tail   6

      Head-shield not greatly larger than tail   13

6. (*5*) Glabella greatly expanded in front   7

      Glabella only slightly expanded or not at all   9

Agnostus, x 4.

Eodiscus, x 2 ½.

Trinucleus, x 2/3.

Harpes, x 1 ½.

7. **(6)** Thorax with 5 or 6 segments. Glabella convex, projecting beyond margin of head-shield. Very large eyes, which occupy practically all the free cheeks. Axis of thorax broad; pleurae grooved **Cyclopyge** [*Aeglina*] Arenig to Bala Beds.
   Body segments, 10 8

8. **(7)** Glabella with a spherical lobe which projects in front of the cheeks; remainder of glabella narrow and cylindrical, with two pairs of furrows and a deep neck furrow. Cheeks very convex, with a flat border. Eyes on stalks. Pleurae of thorax ridged, and prolonged into spines. Pygidium with 4 segments; pleurae spined .. **Staurocephalus** Bala to Wenlock Limestone.

   Glabella large, spheroidal, with three pairs of furrows; the two anterior are indistinct, the posterior curve backwards and join the deep neck suture. Pleurae of thorax have rounded ends. Pygidium with 3 segments .. .. **Sphaerexochus** Ordovician and Silurian.

9. **(6)** Glabella reaches front margin of head-shield 10
   Glabella falls short of front margin of head-shield 11

10. **(9)** Glabella parabolic; without furrows. Eyes small, and near middle of cheeks. Long genal spines. Thoracic segments, 14 or 15. Pygidium short, margin with two teeth; axis with 4 or 5 segments .. **Angelina** Tremadoc.

    Glabella convex, oblong, or ovoid; with three pairs of furrows, which sometimes continue across, the last pair joining with the neck-furrow. Eyes prominent. Thorax with usually 11 segments; pleurae grooved and prolonged into spines. Pygidium with 4 segments, lateral lobes with backwardly-directed spines .. .. .. **Cheiruridae** Tremadoc to Devonian

11. **(9)** Glabella broadens in front. Body large, elongated, narrows towards the rear. Head-shield broad, semicircular, with a border, and long genal spines. Glabella has 2 to 4 furrows, some of which continue across. Eyes large and arched. Thorax of 16 to 20 segments; pleurae grooved and prolonged into long, backwardly-directed spines. Pygidium plate-like; axis with 2 to 8 segments .. **Paradoxides** Middle Cambrian.
    Glabella does not broaden in front 12

12. **(11)** Without eyes. Head-shield semicircular, with a furrow within the border; with genal spines, which are often broken off. Axial furrows deep. Glabella with three or four backwardly-directed furrows. Thorax has 14 or 15 segments, and grooved pleurae. Axis of pygidium with from 2 to 8 segments .. .. **Conocoryphe** Lower Cambrian to Tremadoc.

    Eyes present; a little in front of middle of cheeks, and united to the front of the glabella by an eye line. Usually three pairs of furrows in glabella. Thorax with 12 to 15 segments (typically 14), pleurae with short points. Pygidium with 3 or 4 segments indicated on axis **Olenus** Lingula Flags to Tremadoc.

Cyclopyge, x2.

Staurocephalus,
x 1½.

Sphaerexochus,
x 2/3.

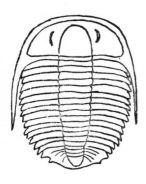

Angelina, x 2/3.

Cheirurus, x 2/3.

Paradoxides, x 1/2.

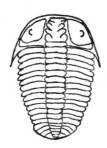

Conocoryphe, x 2/3.

Olenus, x 1.

Calymene, x 1.

13. (*5*) Head-shield markedly larger than pygidium 14

Head-shield approximately equal in size to pygidium 17

14. (*13*) Glabella broader behind than in front; inflated, with three pairs of lateral furrows separating three globular lobes on each side. Eyes small and prominent. Thorax of 13 segments, with a prominent axis. Pleurae grooved. Pygidium with 6 to 11 segments. Specimens are frequently found rolled like a wood-louse .. .. .. **Calymene** Arenig to Upper Ludlow.

Glabella broader in front than in rear 15

15. (*14*) Head-shield covered with tubercles, with a flat border and pointed genal angles. Furrows on glabella indistinct or absent. Eyes small, on short stalks. Thorax with 11 segments and ridged pleurae, which are produced into spines. Pygidium long, narrow, and triangular, with more segments on the axis than there are pleurae .. **Encrinurus** Bala to Upper Ludlow.

Head-shield not covered with tubercles 16

16. (*15*) Glabella inflated and much expanded in front; three or four pairs of indistinct furrows. Eyes large and faceted. No genal spines. Thorax with 11 segments and grooved pleurae. Pygidium rounded in rear **Phacops** Silurian and Devonian.

Glabella not greatly expanded in front; three pairs of distinct furrows, and a fourth furrow which is continuous across rear of glabella. Eyes large and faceted. Long genal spines. Thorax with 11 segments; pleurae often spined .. .. **Dalmanites** Silurian.

17. (*13*) Head-shield triangular; genal angles rounded; furrows on glabella indistinct or absent. Body large, tapering from front to rear; trilobation indistinct. Thorax with 13 segments. Pygidium triangular with 10 to 14 segments .. .. **Trimerus** Arenig to Devonian.

Head-shield semicircular 18

18. (*17*) Glabella indistinctly defined, save at the rear end. Eyes wide apart. Thorax usually with 10 segments; pleurae neither grooved nor ridged. Pygidium large, and very like the head-shield; axis indistinct, segments not visible laterally .. .. **Bumestus** Arenig to Wenlock.

Glabella well defined 19

19. (*18*) Glabella has four or five well-marked lateral furrows. Eyes large. Thorax of 8 segments, axis narrow, distinct; pleurae grooved and usually with pointed ends. Pygidium consists of numerous segments **Ogygiocaris** Tremadoc to Llandeilo.

Glabella indistinctly furrowed. Eyes large. Thorax of 8 segments, with a rather broad axis. Pleurae obliquely grooved, with rounded ends. Pygidium of numerous segments .. .. .. **Asaphus** Tremadoc to Bala.

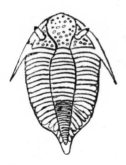

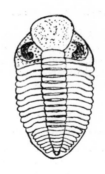

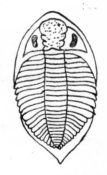

Encrinurus, x1.   *Phacops,* x 1½.   *Dalmanites,* x1.

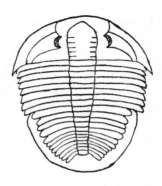

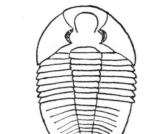

Bumestus x1

Trimerus, x 2/3.   *Ogygiocaris,* x 2/3.

Asaphus, x1/2.   *Bronteus,* x 2/3.

Glabella expands rapidly in front, with three lateral furrows in some species, none in others. Eyes crescentic, situated near the posterior border of head-shield. Thorax of 10 segments, with ridged pleurae. Pygidium very large, fan-shaped; axis very short; lateral areas large, with radiating grooves   ..   .. **Bronteus**
Bala to Devonian.

PLANTAE

Fossil remains of plants are almost always found in a fragmentary condition; roots, stems, leaves, and fruits are rarely found attached to one another. Plant remains are normally not of great utility for purposes of correlation. Their presence in quantity in a stratum suggests that the bed was formed in proximity to dry land, possibly in a swamp or delta, while root-beds indicate fossil soils.

The most likely places in which to search for well-preserved remains of plants are the tip-heaps at coal-mines, and since in Great Britain, these are derived from strata of Carboniferous age, our scheme, unless otherwise stated, is restricted to the determination of stems and leaves of the more common genera of plants which are to be found on these dumps.

As a matter of convenience, we have dealt separately with stems and leaves, these being the commonest fossils.

Stems

1. The stem is "jointed" like that of a bamboo, the joints are fluted, the flutings alternating at the nodes which separate the joints   2
    The stem is not divided by nodes into joints 3

2. The nodes are surrounded by sheaths ..   .. **Equisetites**
    Rhaetic to Wealden.
    The nodes are bare   ..   .. **Calamites**

3. The surface of the stem carries more or less rhomboidal or lozenge-shaped leaf-scars, which are arranged *spirally* ..   ..   .. **Lepidodendron**
    Devonian to Carboniferous.
    The stem bears small scars of various shapes which are arranged in vertical rows   ..   .. **Sigillaria**

Leaves

1. The leaves are fern-like, and divided into small pinnules   2
    The leaves are not fern-like   9

2. (*1*) The secondary veins form a network 3
    The secondary veins are forked or simple, not forming a network .. 4

3. (*2*) The pinnules are attached by a single point; the base is more or less heart-shaped   ..   .. **Linopteris**
    The pinnules are attached by the whole width of the base, often running together   ..   .. **Lonchopteris**

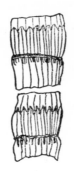

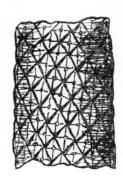

Calamites, x 1/4.

Equisetites. x1.

Lepidodendron,
x 1/5

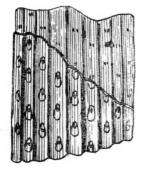

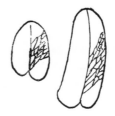

Linopteris, x 1½

Sigillaria, x 1/4.

Lonchopteris, x 1½.

Neuropteris,
the single pinnule is *x 1½.*

Sphenopteris, x 2/3.

259

4. (*2*) The pinnules are attached to the stem at a single point   5

The pinnules are attached by the whole width of the base   6

5. (*4*) Base of pinnule more or less heart-shaped; the mid-rib forks several times and gives off many secondary veins which arch   ..   **Neuropteris** Upper Palaeozoic.

Pinnules generally lobed, small and often wedge-shaped at base; veins radiate in a fan-like manner from the base of the pinnule   **Sphenopteris** Upper Palaeozoic.

6. (*4*) Mid-rib not well marked; does not reach apex of pinnule. Several veins enter pinnule, then fork several times, producing secondary veins which arch   ..   ..   **Odontopteris**

Mid-rib well marked, reaching apex of pinnule   7

7. (*6*) Secondary veins many, almost at right angles to mid-rib. Pinnules long and linear ..   ..   **Alethopteris**

Secondary veins comparatively few   8

8. (*7*) Pinnules short, margins often nearly parallel, secondary veins almost at right angles to mid-rib. Pinnules not contracted at base   ..   **Pecopteris**

Pinnules large and leathery. Secondary veins strong and prominent

Mariopteris

9. (*1*) Leaves in whorls surrounding the stem, in multiples of three. Bases separate, never united to form a collar round the stem. Leaves wedge-shaped; the same plant may bear undivided (entire) leaves on the larger stems, and, on the smaller, leaves which are more or less deeply cleft from the apex towards the base ..   ..   **Sphenophyllum**

Leaves in whorls, united at the base to form a small collar round the stem (not always observable in specimens). From about a dozen to thirty-two leaves in a whorl ..   ..   **Annularia**

FOSSILS AS STRATIGRAPHICAL INDICES

The value of fossils in the correlation and "dating" of strata has been pointed out on p. 187, and it is necessary now to amplify that statement somewhat and to show how the information derived from them may be applied. In the hands of an expert, fossils enable "zoning" to be carried out within very narrow limits; this of course, presupposes a far deeper knowledge of palaeontology than is available to readers of this book, and demands a detailed study of species and varieties so that they can be identified with accuracy and certainty. The beginner should, however, have some broad general idea of the ranges in time of the large divisions of the animal (particularly the invertebrates) kingdom, and be able to form an opinion of the system, if not the formation, from which he is collecting.

Odontopteris, x1.

Pecopteris, x1.

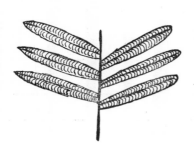

Alethopteris, x 2.

Mariopteris, x 2.

Sphenophyllum,
x 1.

Annularia, x 1½.

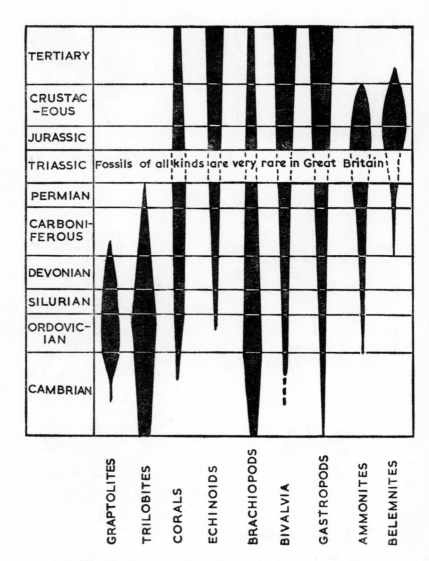

Fig. 60. RANGE IN TIME OF IMPORTANT GROUPS OF FOSSILS.

The most useful fossils for purposes of correlation are those which have a restricted vertical and a wide areal distribution. A general idea of the distribution in time of the groups which have been dealt with in the Determinative Tables, is given diagrammatically in Fig. 60, and it is hoped that by the aid of this figure and the notes in the Determinative Tables, the student will be able to form a preliminary opinion of the age of a deposit which he is studying in the field. The notes and diagrams are drawn up on the plan which is common to the various sections of this book, the data (here, the names of the fossils) are used as a means of deducing geological age; at the same time, the diagrams can be used to form an idea of the fossils likely to be found in rocks whose age is known.

It is desirable here to stress the danger of arguing from *negative data*. For example, graptolites and trilobites are characteristic of Palaeozoic rocks; their absence, however, does not indicate that a rock is of some other age. The conditions under which the deposits were laid down may have been unfavourable to the growth of graptolites and trilobites, or the traces thereof may have been obliterated as the result of subsequent alterations in the rocks. Ammonites and belemnites are well known to be common in strata of Jurassic and Cretaceous age; the Purbeck and Wealden rocks are, however, quite free from either ammonites and belemnites, since both are freshwater formations. The tables and diagrams which follow are open, therefore, to one-way interpretation only. The presence of an assemblage of fossils has a positive significance; its absence, however, does not legitimately lead to opposite conclusions.

APPENDIX I

SAFETY PRECAUTIONS

While the pursuit of field geology cannot be included among the more hazardous occupations, there are possibilities of accident which can be minimised if precautions are taken. We have, therefore, considered it desirable to include a few notes on the subject of safety.

When working on steep or precipitous ground, watch your step and make sure that your foothold is secure; there is always a risk of becoming so occupied with your observations that you may pay too little heed to the risks that are inherent in climbing. Included among these is the possibility of approaching too closely to the edge of a cliff or quarry-face; there is often a certain amount of overhang, and the rock at the lip is often rotten. Care is also necessary in negotiating steep scree-covered slopes; once a scree is set in motion, it may be almost impossible to control one's movements, and there is a danger from boulders from higher up the slope, which may come whizzing down and strike the climber.

In collecting from quarries or cliffs, it is safer to take specimens from the floor of the section. Never risk trying to dislodge a specimen from above your head. The removal of material from a vertical face, consisting of poorly consolidated sandstones, some limestones and weathered igneous rocks, requires special care. Irregular bedding, jointing, and crumbling blocks resulting from long weathering (especially in abandoned quarries), tend to cause unstable conditions. A single blow from a hammer on a face consisting of these "awkward" rocks (of which chalk is one), may dislodge large blocks from above and result in heavy falls of material.

Always avoid working a section where the rock overhangs or is undercut. To do so will almost invariably cause falls and possible casualties.

Remember also, that though quarry managers will generally give complete freedom of access to their workings, they accept no responsibility for accidents which may occur.

Always ascertain whether blasting takes place in a quarry you want to examine, and if so, at what times; noon and four o'clock in the afternoon are often the times when danger from blasting is likely.

APPENDIX II

THE GEOLOGICAL COLUMN

In the following table or scheme, we have endeavoured to give a reasonably complete list of the various geological formations which occur in Britain, under the names that are applied and with notes on their general lithology as seen in their *type areas*.

POST-PLIOCENE OR QUATERNARY

Recent and Glacial. River alluvium, gravels, peat-bogs, blown sands, raised beaches, etc.

Boulder-clays, morainic materials, glacial sands.

CAINOZOIC OR TERTIARY

Index letters of Geological Survey

PLIOCENE

k 2.   *Forest Bed Series.* Estuarine and fresh-water lignite and clay.

Weybourne Crag. Sand with patches of shells.

Chillesford Clay and Sand.

Norwich Crag. Shelly sand and gravel.

k 1.   *Red Crag.* Sand with vast numbers of shells.

Coralline or White Crag. Shelly sands with many polyzoa.

MIOCENE   **Absent in Great Britain.**

OLIGOCENE

i 11.   *Hamstead Beds.* Marls and clays; mainly freshwater.

i 10.   *Bembridge Marls and Limestone.* Marine above, freshwater below.

i 9.   *Osborne Beds.* Marls, shales, and limestone with freshwater shells.

i 8.   *Headon Beds.* Brackish, freshwater, and marine marls, sands, and limestone.

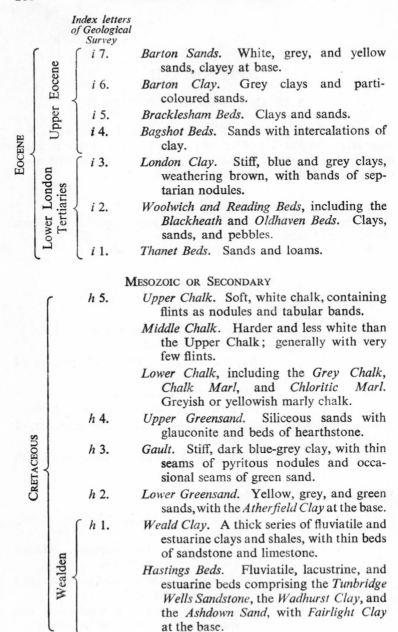

Index letters of Geological Survey

EOCENE

Upper Eocene

i 7.   *Barton Sands.* White, grey, and yellow sands, clayey at base.

i 6.   *Barton Clay.* Grey clays and particoloured sands.

i 5.   *Bracklesham Beds.* Clays and sands.

i **4.**   *Bagshot Beds.* Sands with intercalations of clay.

Lower London Tertiaries

i 3.   *London Clay.* Stiff, blue and grey clays, weathering brown, with bands of septarian nodules.

i 2.   *Woolwich and Reading Beds,* including the *Blackheath* and *Oldhaven Beds.* Clays, sands, and pebbles.

i 1.   *Thanet Beds.* Sands and loams.

MESOZOIC OR SECONDARY

CRETACEOUS

h **5.**   *Upper Chalk.* Soft, white chalk, containing flints as nodules and tabular bands.

Middle Chalk. Harder and less white than the Upper Chalk; generally with very few flints.

Lower Chalk, including the *Grey Chalk, Chalk Marl,* and *Chloritic Marl.* Greyish or yellowish marly chalk.

h **4.**   *Upper Greensand.* Siliceous sands with glauconite and beds of hearthstone.

h **3.**   *Gault.* Stiff, dark blue-grey clay, with thin seams of pyritous nodules and occasional seams of green sand.

h **2.**   *Lower Greensand.* Yellow, grey, and green sands, with the *Atherfield Clay* at the base.

Wealden

h **1.**   *Weald Clay.* A thick series of fluviatile and estuarine clays and shales, with thin beds of sandstone and limestone.

Hastings Beds. Fluviatile, lacustrine, and estuarine beds comprising the *Tunbridge Wells Sandstone,* the *Wadhurst Clay,* and the *Ashdown Sand,* with *Fairlight Clay* at the base.

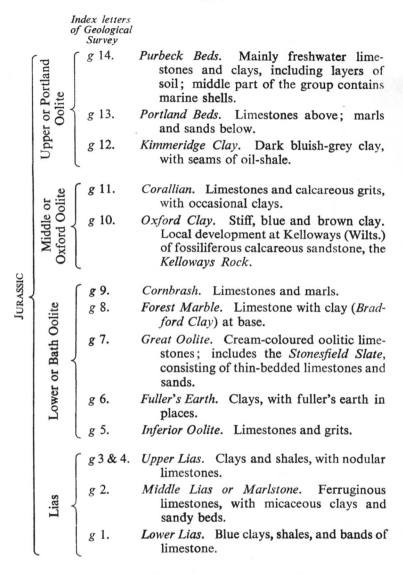

*Index letters
of Geological
Survey*

JURASSIC

Upper or Portland Oolite

g 14. *Purbeck Beds.* Mainly freshwater limestones and clays, including layers of soil; middle part of the group contains marine shells.

g 13. *Portland Beds.* Limestones above; marls and sands below.

g 12. *Kimmeridge Clay.* Dark bluish-grey clay, with seams of oil-shale.

Middle or Oxford Oolite

g 11. *Corallian.* Limestones and calcareous grits, with occasional clays.

g 10. *Oxford Clay.* Stiff, blue and brown clay. Local development at Kelloways (Wilts.) of fossiliferous calcareous sandstone, the *Kelloways Rock.*

Lower or Bath Oolite

g 9. *Cornbrash.* Limestones and marls.

g 8. *Forest Marble.* Limestone with clay (*Bradford Clay*) at base.

g 7. *Great Oolite.* Cream-coloured oolitic limestones; includes the *Stonesfield Slate*, consisting of thin-bedded limestones and sands.

g 6. *Fuller's Earth.* Clays, with fuller's earth in places.

g 5. *Inferior Oolite.* Limestones and grits.

Lias

g 3 & 4. *Upper Lias.* Clays and shales, with nodular limestones.

g 2. *Middle Lias or Marlstone.* Ferruginous limestones, with micaceous clays and sandy beds.

g 1. *Lower Lias.* Blue clays, shales, and bands of limestone.

f g. Rhaetic or Penarth Beds. Red, green, and grey marls, black shales and pale limestone (*White Lias*), with bone-bed containing remains of fish and saurians.

Mesozoic or Secondary

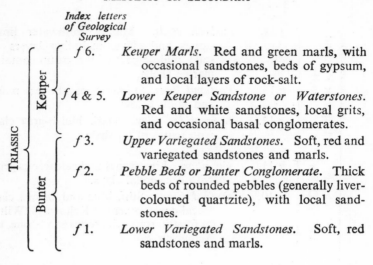

*Index letters
of Geological
Survey*

TRIASSIC

Keuper

f 6.　*Keuper Marls.*　Red and green marls, with occasional sandstones, beds of gypsum, and local layers of rock-salt.

f 4 & 5.　*Lower Keuper Sandstone or Waterstones.*　Red and white sandstones, local grits, and occasional basal conglomerates.

Bunter

f 3.　*Upper Variegated Sandstones.*　Soft, red and variegated sandstones and marls.

f 2.　*Pebble Beds or Bunter Conglomerate.*　Thick beds of rounded pebbles (generally liver-coloured quartzite), with local sandstones.

f 1.　*Lower Variegated Sandstones.*　Soft, red sandstones and marls.

Palaeozoic

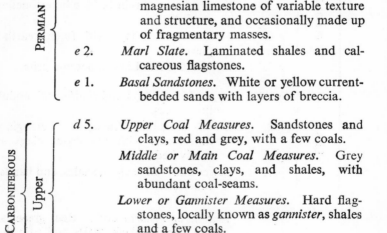

PERMIAN

e 5.　*Upper Permian Sandstone.*　Red sandstones and red clays with gypsum.

e 3 & 4.　*Magnesian Limestone.*　Yellow and white magnesian limestone of variable texture and structure, and occasionally made up of fragmentary masses.

e 2.　*Marl Slate.*　Laminated shales and calcareous flagstones.

e 1.　*Basal Sandstones.*　White or yellow current-bedded sands with layers of breccia.

CARBONIFEROUS

Upper

d 5.　*Upper Coal Measures.*　Sandstones and clays, red and grey, with a few coals.

Middle or Main Coal Measures.　Grey sandstones, clays, and shales, with abundant coal-seams.

Lower or Gannister Measures.　Hard flagstones, locally known as *gannister*, shales and a few coals.

d 4.　*Millstone Grit.*　Grits and sandstones, with shales and clay.

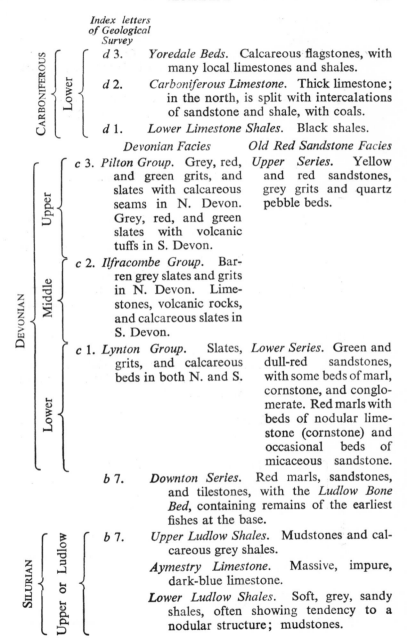

Index letters of Geological Survey

CARBONIFEROUS — Lower

d 3.   *Yoredale Beds.* Calcareous flagstones, with many local limestones and shales.

d 2.   *Carboniferous Limestone.* Thick limestone; in the north, is split with intercalations of sandstone and shale, with coals.

d 1.   *Lower Limestone Shales.* Black shales.

DEVONIAN

Devonian Facies	*Old Red Sandstone Facies*

Upper

c 3. *Pilton Group.* Grey, red, and green grits, and slates with calcareous seams in N. Devon. Grey, red, and green slates with volcanic tuffs in S. Devon.

Upper Series. Yellow and red sandstones, grey grits and quartz pebble beds.

Middle

c 2. *Ilfracombe Group.* Barren grey slates and grits in N. Devon. Limestones, volcanic rocks, and calcareous slates in S. Devon.

Lower

c 1. *Lynton Group.* Slates, grits, and calcareous beds in both N. and S.

Lower Series. Green and dull-red sandstones, with some beds of marl, cornstone, and conglomerate. Red marls with beds of nodular limestone (cornstone) and occasional beds of micaceous sandstone.

b 7.   *Downton Series.* Red marls, sandstones, and tilestones, with the *Ludlow Bone Bed*, containing remains of the earliest fishes at the base.

SILURIAN — Upper or Ludlow

b 7.   *Upper Ludlow Shales.* Mudstones and calcareous grey shales.

Aymestry Limestone. Massive, impure, dark-blue limestone.

Lower Ludlow Shales. Soft, grey, sandy shales, often showing tendency to a nodular structure; mudstones.

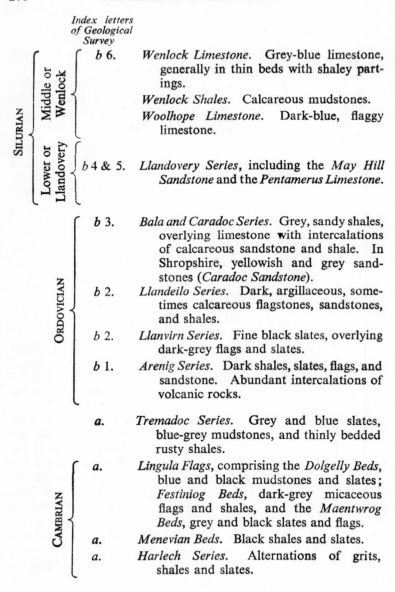

Index letters of Geological Survey

SILURIAN

Middle or Wenlock

b 6. *Wenlock Limestone.* Grey-blue limestone, generally in thin beds with shaley partings.
Wenlock Shales. Calcareous mudstones.
Woolhope Limestone. Dark-blue, flaggy limestone.

Lower or Llandovery

b 4 & 5. *Llandovery Series,* including the *May Hill Sandstone* and the *Pentamerus Limestone.*

ORDOVICIAN

b 3. *Bala and Caradoc Series.* Grey, sandy shales, overlying limestone with intercalations of calcareous sandstone and shale. In Shropshire, yellowish and grey sandstones (*Caradoc Sandstone*).

b 2. *Llandeilo Series.* Dark, argillaceous, sometimes calcareous flagstones, sandstones, and shales.

b 2. *Llanvirn Series.* Fine black slates, overlying dark-grey flags and slates.

b 1. *Arenig Series.* Dark shales, slates, flags, and sandstone. Abundant intercalations of volcanic rocks.

a. *Tremadoc Series.* Grey and blue slates, blue-grey mudstones, and thinly bedded rusty shales.

CAMBRIAN

a. *Lingula Flags,* comprising the *Dolgelly Beds,* blue and black mudstones and slates; *Festiniog Beds,* dark-grey micaceous flags and shales, and the *Maentwrog Beds,* grey and black slates and flags.

a. *Menevian Beds.* Black shales and slates.

a. *Harlech Series.* Alternations of grits, shales and slates.

PRE-CAMBRIAN (ARCHEAN)

Chiefly metamorphic and igneous, with some sedimentary rocks.

SUGGESTIONS FOR FURTHER READING

For the furtherance of his studies, the student should take any opportunity which is available of consulting one or more of the following works, some of which appear in various editions.

GENERAL GEOLOGY

W. W. WATTS: *Geology for Beginners* (Macmillan).

A. E. TRUEMAN: *Introduction to Geology* (Thomas Murby).
Geology and Scenery of England and Wales (Pelican Series).

A. HOLMES: *Principles of Physical Geology* (Thomas Nelson).

C. LAPWORTH: *Intermediate Textbook of Geology* (William Blackwood).

HISTORICAL GEOLOGY

L. D. STAMP: *An Introduction to Stratigraphy* (Thomas Murby).

A. K. WELLS and J. F. KIRKALDY: *Outline of Geological History* (Thomas Murby).

A. J. JUKES-BROWNE: *Stratigraphical Geology* (Edward Stanford).

FOSSILS

A. MORLEY DAVIES: *Introduction to Palaeontology* (Thomas Murby).
Tertiary Faunas, Vol. I (Thomas Murby).

H. WOODS: *Elementary Palaeontology: Invertebrate* (Cambridge University Press).

K. A. VON ZITTEL: *Textbook of Palaeontology*, Vol. I, "Invertebrate" (Macmillan).

E. NEAVERSON: *Stratigraphical Palaeontology* (Macmillan).

H. L. HAWKINS: *Invertebrate Palaeontology* (Methuen).

R. CROOKALL: *Coal Measure Plants* (Edward Arnold).

PALAEONTOGRAPHICAL SOCIETY: *Monographs Descriptive of British Fossils.* These are essential for purposes of detailed identification.

MINERALS

F. RUTLEY, rewritten by H. H. READ: *Introduction to Mineralogy* (Thomas Murby).

ROCKS

S. J. SHAND: *The Study of Rocks* (Thomas Murby).

F. H. HATCH and A. K. WELLS: *Petrology of the Igneous Rocks* (Allen and Unwin).

F. H. HATCH and R. H. RASTALL: *Petrology of the Sedimentary Rocks* (Allen and Unwin).

MAPS AND MAP-READING

ORDNANCE SURVEY: Pamphlets describing (i) The Large-Scale, (ii) The Medium-Scale, and (iii) The Small-Scale Ordnance Maps of Great Britain.

GEOLOGICAL SURVEY: The twenty-five and the ten miles to the inch geological maps of the British Isles give an excellent generalised idea of the outcrops of the various rocks.

For special districts, there are numerous geological maps available on a scale of one inch to one mile.

G. L. ELLES: *The Study of Geological Maps* (Cambridge University Press).

A. R. DWERRYHOUSE: *Geological and Topographical Maps* (Edward Arnold).

J. PLATT: *Simple Geological Structures.* A series of notes and map exercises (Thomas Murby).

E. GREENLY and H. WILLIAMS: *Methods in Geological Surveying* (Thomas Murby).

REGIONAL GEOLOGY

GEOLOGICAL SURVEY: *British Regional Geology.* Covers Great Britain in eighteen Guides.
Sheet and District Memoirs.

GEOLOGISTS' ASSOCIATION: *Proceedings.* Papers and Reports of Field Meetings.

GENERAL INDEX

ANIMAL life, as an aid to mapping, 52
Anticlines, 93
Apparatus for the field, 5
Apparent dip, 16, 17, 94
Aquifer, 104
Artesian springs, 105
Ashover (Derbyshire), mapping at, 63 et seq.
Assemblages, fossil, 187, 188
Augen structure, 185
Auger, the, 12, 54

BAG, collecting, 11
Bead tests, blowpipe, 156
Bedding, 39
— current or false, 16
— true, 17
Blow-holes, 106
Blowpipe, the, 12, 152
— analysis, 152 et seq.
— reagents, 157
Borings, as aids to mapping, 54
Boundary lines, in relation to shape of ground, 21
— — tracing or plotting, 48, 78 et seq.
Butt Shales, 89

CARBONIFEROUS Limestone, 72, 89, 108
Carborundum slip, 11
Centroclinal structure, 97
Chalk and water supply, 110
Charcoal, for blowpipe analysis, 155
Chatsworth Grit, 89
Chisels, cold, 9, 118
Claypits, 118
Clay-with-Flints, 50
Cleavage in rocks, 183
Cliff sections, 48
Clinometer, the, 10, 15
Clothing, for the field, 13
Coastal erosion; deposition, 35
— sand dunes, 36
Cobalt glass, for flame tests, 155
Collecting, 113 et seq.
— bag, 11
Colour of rocks, 168
Colouring maps, 87
Columnar jointing, 183
Compass, the, 9, 42, 43
— clinometer, 10

DELTA, 34
Denudation, 53
Derbyshire (Ashover), mapping in, 63 et seq.
Dip of rocks; apparent, 16, 17, 94
— — — determination of, 10, 15 et seq., 100
— — — quaquaversal, 93
Drumlins, 35
Dykes, mapping, 53, 56
Dry valleys, 33

ECOLOGY, 52
Equipment for the field, 5
Eruptive or igneous rocks, 176 et seq.
Exposures, general observations, 48

FAULTS and faulting, 33, 58 et seq., 98 et seq.
Feature-mapping, 39, 52
Field identifications, 119 et seq.
Flames, blowpipe, 153
— tests for, 154
Flints, 50
Foliated or metamorphic rocks, 183 et seq.
Foliation, 183
Footwear for the field, 13
Fossils as stratigraphical indices, 260
— collecting, 117
— correlation of strata by, 260
— general observations, 40
— in relation to bedding, 16
— use and determination of, 186 et seq.

GAPING Gill Hole, 33
Geological column, the, 265 et seq.
Glass tubes, for blowpipe analysis, 156
Gorge, a, 32
Gravels, mapping of, 57
Green-lining exposures, 43, 48, 58
Gridded maps (National Grid), 28, 43

HAMMER, the, 6
Hardness of minerals, 124
— — rocks, 168
"Heavy" minerals, 116
High-level gravels, 57
Hill creep, 16

Hills, in relation to mapping, 31
— long ranges, 31
— flat-topped, 32
Holmes, Prof. A., on texture of rocks, 168

IGNEOUS rocks, 176 *et seq.*
Ingleborough, 33
Inliers, 81, 93, 102
Intrusive contacts, mapping of, 56

JOINTING, 39
— columnar, 183

"KEY" to geological formations, 87
Knife, Putty, 11

LABELLING specimens, 113
Lens, the, 9
Limestones, 108, 117
— and water supply, 108
Lithoidal rocks, 178, 181
Lithological maps, 28
Lustre-mottling, 181

MAP-CASE, the, 6, 30
Map, preliminary study, 30
Mapping, geological, 26 *et seq.*
Maps, geological, 5, 26 *et seq.*
— — care of, 30
— — completing, 86
— — interpretation of, 91 *et seq.*
— — scale of, 27
— — sections across, 92
— — signs and symbols, 27, 29
— — six-inch Ordnance, 5, 28
— — with National Grid, 28, 43
Measuring sections, 45 *et seq.*
Metamorphic rocks, 183 *et seq.*
Microlites, 178
Millstone Grit series, 89
Mine-dumps, 40, 55
Minerals, associated, 40, 115, 125
— collecting, 115
— general observations, 40
— hardness of, 124
— "heavy", 116
— identification of, 123 *et seq.*
— streak of, 123, 124
Moraines, glacial, 34

NATIONAL grid lines, 28, 43
Nick point, 33
Notebook, field, 10, 11

OVERLAPS, 58, 62
Outcrop, width, of, in relation to dip and slope of ground, 20
Outliers, 102
Oxbow lakes, 34

PACKING specimens, 113
Panning, 116
Peat, 57
Pebble-beds, 169
Pencils, 11
Permeability or porosity of rocks, 106, 108
Phenocrysts, 178
Physical features, preliminary study of, 30
Plant life, as an aid to mapping, 39, 52, 83
Platinum wire, 152
Plotting bearings and boundaries, 42 *et seq.*
Porosity of rocks, 106
Pot hole, 33
Principles of mapping, application, 63 *et seq.*
Protractor, as a clinometer, 10

QUAQUAVERSAL dip, 93
Quarry sections, 41

RAILWAY cuttings, 49
Rainfall, 104
Rain-pitting, in relation to bedding, 39
Raised beaches, 35
Reagents, for blowpipe analysis, 157
Ripple-marks, in relation to bedding, 16, 39
River and stream sections, 49
Rivers, in relation to mapping, 32 *et seq.*
Road-cuttings, 41, 49
Rocks, collecting, 114
— colour of, 168
— general observations, 38, 167
— hardness of, 168
— identification, 166 *et seq.*
— igneous, 176 *et seq.*
— lithoidal, 178, 181
— metamorphic, 183 *et seq.*
— sedimentary, 168 *et seq.*
— structure and texture of, 167
Romer, the, 6
Ruck-sack, the, 11
Rule and clinometer, combined, 10

SAFETY precautions, 264
Salt marshes, 36
Sand dunes, 36

Sands, in relation to water supply, 108
Scale of maps, 27
Sections, across geological maps, 92
— examining and recording, 41 *et seq.*
Sedimentary rocks, 168 *et seq.*
Shading maps, 88
Shape of ground; feature-mapping, 39, 52
Signs and symbols used on geological maps, 27, 29
Sills, mapping of, 56
Six-inch Ordnance maps, 5, 28
Sketching, in relation to sections, 45
Slickensides, 68
Slopes, steep, 31
Smash-zones, 59
Soil-creep, 16, 52
Soils and subsoils, examination of, 50
Springs, as aids to mapping, 33, 104 *et seq.*
Strata, correlation of, by fossils, 260
Streak of minerals, 123, 124
Stream sections, 49
Strike of rocks, determination of, 15, 17
Structure of rocks, 167
Sun cracks, in relation to bedding, 16, 39
Superficial deposits, 57
Swallow hole, 33
Symbols used on geological maps, 27, 29
Synclines, 96, 98

TEMPORARY sections, 41, 49
Terraces, 34, 57
Terracettes, 16
Texture of rocks, 167, 178

Thickness of beds, calculation of, 21
Three dimensions, thinking in, 15
Three-point problem, the, 18
Thrusts, 99, 102
Time ranges, by distribution of fossil groups, 263
Tip-heaps, 55
Tracing or plotting boundary lines, 48
Trowel, the, 11
True bedding, 16

UNCONFORMITIES, at Ingleton, 61, 100
Underground water, 105, 106

VALLEYS; U-shaped, V-shaped, 33, 34
Vegetation, as an aid to mapping, 39, 52, 83

WATER-COLOURS, for geological maps, 87
Waterfalls, in relation to mapping, 32
Water supply, 103 *et seq.*
— tables, 106
Weathering of metallic minerals, 125
— — rocks, 53
Wells and borings, as aids to mapping, 54

YOREDALE, Beds, 89

ZONES, fossil, 187

INDEX OF MINERALS

ACTINOLITE, 143
Almandine, 129
Amphiboles, Actinolite, 143
— Hornblende, 147
Andalusite (Chiastolite), 130
Anglesite, 149
Anhydrite, 149
Antimonite (Stibnite), 135
Apatite, 151
Aragonite, 149
Arsenopyrite (Mispickel), 133
Augite, 147
Azurite, 141

BARYTES ("Heavy Spar"), 145, 149
Bauxite, 145

Beryl, 131
Biotite, 145
Blende, Zinc, 69, 137, 145
Bog Iron Ore, 137
Bornite (Erubescite), 133

CALAMINE, 151
Calcite, 68, 149
Carbon (Graphite), 135
Cassiterite (Tinstone), 129, 139, 147
Celestite, 149
Cerrussite, 151
Chalcedony, 129
Chalcocite (Copper Glance), 135
Chalcopyrite (Copper Pyrites), 133
Chalybite, 145, 149

Chert, 129
Chiastolite, 183
Chlorite, 141
Chromite, 137
Chrysocolla, 141
Cinnabar, 139
Clay-Ironstone, 145, 149
Cobaltite, 133
Copper Glance, 135
— Pyrites, 133
Corundum, 131
Cryolite, 147
Cuprite, 139

DIALLAGE, 143
Diamond, 131
Disthene, 143
Dolomite, 145, 149

EPIDOTE, 143
Erubescite, 133

FELSPAR, Orthoclase, 151
— Plagioclase, 151
— Sanidine, 151
Flint, 129
Fluorspar, 68, 141, 151

GALENA, 69, 135, 163, 164
Garnet, 129
Gold, Native, 137
Graphite (Carbon), 135
Grossularite, 129
Gypsum, 147

HEAVY Spar, 145, 149
Hematite (Specular Iron), 139
Hornblende, 147
Horse-flesh ore, 133

ILMENITE (Titanoferrite), 135
Indicolite, 129

KUPFERNICKEL, 133
Kyanite (Disthene), 143, 183

LEUCITE, 151
Limonite, 137
Lodestone, 135

MALACHITE, 141
Magnesite, 149
Magnetic Pyrites, 133
Magnetite (Lodestone), 135
Marcasite, 133
Melanite, 129
Mica, Biotite, 145
— Muscovite, 147
Millerite, 133
Mispickel, 133
Molybdenite, 137
Muscovite, 147

NATIVE Gold, 137
— Silver, 137
Nepneline, 151
Niccolite (Kupfernickel), 133

OCHRE, Yellow, 137
Olivine, 143
Orthoclase Felspar, 151

PHOSPHORITE, 143, 151
Plagioclase Felspar, 151
Psilomelane, 135, 165
Pyrite, 133
Pyrolusite, 135, 165
Pyromorphite, 137, 141
Pyrope, 129
Pyroxene, Augite, 147
— Diallage, 143
Pyrrhotite (Magnetic Pyrites), 133

QUARTZ (Rock Crystal), 129

RHODOCHROSITE, 145
Rock Crystal, 129
— Phosphate, 143, 151
Rubellite, 129
Rutile, 139

SANIDINE, 151
Schorl, 129
Selenite, 147
Serpentine, 141, 145
Siderite, Chalybite (Clay-Ironstone), 145, 149
Silver, Native, 137
Smaltite, 133
Smithsonite (Calamine), 151
Specular Iron, 139
Sphalerite (Zinc Blende), 69, 137, 145, 164
Sphene (Titanite), 145

Staurolite, 183
Steatite, 141, 147
Stibnite (Antimonite), 135

TALC (Steatite), 141, 147
Tetrahedrite, 135
Tinstone (Cassiterite), 129, 139, 147
Titanite, 145
Titanoferrite, 135
Topaz, 131

Tourmaline, 129

WAD, 135
Wolframite, 135, 139

YELLOW Ochre, 137

ZINC Blende, 69, 137, 145
Zircon, 131

INDEX OF ROCKS

AGGLOMERATES, 172
Alluvium, 57
Andesite, 177, 182
— glass, 177, 183
Anthracitic coal, 171, 175
Argillaceous limestone, 173
Arkose, 169, 170
Ash, volcanic, 172
Augen gneiss, 184, 185

BASALT, 177, 182
Bituminous coal, 175
— limestone, 173
— shale, 171, 174, 175
Boulder-clay, 50, 58, 171, 174
Breccias, 169, 170
— crush-, 172
— fault-, 59, 172

CANNEL coal, 171, 175
Carbonaceous shale, 171, 174
Chalk, 170, 173
Chert, 51, 67, 170, 172
Chiastolite slate, 184, 185
China-clay, 174
Clays, 171, 174
Coal, 171, 175
Conglomerates, 169, 170
Crush-breccia, 172
Crystalline limestone, 184

DIORITE, 177, 180
Dolerite, 177, 182
Dolomite, 184
Dolomitic conglomerate, 169
— limestone, 173
— marble, 184

FAULT-BRECCIA, 59, 172
Felsite, 176, 181
Felspathic sandstone, 169
Ferruginous sandstone, 169
Fire-clay, 174
Flint, 50, 170, 172
Fullers' earth, 171, 174

GABBRO, 177, 180
Glauconitic sandstone, 169
Gneiss, 184, 185
Granite, 176, 180
Granulite, 184, 185
Grit, 74 et seq., 169, 170

KAOLIN, 174

LIGNITE, 171, 175
Limestones, 110, 170, 172, 173, 184
Loam, 174

MAGNESIAN (dolomitic) limestone,
170, 173
Marl, marlstone, 170, 173
Micaceous sandstone, 169
Microlites, 178
Mudstone, 171, 174

OBSIDIAN, 176, 183
Oil shale, 171
Oolitic limestone, 170, 173

PAPER-SHALE, 174
Peat, 57, 171, 175
Peridotite, 177, 181
Phyllite, 184, 185

Picrite, 177, 181
Pin-holed chert, 172
Pipe-clay, 174
Pisolitic limestone, 170, 173
Pitchstone, 176, 183
Porphyries, 176, 181
Porphyrites, 176, 182

QUARTZITE, 169, 184

RHYOLITE, 176, 182

SANDS, 168
Sandstones, 109, 168, 169, 170
Schist, 184, 185

Serpentine and serpentine rocks, 177, 181
Shales, 69, 118, 171, 174
Siliceous limestone, 173
Slates, 118, 184, 185
Spotted slate, 184, 185
Statuary marble, 184
Syenite, 176, 180

TACHYLITE, 177, 183
Till, 174
Toadstone (tuff), 68 *et seq.*, 89
Trachyte, 176, 182
Tuff, volcanic, 172

VOLCANIC ash, 172
— tuff, 172

INDEX OF FOSSILS

ACANTHOCERAS, 246, 247
Acrosalenia, 206, 207
Actinozoa or corals, 190
Aeglina, 254
Agnostus, 252, 253
Alethopteris, 260, 261
Amaltheus, 248, 249
Ammonitina, 242
Ampullina, 238
Anahoplites, 249
Ancyloceras, 244, 245
Angelina, 254, 255
Annularia, 260, 261
Arca, 222, 223
Architectonica (*Solarium*), 238, 239
Arctica, 226, 227
Arietitidae, 248, 251
Asaphus, 256, 257
Astarte, 226, 227
Athyris, 218, 219
Atrypa, 218, 219
Aulophyllum, 202, 203
Avicula, 230

BELEMNITES, 244, 245
Bellerophon, 235, 236
Brachiopoda, 190, 191, 212
Bronteus, 257, 258
Buccinum, 240, 241
Bumestus, 256, 257

CALAMITES, 258, 259
Calceola, 200, 201
Calymene, 255, 256

Caninia, 200, 201
Carbonicola, 82
Cardiaster, 210
Cardinia, 226, 227
Cardioceras, 248, 249
Cardita, 224, 225
Cardium, 224, 225
Cephalopoda, 190, 242
Ceratites, 242, 243
Cerithium, 236, 237
Chama, 230, 231
Cheiruridae, 254, 255
Chlamys, 230, 231
Chonetidae, 216, 217
Cidaris, 207, 208
Climacograptus, 196
Clonograptus, 194
Clypeus, 210, 211
Collyrites, 205, 208, 209
Conchidium, 220, 221
Conocoryphe, 254, 255
Conorbis, 240, 241
Conulus (*Echinoconus*), 208, 209
Conus, 238, 239
Corals, 190, 196
Corbula, 230, 231
Corbicula, 226, 229
Crania, 214, 215
Crassatella, 226, 227
Crinoids, 67, 212, 213
Crioceras, 244, 245
Cyathaxonia, 202, 203
Cyathaxoniicae, 200, 201
Cyclopyge (*Aeglina*), 254, 255
Cyphosoma, 208
Cypraea, 238

Cyrtia, 214, 215
Cyrtinid, 214, 215

DACTYLIOCERAS, 244, 247
Dalmanites, 256, 257
Dibunophyllum, 67, 72, 192, 202, 203
Dicellograptus, 196
Dichograptus, 194
Dicoelosia, 216, 217
Dicranograptus, 196
Dictyonema, 194
Didymograptus, 196
Diplograptus, 196
Diplopodia, 208, 209
Discoides, 208, 209
Douvilleiceras, 246, 247
Dunbarella, 82, 230, 231

ECHINOBRISSUS, 210
Echinoconus, 208
Echinocorys, 205, 210, 211
Echinodermata, 202
Emarginula, 234, 235
Encrinurus, 256, 257
Eodiscus, 252, 253
Equisetites, 258, 259
Euomphalus, 236, 237
Euhoplites, 249
Exogyra, 232, 233, 249

FAVOSITES, 198
Fissurella, 234
Fusinus, 240, 241

GASTROPODA, 190, 232
Gervillia, 224, 225
Glycimeris (Pectunculus), 222, 223
Goniatites, 242, 243
Goniophyllum, 200, 201
Graptolites, 194
Gryphaea, 232, 233

HALYSITES, 200, 201
Hamites, 244, 245
Harpes, 252, 253
Harpoceras, 248, 251
Heliolites, 198
Hemicidaris, 206, 207
Hildoceras, 248, 251
Holaster, 210, 211
Holectypus, 208, 209
Homomya, 228
Hoplitidae, 246

INOCERAMUS, 232, 233
Irregularia, 206
Isastrea, 202, 203
Isognomon, 224, 225

KOSMOCERAS, 246, 249

LAMELLIBRANCHIA, 190
Lepidodendron, 74, 82, 258, 259
Leptaena, 216, 217
Lima, 230, 231
Limnea, 238, 239
Lingula, 214, 215
Linopteris, 258, 259
Liparoceras, 246, 247
Lithostrotion, 67, 72, 202, 203
Lonchopteris, 258, 259
Lonsdaleia, 72, 202, 203
Lucina, 226, 227

MACROCEPHALITES, 244, 245
Mactra, 228, 229
Mariopteris, 260, 261
Melania, 236, 237
Meleagrinella, 230, 231
Meretricinae, 228, 229
Meristina, 218, 219
Michelinia, 198
Micraster, 210, 211
Modiolus, 226, 227
Monograptus, 196
Montlivaltia, 202, 203
Murex, 240, 241
Mytilus, 224, 225

NASSA, 240, 241
Natica, 238, 239
Nautilus, 242, 243
Neptunea, 240, 241
Neuropteris, 259, 260
Nucleolites (Echinobrissus), 210, 211
Nuculid, 222, 223
Nuculanid, 222, 223

ODONTOPTERIS, 260, 261
Ogygiocaris, 256, 257
Olenus, 254, 255
Orbiculoidea, 214, 215
Orthacea, 216
Orthis, 215
Orthoceras, 244, 245
Ostrea, 232, 233
Oxynoticeras, 248, 251